Solutions Manual for Essentials of Statistics for Business and Economics

Seventh Edition

D1543868

Anderson | Sweeney | Williams | Camm | Cochran

CENGAGE
Learning·

Australia • Brazil • Japan • Korea • Mexico • Singapore • Spain • United Kingdom • United States

CENGAGE
Learning·

Solutions Manual for Essentials of Statistics for Business and Economics

Solutions Manual for Essentials of Statistics for Business and Economics, Seventh Edition
Anderson | Sweeney | Williams | Camm | Cochran

© 2015 Cengage Learning. All rights reserved.

Senior Manager, Student Engagement:

Linda deStefano

Janey Moeller

Manager, Student Engagement:

Julie Dierig

Marketing Manager:

Rachael Kloos

Manager, Production Editorial:

Kim Fry

Manager, Intellectual Property Project Manager:

Brian Methe

Senior Manager, Production and Manufacturing:

Donna M. Brown

Manager, Production:

Terri Daley

For product information and technology assistance, contact us at
Cengage Learning Customer & Sales Support, 1-800-354-9706

For permission to use material from this text or product,
submit all requests online at **cengage.com/permissions**
Further permissions questions can be emailed to
permissionrequest@cengage.com

This book contains select works from existing Cengage Learning resources and was produced by Cengage Learning Custom Solutions for collegiate use. As such, those adopting and/or contributing to this work are responsible for editorial content accuracy, continuity and completeness.

Compilation © 2014 Cengage Learning

ISBN-13: 978-1-305-29314-4

ISBN-10: 1-305-29314-2

WCN: 01-100-101

Cengage Learning

5191 Natorp Boulevard
Mason, Ohio 45040
USA

Cengage Learning is a leading provider of customized learning solutions with office locations around the globe, including Singapore, the United Kingdom, Australia, Mexico, Brazil, and Japan. Locate your local office at: **international.cengage.com/region.**

Cengage Learning products are represented in Canada by Nelson Education, Ltd.
For your lifelong learning solutions, visit **www.cengage.com/custom.**
Visit our corporate website at **www.cengage.com.**

Printed in the United States of America

Contents

Chapter

Preface

The purpose of *Essentials of Statistics for Business and Economics* is to provide students, primarily in the fields of business administration and economics, with a sound conceptual introduction to the field of statistics and its many applications. The text is applications-oriented and has been written with the needs of the nonmathematician in mind.

The solutions manual furnishes assistance by identifying learning objectives and providing detailed solutions for all exercises in the text.

Note: The solutions to the case problems are included in a separate manual .

Acknowledgements

We would like to provide special recognition to Catherine J. Williams for her efforts in preparing the solutions manual.

David R. Anderson
Dennis J. Sweeney
Thomas A. Williams
Jeffrey D. Camm
James J. Cochran

Chapter 1
Data and Statistics

Learning Objectives

1. Obtain an appreciation for the breadth of statistical applications in business and economics.

2. Understand the meaning of the terms elements, variables, and observations as they are used in statistics.

3. Obtain an understanding of the difference between categorical, quantitative, crossectional and time series data.

4. Learn about the sources of data for statistical analysis both internal and external to the firm.

5. Be aware of how errors can arise in data.

6. Know the meaning of descriptive statistics and statistical inference.

7. Be able to distinguish between a population and a sample.

8. Understand the role a sample plays in making statistical inferences about the population.

9. Know the meaning of the term data mining.

10. Be aware of ethical guidelines for statistical practice.

Solutions:

1. Statistics can be referred to as numerical facts. In a broader sense, statistics is the field of study dealing with the collection, analysis, presentation and interpretation of data.

2. a. The ten elements are the ten cars

    b. 5 variables: Size, Cylinders, City MPG, Highway MPG, and Fuel

    c. Categorical variables: Size and Fuel

       Quantitative variables: Cylinders, City MPG, and Highway MPG

    d.

Variable	Measurement Scale
Size	Ordinal
Cylinders	Ratio
City MPG	Ratio
Highway MPG	Ratio
Fuel	Nominal

3. a. Average mpg for city driving = 182/10 = 18.2 mpg

    b. Average mpg for highway driving = 261/10 = 26.1 mpg

       On average, the miles per gallon for highway driving is 26.1 – 18.2 = 7.9 mpg greater compared to city driving.

    c. 3 of 10 or 30% have four cylinder engines

    d. 6 of 10 or 60% use regular fuel

4. a. There are eight elements in this data set; each element corresponds to one of the eight models of cordless telephones

    b. Categorical variables: Voice Quality and Handset on Base

       Quantitative variables: Price, Overall Score, and Talk Time

    c. Price – ratio measurement
       Overall Score – interval measurement
       Voice Quality – ordinal measurement
       Handset on Base – nominal measurement
       Talk Time – ratio measurement

5. a. Average Price = 545/8 = $68.13

    b. Average Talk Time = 71/8 = 8.875 hours

    c. Percentage rated Excellent: 2 of 8   2/8 = .25, or 25%

    d. Percentage with Handset on Base: 4 of 8   4/8 = .50, or 50%

6. a. Categorical

    b. Quantitative

    c.   Categorical

    d.   Quantitative

    e.   Quantitative

7.   a.   Each question has a yes or no categorical response.

    b.   Yes and no are the labels for the customer responses. A nominal scale is being used.

8.   a.   1015

    b.   Categorical

    c.   Percentages

    d.   .10(1015) = 101.5

        101 or 102 respondents said the Federal Bank is doing a good job.

9.   a.   Categorical

    b.   30 of 71; 42.3%

10. a.   Categorical

    b.   Percentages

    c.   44 of 1080 respondents or approximately 4% strongly agree with allowing drivers of motor vehicles to talk on a hand-held cell phone while driving.

    d.   165 of the 1080 respondents or 15% of said they somewhat disagree and 741 or 69% said they strongly disagree. Thus, there does not appear to be general support for allowing drivers of motor vehicles to talk on a hand-held cell phone while driving.

11. a.   Quantitative; ratio

    b.   Categorical; nominal

    c.   Categorical; ordinal

    d.   Quantitative; ratio

    e.   Categorical; ordinal. The response to this question was recorded as a numerical value from 1 to 10. While the data are numerical, they are not quantitative. The numerical values from 1 to 10 represent categories that *order* the overall rating somewhere between unacceptable and truly exceptional. The data may be ordered by response category with a higher number category indicating a higher overall rating.

        While we prefer the categorical; ordinal answer above, at times statisticians may *make the assumption* that the numerical responses are equal-interval measures on a quantitative scale from 1 to 10. When this assumption is made, the data may be considered quantitative with an interval scale of measurement. In this case, additional statistical computations such as the average overall rating become helpful in summarizing the data.

12. a. The population is all visitors coming to the state of Hawaii.

    b. Since airline flights carry the vast majority of visitors to the state, the use of questionnaires for passengers during incoming flights is a good way to reach this population. The questionnaire actually appears on the back of a mandatory plants and animals declaration form that passengers must complete during the incoming flight. A large percentage of passengers complete the visitor information questionnaire.

    c. Questions 1 and 4 provide quantitative data indicating the number of visits and the number of days in Hawaii. Questions 2 and 3 provide categorical data indicating the categories of reason for the trip and where the visitor plans to stay.

13. a. Federal spending measured in trillions of dollars

    b. Quantitative

    c. Time series

    d. Federal spending has increased over time

14. a. The graph of the time series follows:

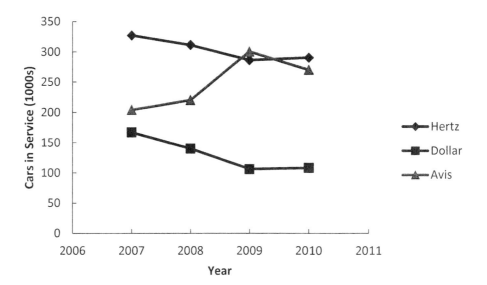

    b. In 2007 and 2008 Hertz was the clear market share leader. In 2009 and 2010 Hertz and Avis have approximately the same market share. The market share for Dollar appears to be declining.

c. The bar chart for 2010 is shown below.

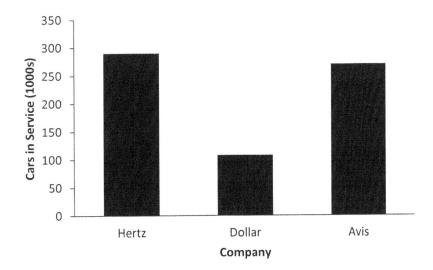

This chart is based on cross-sectional data.

15. a. Quantitative – number of new drugs approved

   b. Time series

   c. July; 1100

   d. 2.9%; Yes, because most recreational boating takes place during the summer months.

   e. The bar graph follows the shape of a bell curve.

16. The answer to this exercise depends on updating the time series of the average price per gallon of conventional regular gasoline as shown in Figure 1.1. Contact the website www.eia.doe.gov to obtain the most recent time series data. The answer should focus on the most recent changes or trend in the average price per gallon.

17. Internal data on salaries of other employees can be obtained from the personnel department. External data might be obtained from the Department of Labor or industry associations.

18. a. 684/1021; or approximately 67%

   b. 612

   c. Categorical

19. a. All subscribers of Business Week in North America at the time the survey was conducted.

   b. Quantitative

   c. Categorical (yes or no)

   d. Crossectional - all the data relate to the same time.

e. Using the sample results, we could infer or estimate 59% of the population of subscribers have an annual income of $75,000 or more and 50% of the population of subscribers have an American Express credit card.

20. a. 43% of managers were bullish or very bullish.

   21% of managers expected health care to be the leading industry over the next 12 months.

   b. We estimate the average 12-month return estimate for the population of investment managers to be 11.2%.

   c. We estimate the average over the population of investment managers to be 2.5 years.

21. a. The two populations are the population of women whose mothers took the drug DES during pregnancy and the population of women whose mothers did not take the drug DES during pregnancy.

   b. It was a survey.

   c. 63 / 3.980 = 15.8 women out of each 1000 developed tissue abnormalities.

   d. The article reported "twice" as many abnormalities in the women whose mothers had taken DES during pregnancy. Thus, a rough estimate would be 15.8/2 = 7.9 abnormalities per 1000 women whose mothers had *not* taken DES during pregnancy.

   e. In many situations, disease occurrences are rare and affect only a small portion of the population. Large samples are needed to collect data on a reasonable number of cases where the disease exists.

22. a. The population consists of all customers of the chain's stores in Charlotte, North Carolina.

   b. Some of the ways that could be used to collect the data are as follows:

   • Customers entering or leaving the store could be surveyed

   • A survey could be mailed to customers who have a shopper's club card for the stores

   • Customers could be given a printed survey when they check out

   • Customers could be given a coupon that asks them to complete a brief on-line survey; if they do, they will receive a 5% discount on their next shopping trip.

23. a. This finding is applicable to the population of all American adults.

   b. This finding is applicable to the population of American adults that own a cellphone and/or a tablet computer.

   c. They conducted a sample survey. It would be way too costly to survey all American adults or all American adults who own cellphones and/or tablet computers. As we will see later in the text, very good results can be obtained using a sample survey.

   d. These results should be quite interesting to restaurant owners. It suggests that it would be worthwhile for them to have a website and to consider advertising through an internet search company, such as Google.

24. a. This is a statistically correct descriptive statistic for the sample.

    b. An incorrect generalization since the data was not collected for the entire population.

    c. An acceptable statistical inference based on the use of the word "estimate."

    d. While this statement is true for the sample, it is not a justifiable conclusion for the entire population.

    e. This statement is not statistically supportable. While it is true for the particular sample observed, it is entirely possible and even very likely that at least some students will be outside the 65 to 90 range of grades.

25. a. There are five variables: Exchange, Ticker Symbol, Market Cap, Price/Earnings Ratio and Gross Profit Margin.

    b. Categorical variables: Exchange and Ticker Symbol

       Quantitative variables: Market Cap, Price/Earnings Ratio, Gross Profit Margin

    c. Exchange variable:

Exchange	Frequency	Percent Frequency
AMEX	5	(5/25) 20%
NYSE	3	(3/25) 12%
OTC	17	(17/25) 68%
	25	

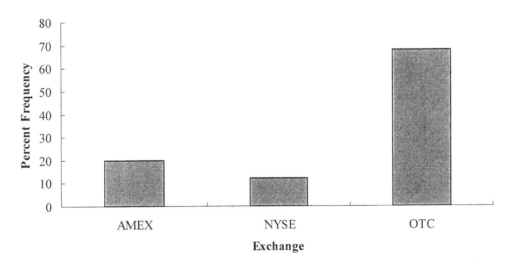

    d. Gross Profit Margin variable:

Gross Profit Margin	Frequency
0.0 – 14.9	2
15.0 – 29.9	6
30.0 – 44.9	8
45.0 – 59.9	6
60.0 – 74.9	3

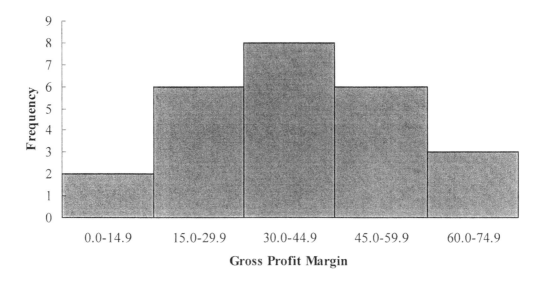

e. Sum the Price/Earnings Ratio data for all 25 companies.

Sum = 505.4

Average Price/Earnings Ratio = Sum/25 = 505.4/25 = 20.2

Chapter 2
Descriptive Statistics: Tabular and Graphical Displays

Learning Objectives

1. Learn how to construct and interpret summarization procedures for qualitative data such as: frequency and relative frequency distributions, bar graphs and pie charts.

2. Learn how to construct and interpret tabular summarization procedures for quantitative data such as: frequency and relative frequency distributions, cumulative frequency and cumulative relative frequency distributions.

3. Learn how to construct a dot plot and a histogram as graphical summaries of quantitative data.

4. Learn how the shape of a data distribution is revealed by a histogram. Learn how to recognize when a data distribution is negatively skewed, symmetric, and positively skewed.

5. Be able to use and interpret the exploratory data analysis technique of a stem-and-leaf display.

6. Learn how to construct and interpret cross tabulations, scatter diagrams, side-by-side and stacked bar charts.

7. Learn best practices for creating effective graphical displays and for choosing the appropriate type of display.

Solutions:

1.

Class	Frequency	Relative Frequency
A	60	60/120 = 0.50
B	24	24/120 = 0.20
C	36	36/120 = 0.30
	120	1.00

2. a. $1 - (.22 + .18 + .40) = .20$

   b. $.20(200) = 40$

   c/d.

Class	Frequency	Percent Frequency
A	.22(200) = 44	22
B	.18(200) = 36	18
C	.40(200) = 80	40
D	.20(200) = 40	20
Total	200	100

3. a. $360° \times 58/120 = 174°$

   b. $360° \times 42/120 = 126°$

   c.

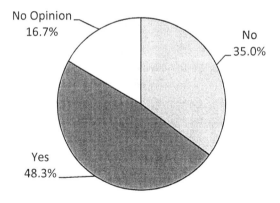

d.

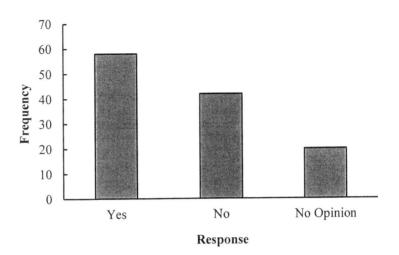

4. a. These data are categorical.

    b.

Show	Relative Frequency	% Frequency
Jep	10	20
JJ	8	16
OWS	7	14
THM	12	24
WoF	13	26
Total	50	100

    c.

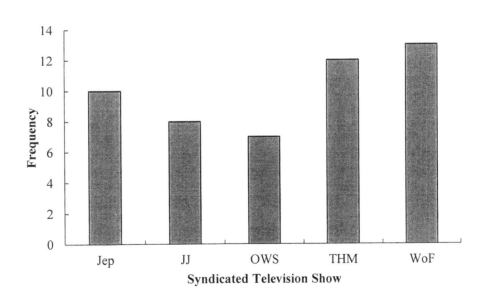

Syndicated Television Shows

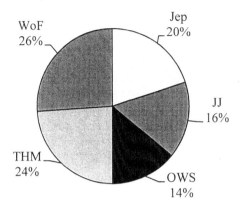

d. The largest viewing audience is for *Wheel of Fortune* and the second largest is for *Two and a Half Men*.

5. a.

Name	Frequency	Relative Frequency	Percent Frequency
Brown	7	0.14	14%
Johnson	10	0.20	20%
Jones	7	0.14	14%
Miller	6	0.12	12%
Smith	12	0.24	24%
Williams	8	0.16	16%
Total:	50	1	100%

b.

Common U.S. Last Names

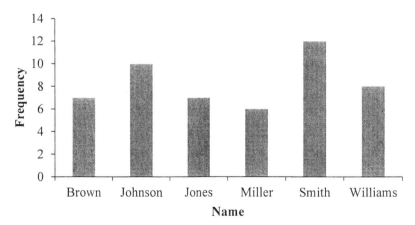

c.

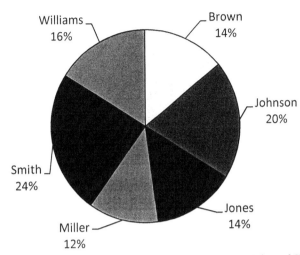

Common U.S. Last Names

d. The three most common last names are Smith (24%), Johnson (20%), and Williams (16%)

6. a.

Network	Relative Frequency	% Frequency
ABC	6	24
CBS	9	36
FOX	1	4
NBC	9	36
Total:	25	100

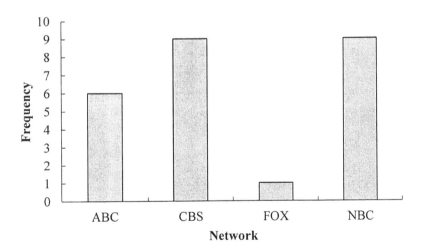

b. For these data, NBC and CBS tie for the number of top-rated shows. Each has 9 (36%) of the top 25. ABC is third with 6 (24%) and the much younger FOX network has 1(4%).

2 - 5

7. a.

Rating	Frequency	Percent Frequency
Excellent	20	40
Very Good	23	46
Good	4	8
Fair	1	2
Poor	2	4
	50	100

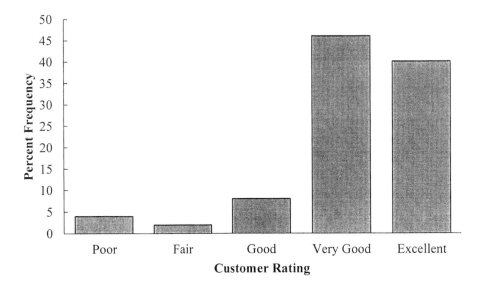

Management should be very pleased with the survey results. 40% + 46% = 86% of the ratings are very good to excellent. 94% of the ratings are good or better. This does not look to be a Delta flight where significant changes are needed to improve the overall customer satisfaction ratings.

b. While the overall ratings look fine, note that one customer (2%) rated the overall experience with the flight as Fair and two customers (4%) rated the overall experience with the flight as Poor. It might be insightful for the manager to review explanations from these customers as to how the flight failed to meet expectations. Perhaps, it was an experience with other passengers that Delta could do little to correct or perhaps it was an isolated incident that Delta could take steps to correct in the future.

8. a.

Position	Frequency	Relative Frequency
Pitcher	17	0.309
Catcher	4	0.073
1st Base	5	0.091
2nd Base	4	0.073
3rd Base	2	0.036
Shortstop	5	0.091
Left Field	6	0.109
Center Field	5	0.091
Right Field	7	0.127
	55	1.000

b. Pitchers (Almost 31%)

c. 3rd Base (3 – 4%)

d. Right Field (Almost 13%)

e. Infielders (16 or 29.1%) to Outfielders (18 or 32.7%)

9. a.

Living Area	Live Now	Ideal Community
City	32%	24%
Suburb	26%	25%
Small Town	26%	30%
Rural Area	16%	21%
Total	100%	100%

b. Where do you live now?

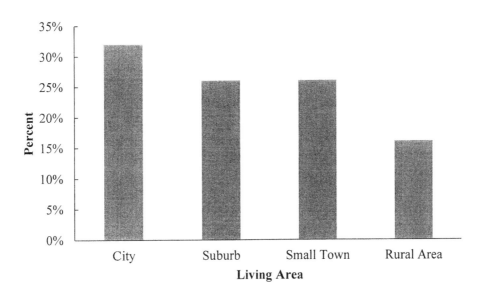

What do you consider the ideal community?

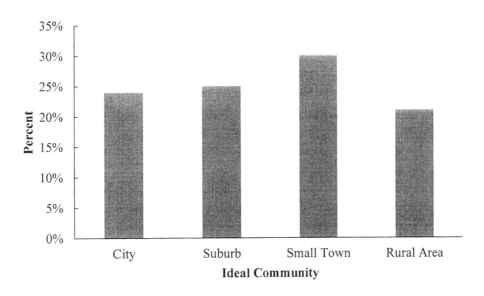

c. Most adults are now living in a city (32%).

d. Most adults consider the ideal community a small town (30%).

e. Percent changes by living area: City –8%, Suburb –1%, Small Town +4%, and Rural Area +5%. Suburb living is steady, but the trend would be that living in the city would decline while living in small towns and rural areas would increase.

10. a.

Rating	Frequency
Excellent	187
Very Good	252
Average	107
Poor	62
Terrible	41
Total	649

b.

Rating	Percent Frequency
Excellent	28.8
Very Good	38.8
Average	16.5
Poor	9.6
Terrible	6.3
Total	100.0

c.

d. 28.8% + 38.8 = 67.6% of the guests at the Sheraton Anaheim Hotel rated the hotel as Excellent or Very Good. But, 9.6% + 6.3% = 15.9% of the guests rated the hotel as poor or terrible.

e. The percent frequency distribution for Disney's Grand Californian follows:

Rating	Percent Frequency
Excellent	48.1
Very Good	31.0
Average	11.9
Poor	6.4
Terrible	2.6
Total	100.0

48.1% + 31.0% = 79.1% of the guests at the Sheraton Anaheim Hotel rated the hotel as Excellent or Very Good. And, 6.4% + 2.6% = 9.0% of the guests rated the hotel as poor or terrible.

Compared to ratings of other hotels in the same region, both of these hotels received very favorable ratings. But, in comparing the two hotels, guests at Disney's Grand Californian provided somewhat better ratings than guests at the Sheraton Anaheim Hotel.

11.

Class	Frequency	Relative Frequency	Percent Frequency
12–14	2	0.050	5.0
15–17	8	0.200	20.0
18–20	11	0.275	27.5
21–23	10	0.250	25.0
24–26	9	0.225	22.5
Total	40	1.000	100.0

12.

Class	Cumulative Frequency	Cumulative Relative Frequency
less than or equal to 19	10	.20
less than or equal to 29	24	.48
less than or equal to 39	41	.82
less than or equal to 49	48	.96
less than or equal to 59	50	1.00

13.

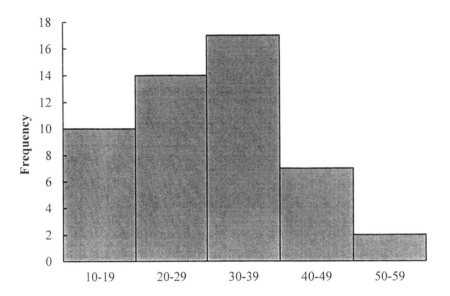

14. a.

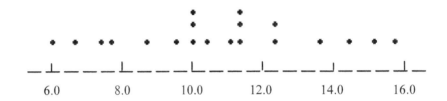

b/c.

Class	Frequency	Percent Frequency
6.0 – 7.9	4	20
8.0 – 9.9	2	10
10.0 – 11.9	8	40
12.0 – 13.9	3	15
14.0 – 15.9	3	15
	20	100

15.   Leaf Unit = .1

6	3
7	5 5 7
8	1 3 4 8
9	3 6
10	0 4 5
11	3

16.   Leaf Unit = 10

11	6
12	0 2
13	0 6 7
14	2 2 7
15	5
16	0 2 8
17	0 2 3

17. a/b.

Waiting Time	Frequency	Relative Frequency
0 – 4	4	0.20
5 – 9	8	0.40
10 – 14	5	0.25
15 – 19	2	0.10
20 – 24	1	0.05
Totals	20	1.00

c/d.

Waiting Time	Cumulative Frequency	Cumulative Relative Frequency
Less than or equal to 4	4	0.20
Less than or equal to 9	12	0.60
Less than or equal to 14	17	0.85
Less than or equal to 19	19	0.95
Less than or equal to 24	20	1.00

e. $12/20 = 0.60$

18. a., b, c

PPG	Frequency	Relative Frequency	Cumulative Percent Frequency
10-11.9	1	.02	2
12-13.9	3	.06	8
14-15.9	7	.14	22
16-17.9	19	.38	60
18-19.9	9	.18	78
20-21.9	4	.08	86
22-23.9	2	.04	90
24-25.9	0	.00	90
26-27.9	3	.06	96
28-29.9	2	.04	100
Total	50		

d.

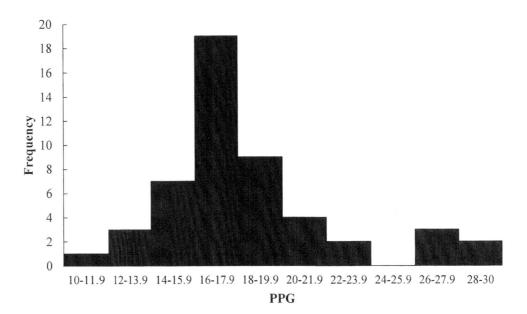

e. There is skewness to the right.

f. $(11/50)(100) = 22\%$

19. a. The largest number of tons is 236.3 million (South Louisiana). The smallest number of tons is 30.2 million (Port Arthur).

b.

Millions Of Tons	Frequency
25-50	11
50-75	9
75-100	2
100-125	0
125-150	1
150-175	0
175-200	0
200-225	0
225-250	2

c.

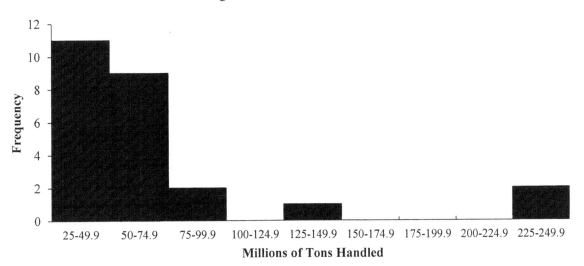

Most of the top 25 ports handle less than 75 million tons. Only five of the 25 ports handle above 75 million tons.

20. a.   Lowest = 12, Highest = 23

b.

Hours in Meetings per Week	Frequency	Percent Frequency
11-12	1	4%
13-14	2	8%
15-16	6	24%
17-18	3	12%
19-20	5	20%
21-22	4	16%
23-24	4	16%
	25	100%

c.

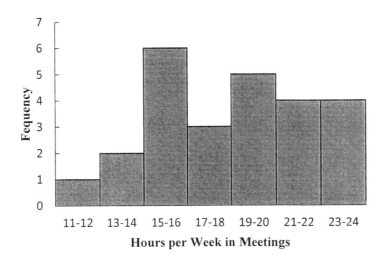

The distribution is slightly skewed to the left.

21. a/b/c/d.

Revenue	Frequency	Relative Frequency	Cumulative Frequency	Cumulative Relative Frequency
0-49	6	.12	6	.12.
50-99	29	.58	35	.70
100-149	11	.22	46	.92
150-199	0	.00	46	.92
200-249	1	.02	47	.94
250-299	1	.02	48	.96
300-349	0	.00	48	.96
350-399	0	.00	48	.96
400-449	2	.04	50	1.00
Total	50	1.00		

e. The majority of the large corporations (40) have revenues in the $50 billion to $149 billion range. Only 4 corporations have revenues of over $200 billion and only 2 corporations have revenues over $400 billion. .70, or 70%, of the corporations have revenues under $100 billion. .30, or 30%, of the corporations have revenues of $100 billion or more.

f.

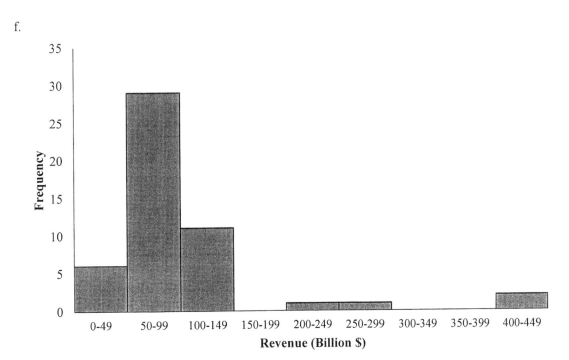

The histogram shows the distribution is skewed to the right with four corporations in the $200 to $449 billion range.

g. Exxon-Mobil is America's largest corporation with an annual revenue of $443 billion. Wal-Mart is the second largest corporation with annual revenue of $406 billion. All other corporations have annual revenues less than $300 billion. Most (92%) have annual revenues less than $150 billion.

22. a.

# U.S. Locations	Frequency	Percent Frequency
0-4999	10	50
5000-9999	3	15
10000-14999	2	10
15000-19999	1	5
20000-24999	0	0
25000-29999	1	5
30000-34999	2	10
35000-39999	1	5
Total:	20	100

b.

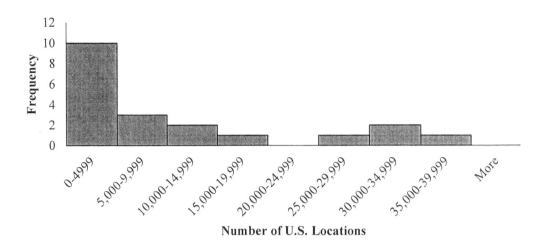

Number of U.S. Locations

c. The distribution is skewed to the right. The majority of the franchises in this list have fewer than 20,000 locations (50% + 15% + 15% = 80%). McDonald's, Subway and 7-Eleven have the highest number of locations.

23. a/b.

Computer Usage (Hours)			Frequency	Relative Frequency
0.0	–	2.9	5	0.10
3.0	–	5.9	28	0.56
6.0	–	8.9	8	0.16
9.0	–	11.9	6	0.12
12.0	–	14.9	3	0.06
		Total	50	1.00

c.

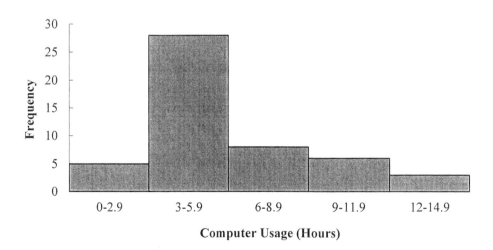

Computer Usage (Hours)

d. The majority of the computer users are in the 3 to 6 hour range. Usage is somewhat skewed toward the right with 3 users in the 12 to 14.9 hour range.

24.   Median Pay

```
 6 | 6 7 7
 7 | 2 4 6 7 7 8 9
 8 | 0 0 1 3 7
 9 | 9
10 | 0 6
11 | 0
12 | 1
```

The median pay for these careers is generally in the $70 and $80 thousands. Only four careers have a median pay of $100 thousand or more. The highest median pay is $121 thousand for a finance director.

Top Pay

```
10 | 0 6 9
11 | 1 6 9
12 | 2 5 6
13 | 0 5 8 8
14 | 0 6
15 | 2 5 7
16 |
17 |
18 |
19 |
20 |
21 | 4
22 | 1
```

The most frequent top pay is in the $130 thousand range. However, the top pay is rather evenly distributed between $100 and $160 thousand. Two unusually high top pay values occur at $214 thousand for a finance director and $221 thousand for an investment banker. Also, note that the top pay has more variability than the median pay.

25.

9	8 9
10	2 4 6 6
11	4 5 7 8 8 9
12	2 4 5 7
13	1 2
14	4
15	1

26. a.

2	1 4
2	6 7
3	0 1 1 1 2 3
3	5 6 7 7
4	0 0 3 3 3 3 3 4 4
4	6 6 7 9
5	0 0 0 2 2
5	5 6 7 9
6	1 4
6	6
7	2

    b.   Most frequent age group: 40-44 with 9 runners

    c.   43 was the most frequent age with 5 runners

27. a.

		y		
		1	2	Total
	A	5	0	5
x	B	11	2	13
	C	2	10	12
	Total	18	12	30

b.

		y		
		1	2	Total
	A	100.0	0.0	100.0
x	B	84.6	15.4	100.0
	C	16.7	83.3	100.0

c.

		y	
		1	2
	A	27.8	0.0
x	B	61.1	16.7
	C	11.1	83.3
	Total	100.0	100.0

d. Category A values for x are always associated with category 1 values for y. Category B values for x are usually associated with category 1 values for y. Category C values for x are usually associated with category 2 values for y.

28. a.

		y				
		20-39	40-59	60-79	80-100	Grand Total
	10-29			1	4	5
x	30-49	2		4		6
	50-69	1	3	1		5
	70-90	4				4
	Grand Total	7	3	6	4	20

b.

		y				
		20-39	40-59	60-79	80-100	Grand Total
	10-29			20.0	80.0	100
x	30-49	33.3		66.7		100
	50-69	20.0	60.0	20.0		100
	70-90	100.0				100

c.

		y			
		20-39	40-59	60-79	80-100
x	10-29	0.0	0.0	16.7	100.0
	30-49	28.6	0.0	66.7	0.0
	50-69	14.3	100.0	16.7	0.0
	70-90	57.1	0.0	0.0	0.0
	Grand Total	100	100	100	100

d. Higher values of x are associated with lower values of y and vice versa

29. a.

Average Miles per Hour

Make	130-139.9	140-149.9	150-159.9	160-169.9	170-179.9	Total
Buick	100.00	0.00	0.00	0.00	0.00	100.00
Chevrolet	18.75	31.25	25.00	18.75	6.25	100.00
Dodge	0.00	100.00	0.00	0.00	0.00	100.00
Ford	33.33	16.67	33.33	16.67	0.00	100.00

b. 25.00 + 18.75 + 6.25 = 50 percent

c.

Average Miles per Hour

Make	130-139.9	140-149.9	150-159.9	160-169.9	170-179.9
Buick	16.67	0.00	0.00	0.00	0.00
Chevrolet	50.00	62.50	66.67	75.00	100.00
Dodge	0.00	25.00	0.00	0.00	0.00
Ford	33.33	12.50	33.33	25.00	0.00
Total	100.00	100.00	100.00	100.00	100.00

d. 75%

30. a.

	Year					
Average Speed	1988-1992	1993-1997	1998-2002	2003-2007	2008-2012	Total
130-139.9	16.7	0.0	0.0	33.3	50.0	100
140-149.9	25.0	25.0	12.5	25.0	12.5	100
150-159.9	0.0	50.0	16.7	16.7	16.7	100
160-169.9	50.0	0.0	50.0	0.0	0.0	100
170-179.9	0.0	0.0	100.0	0.0	0.0	100

b. It appears that most of the faster average winning times occur before 2003. This could be due to new regulations that take into account driver safety, fan safety, the environmental impact, and fuel consumption during races.

31. a.   The crosstabulation of condition of the greens by gender is below.

	Green Condition		
Gender	Too Fast	Fine	Total
Male	35	65	100
Female	40	60	100
Total	75	125	200

The female golfers have the highest percentage saying the greens are too fast: 40/100 = 40%. Male golfers have 35/100 = 35% saying the greens are too fast.

b.   Among low handicap golfers, 1/10 = 10% of the women think the greens are too fast and 10/50 = 20% of the men think the greens are too fast. So, for the low handicappers, the men show a higher percentage who think the greens are too fast.

c.   Among the higher handicap golfers, 39/51 = 43% of the woman think the greens are too fast and 25/50 = 50% of the men think the greens are too fast. So, for the higher handicap golfers, the men show a higher percentage who think the greens are too fast.

d.   This is an example of Simpson's Paradox. At each handicap level a smaller percentage of the women think the greens are too fast. But, when the crosstabulations arc aggregated, the result is reversed and we find a higher percentage of women who think the greens are too fast.

The hidden variable explaining the reversal is handicap level. Fewer people with low handicaps think the greens are too fast, and there are more men with low handicaps than women.

32. a.

	5 Year Average Return						
Fund Type	0-9.99	10-19.99	20-29.99	30-39.99	40-49.99	50-59.99	Total
DE	1	25	1	0	0	0	27
FI	9	1	0	0	0	0	10
IE	0	2	3	2	0	1	8
Total	10	28	4	2	0	1	45

b.

5 Year Average Return	Frequency
0-9.99	10
10-19.99	28
20-29.99	4
30-39.99	2
40-49.99	0
50-59.99	1
Total	45

c.

Fund Type	Frequency
DE	27
FI	10
IE	8
Total	45

d.   The right margin shows the frequency distribution for the fund type variable and the bottom margin shows the frequency distribution for the 5 year average return variable.

e. Higher returns are associated with International Equity funds and lower returns are associated with Fixed Income funds.

33. a.

Fund Type	Expense Ratio (%)						Total
	0-0.24	0.25-0.49	0.50-0.74	0.75-0.99	1.00-1.24	1.25-1.49	
DE	1	1	3	5	10	7	27
FI	2	4	3	0	0	1	10
IE	0	0	1	2	4	1	8
Total	3	5	7	7	14	9	45

b.

Expense Ratio (%)	Frequency	Percent
0-0.24	3	6.7
0.25-0.49	5	11.1
0.50-0.74	7	15.6
0.75-0.99	7	15.6
1.00-1.24	14	31.0
1.25-1.49	9	20.0
Total	45	100

c. Higher expense ratios are associated with Domestic Equity funds and lower expense ratios are associated with Fixed Income fund

34. a.

Bank	2000	2001	2002	2003	2004	2005	2006	2007	2008	2009	2010	2011	2012	Total
AL										3	1	2	1	7
AR		1							1		1			3
AZ			1							5	4	3		13
CA				1					5	17	12	4	1	40
CO										3	6			9
CT			1											1
FL			2		1				2	14	29	13	8	69
GA			1					1	5	25	21	23	10	86
HI	1													1
IA										1		1		2
ID										1				1
IL	1	1	1						1	21	16	9	8	58
IN										1	1	1		3
KS									1	3	3	1	1	9
KY										1				1
LA			1								1	1		3
MA											1			1
MD										2	4		2	8
MI			1						1	4	5	2	1	14
MN									1	6	8	2	4	21
MO									2	3	6	1	4	16
MS											1	1		2
NC										2		2	1	5
NE										1	1	1		3
NH		1												1
NJ				1						2	1	1	1	6
NM											2	1		3
NV									3	3	4	1		11
NY				1						1	3			5
OH		1	1					1		2	2			7
OK										1	1	2	1	5
OR										3	3			6
PA			1					1		1	2	1	2	8
PR											3			3
SC											4	3	2	9
SD										1				1
TN			1										3	4
TX			1						2	5	1	1		10
UT					1					2	3	1		7
VA										1	1	2		4
WA										3	11	3		17
WI				1						1	2	3		7
WV									1					1
WY										1				1
Total	2	4	11	3	4	0	0	3	25	140	157	92	51	492

b. The top three states for bankruptcies over this time period are Georgia (86), Florida (69) and Illinois (58).

c. The frequency distribution over time appears below. Bank failures surged in 2009 and 2010 and then began decreasing in 2011 and 2012.

Year	Number of Bank Failures
2000	2
2001	4
2002	11
2003	3
2004	4
2005	0
2006	0
2007	3
2008	25
2009	140
2010	157
2011	92
2012	51

35. a.

Hwy MPG

Size	15-19	20-24	25-29	30-34	35-39	40-44	Total
Compact	3	4	17	22	5	5	56
Large	2	10	7	3	2		24
Midsize	3	4	30	20	9	3	69
Total	8	18	54	45	16	8	149

b. Midsize and Compact seem to be more fuel efficient than Large.

c.

City MPG

Drive	10-14	15-19	20-24	25-29	30-34	40-44	Total
A	7	18	3				28
F		17	49	19	2	3	90
R	10	20		1			31
Total	17	55	52	20	2	3	149

d. Higher fuel efficiencies are associated with front wheel drive cars.

e.

City MPG

Fuel Type	15-19	20-24	25-29	30-34	35-39	40-44	Total
P	8	16	20	12			56
R		2	34	33	16	8	93
Total	8	18	54	45	16	8	149

f. Higher fuel efficiencies are associated with cars that use regular gas.

36. a.

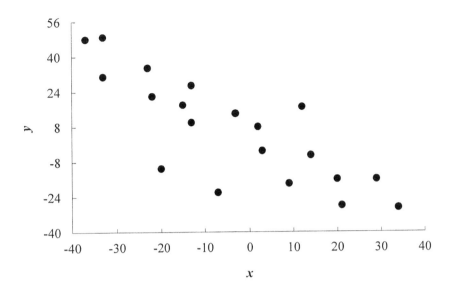

b. There is a negative relationship between x and y; y decreases as x increases.

37. a.

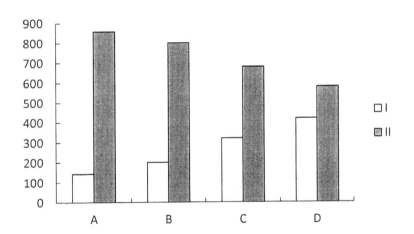

b. As X goes from A to D the frequency for I increases and the frequency of II decreases.

38. a.

		y		
		Yes	No	
	Low	66.667	33.333	100
x	Medium	30.000	70.000	100
	High	80.000	20.000	100

b.

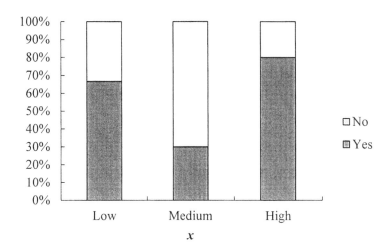

39. a.

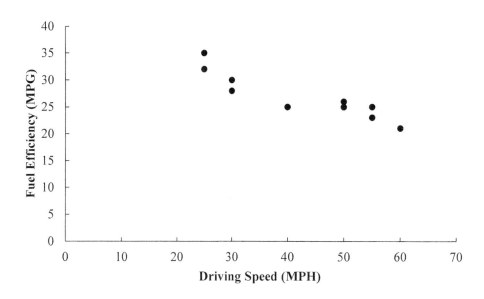

b. For midsized cars, lower driving speeds seem to yield higher miles per gallon.

40. a.

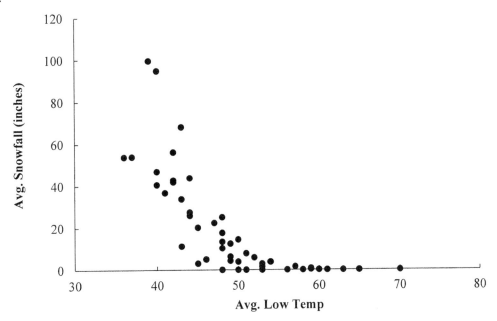

b. Colder average low temperature seems to lead to higher amounts of snowfall.

c. Two cities have an average snowfall of nearly 100 inches of snowfall: Buffalo, N.Y and Rochester, NY. Both are located near large lakes in New York.

41. a.

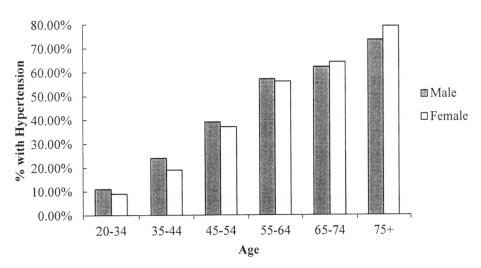

b. The percentage of people with hypertension increases with age.

c. For ages earlier than 65, the percentage of males with hypertension is higher than that for females. After age 65, the percentage of females with hypertension is higher than that for males.

2 - 27

42. a.

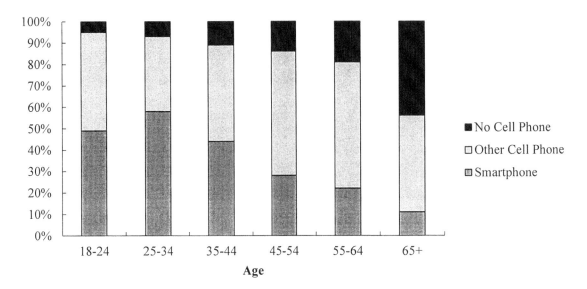

b. After an increase in age 25-34, smartphone ownership decreases as age increases. The percentage of people with no cell phone increases with age. There is less variation across age groups in the percentage who own other cell phones.

c. Unless a newer device replaces the smartphone, we would expect smartphone ownership would become less sensitive to age. This would be true because current users will become older and because the device will become to be seen more as a necessity than a luxury.

43. a.

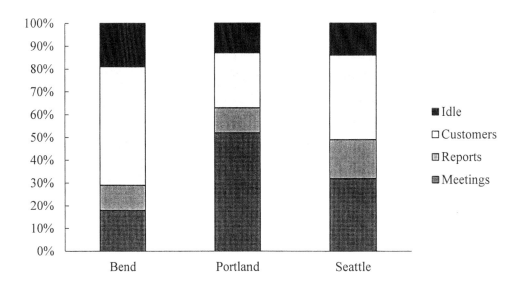

b.

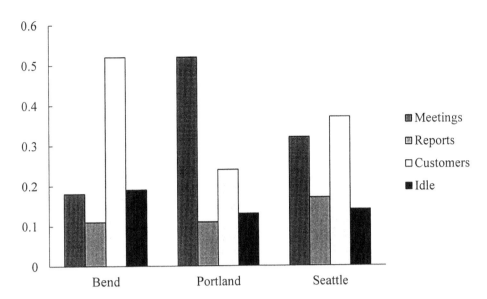

c. The stacked bar chart seems simpler than the side-by-side bar chart and more easily conveys the differences in store managers' use of time.

44. a.

Class	Frequency
800-999	1
1000-1199	3
1200-1399	6
1400-1599	10
1600-1799	7
1800-1999	2
2000-2199	1
Total	30

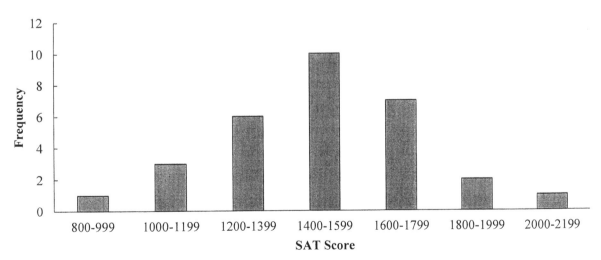

b. The distribution if nearly symmetrical. It could be approximated by a bell-shaped curve.

2 - 29

c. 10 of 30 or 33% of the scores are between 1400 and 1599. The average SAT score looks to be a little over 1500. Scores below 800 or above 2200 are unusual.

45. a.

State	Frequency
Arizona	2
California	11
Florida	15
Georgia	2
Louisiana	8
Michigan	2
Minnesota	1
Texas	2
Total	43

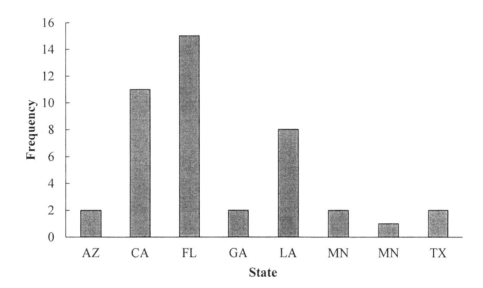

b. Florida has had the most Super Bowl with 15, or 15/43(100) = 35%. Florida and California have been the states with the most Super Bowls. A total of 15 + 11 = 26, or 26/43(100) = 60%. Only 3 Super Bowls, or 3/43(100) = 7%, have been played in the cold weather states of Michigan and Minnesota.

c.

```
0 | 1 3 3 3 3 3 4 4 4 4
0 | 5 7 7 7 9
1 | 0 0 0 1 2 2 3 4
1 | 5 6 7 7 7 7 8 9 9 9
2 | 1 2 3
2 | 5 7 7
3 | 2
3 | 5 6
4 |
4 | 5
```

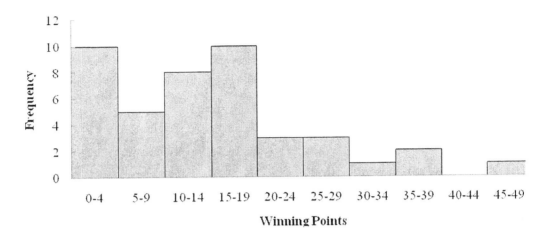

d. The most frequent winning points have been 0 to 4 points and 15 to 19 points. Both occurred in 10 Super Bowls. There were 10 close games with a margin of victory less than 5 points, 10/43(100) = 23% of the Super Bowls. There have also been 10 games, 23%, with a margin of victory more than 20 points.

e. The closest games was the 25th Super Bowl with a 1 point margin. It was played in Florida. The largest margin of victory occurred one year earlier in the 24th Super Bowl. It had a 45 point margin and was played in Louisiana. More detailed information not available from the text information.

    25th Super Bowl: 1991 New York Giants 20 Buffalo Bills 19, Tampa Stadium, Tampa, FL
    24th Super Bowl: 1990 San Francisco 49ers 55 Denver Broncos 10, Superdome, New Orleans, LA

    Note: The data set SuperBowl contains a list of the teams and the final scores of the 43 Super Bowls. This data set can be used in Chapter 2 and Chapter 3 to provide interesting data summaries about the points scored by the winning team and the points scored by the losing team in the Super Bowl. For example, using the median scores, the median Super Bowl score was 28 to 13.

46. a.

Population in Millions	Frequency	% Frequency
0.0 - 2.4	15	30.0%
2.5-4.9	13	26.0%
5.0-7.4	10	20.0%
7.5-9.9	5	10.0%
10.0-12.4	1	2.0%
12.5-14.9	2	4.0%
15.0-17.4	0	0.0%
17.5-19.9	2	4.0%
20.0-22.4	0	0.0%
22.5-24.9	0	0.0%
25.0-27.4	1	2.0%
27.5-29.9	0	0.0%
30.0-32.4	0	0.0%
32.5-34.9	0	0.0%
35.0-37.4	1	2.0%
37.5-39.9	0	0.0%
More	0	0.0%

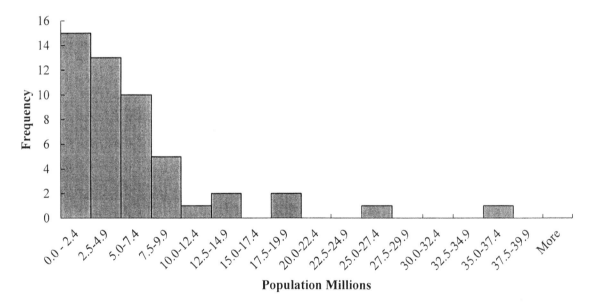

b. The distribution is skewed to the right.

c. 15 states (30%) have a population less than 2.5 million. Over half of the states have population less than 5 million (28 states – 56%). Only seven states have a population greater than 10 million (California, Florida, Illinois, New York, Ohio, Pennsylvania and Texas). The largest state is California (37.3 million) and the smallest states are Vermont and Wyoming (600 thousand).

47. a.

```
 1   8
 2   014
 3   18
 4   007899
 5   012444578
 6   00139
 7   237888
 8   011
 9   1
10   3
11   0289
12   9
13   01
14
15   46
16   68
17
18
19   2
20
21
22
23
24
25
26
27   2
```

b. The majority of the start-up companies in this set have less than $90 million in venture capital. Only 6 of the 50 (12%) have more than $150 million.

48. a.

Industry	Frequency	% Frequency
Bank	26	13%
Cable	44	22%
Car	42	21%
Cell	60	30%
Collection	28	14%
Total	200	100%

b.

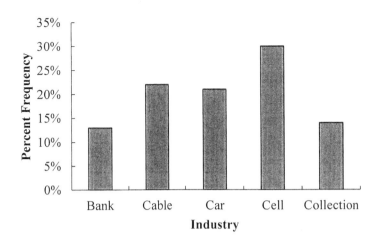

c. The cellular phone providers had the highest number of complaints.

d. The percentage frequency distribution shows that the two financial industries (banks and collection agencies) had about the same number of complaints. Also, new car dealers and cable and satellite television companies also had about the same number of complaints.

49. a.

Yield%	Frequency	Percent Frequency
0.0-0.9	4	13.3
1.0-1.9	2	6.7
2.0-2.9	6	20.0
3.0-3.9	10	33.3
4.0-4.9	3	10.0
5.0-5.9	2	6.7
6.0-6.9	2	6.7
7.0-7.9	0	0.0
8.0-8.9	0	0.0
9.0-9.9	1	3.3
Total	30	100.0

b.

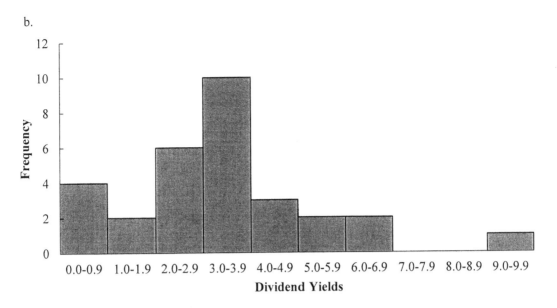

c. The distribution is skewed to the right.

d. Dividend yield ranges from 0% to over 9%. The most frequent range is 3.0% to 3.9%. Average dividend yields looks to be between 3% and 4%. Over 50% of the companies (16) pay from 2.0 % to 3.9%. Five companies (AT&T, DuPont, General Electric, Merck, and Verizon) pay 5.0% or more. Four companies (Bank of America, Cisco Systems, Hewlett-Packard, and J.P. Morgan Chase) pay less than 1%.

e. General Electric had an unusually high dividend yield of 9.2%. 500 shares at $14 per share is an investment of 500($14) = $7,000. A 9.2% dividend yield provides .092(7,000) = $644 of dividend income per year.

50. a.

Age	Below High School	High School Graduate	Some College No Degree	Associate's Degree	Bachelor's Degree	Advanced Degree	Total
25-34	11.6	27.2	18.9	9.5	24.0	8.9	100
35-44	11.7	28.6	16.3	10.3	21.9	11.2	100
45-54	10.4	32.8	16.7	10.6	19.0	10.4	100
55-64	10.4	31.3	17.3	9.2	18.6	13.1	100
65-74	17.0	35.4	15.7	6.6	14.1	11.1	100
75 & older	24.6	37.6	14.0	4.6	11.9	7.3	100

b.

Age	Below High School	High School Graduate	Some College No Degree	Associate's Degree	Bachelor's Degree	Advanced Degree
25-34	18.5	17.9	23.1	21.4	25.4	17.4
35-44	18.4	18.5	19.6	22.9	22.8	21.5
45-54	18.0	23.3	22.0	25.8	21.7	21.9
55-64	14.3	17.7	18.2	17.9	17.0	22.0
65-74	13.9	11.9	9.8	7.6	7.6	11.0
75 & older	16.9	10.6	7.3	4.5	5.4	6.1
Total	100.0	100.0	100.0	100.0	100.0	100.0

Comparing the percent frequency distributions of the Bachelor's Degree versus Advanced Degree, we see that the percentage of advanced degree holders who are older exceeds those holding a bachelor's degree who are older.

51. a. The batting averages for the junior and senior years for each player are as follows:

Junior year:
- Allison Fealey   15/40 = .375
- Emily Janson   70/200 = .350

Senior year:
- Allison Fealey   75/250 = .300
- Emily Janson   35/120 = .292

Because Allison Fealey had the higher batting average in both her junior year and senior year, Allison Fealey should receive the scholarship offer.

b. The combined or aggregated two-year crosstabulation is as follows:

Combined 2-Year Batting

Outcome	A. Fealey	E. Jansen
Hit	90	105
No Hit	200	215
Total At Bats	290	320

Based on this crosstabulation, the batting average for each player is as follows:

Combined Junior/Senior Years
- Allison Fealey   90/290 = .310
- Emily Janson   105/320 = .328

Because Emily Janson has the higher batting average over the combined junior and senior years, Emily Janson should receive the scholarship offer.

c. The recommendations in parts (a) and (b) are not consistent. This is an example of Simpson's Paradox. It shows that in interpreting the results based upon separate or un-aggregated crosstabulations, the conclusion can be reversed when the crosstabulations are grouped or aggregated. When Simpson's Paradox is present, the decision maker will have to decide whether the un-aggregated or the aggregated form of the crosstabulation is the most helpful in identifying the desired conclusion. Note: The authors prefer the recommendation to offer the scholarship to Emily Janson because it is based upon the aggregated performance for both players over a larger number of at-bats. But this is a judgment or personal preference decision. Others may prefer the conclusion based on using the un-aggregated approach in part (a).

52. a.

Job Growth (%)	Size of Company			Total
	Small	Midsized	Large	
-10- (-1)	4	6	2	12
0-9	18	13	29	60
10-19	7	2	4	13
20-29	3	3	2	8
30-39	0	3	1	4
40 or more	0	1	0	1
Total	32	28	38	98

b. Frequency distribution for growth rate.

Job Growth (%)	Total
-10- (-1)	12
0-9	60
10-19	13
20-29	8
30-39	4
40 or more	1
Total	98

Frequency distribution for size of company.

Size	Total
Small	32
Medium	28
Large	38
Total	98

c. Crosstabulation showing column percentages.

	Size of Company		
Job Growth (%)	Small	Midsized	Large
-10- (-1)	13	21	5
0-9	56	46	76
10-19	22	7	11
20-29	9	11	5
30-39	0	11	3
40 or more	0	4	0
Total	100	100	100

d. Crosstabulation showing row percentages.

	Size of Company			
Job Growth (%)	Small	Midsized	Large	Total
-10- (-1)	33	50	17	100
0-9	30	22	48	100
10-19	54	15	31	100
20-29	38	38	25	100
30-39	0	75	25	100
40 or more	0	4	0	100

e. 12 companies had negative job growth: 33% of these were small companies; 50% were midsized companies; and 17% were large companies. So, in terms of avoiding negative job growth, large companies performed better than small and midsized companies. But, although 95% of the large companies had a positive job growth, the growth rate was between 0 and 9% for 76% of these companies. In terms of better job growth rates, midsized companies performed better than either small or large companies. For instance, 26% of the midsized companies had a job growth of at least 20% compared to 9% for small companies and 8% for large companies.

53. a.

	Tution & Fees ($)								
Year Founded	1-5000	10001-15000	15001-20000	20001-25000	25001-30000	30001-35000	35001-40000	40001-45000	Total
1600-1649							1		1
1700-1749							2	1	3
1750-1799								4	4
1800-1849				1	3	3	6	8	21
1850-1899	1		2	2	13	14	13	4	49
1900-1949		1		2	3	4	8		18
1950-2000			2	4		1			7
Total	1	1	4	9	19	22	30	17	103

b.

Year Founded	Tuition & Fees ($)								Grand Total
	1-5000	10001-15000	15001-20000	20001-25000	25001-30000	30001-35000	35001-40000	40001-45000	
1600-1649							100.00		100
1700-1749							66.67	33.33	100
1750-1799								100.00	100
1800-1849				4.76	14.29	14.29	28.57	38.10	100
1850-1899	2.04		4.08	4.08	26.53	28.57	26.53	8.16	100
1900-1949		5.56		11.11	16.67	22.22	44.44		100
1950-2000			28.57	57.14		14.29			100

c. Colleges in this sample founded before 1800 tend to be expensive in terms of tuition.

54. a.

Year Founded	% Graduate													Grand Total
	35-40	40-45	45-50	50-55	55-60	60-65	65-70	70-75	75-80	80-85	85-90	90-95	95-100	
1600-1649													1	1
1700-1749													3	3
1750-1799												1	3	4
1800-1849						1	2	4	2	3	4	3	2	21
1850-1899			1	2	4	3	11	5	9	6	3	4	1	49
1900-1949	1	1	1		1	3		3	2	4	1	1		18
1950-2000	1		1	3			2							7
Grand Total	2	1	3	5	5	7	15	12	13	13	8	9	10	103

b.

Year Founded	% Graduate													Grand Total
	35-40	40-45	45-50	50-55	55-60	60-65	65-70	70-75	75-80	80-85	85-90	90-95	95-100	
1600-1649													100.00	100
1700-1749													100.00	100
1750-1799												25.00	75.00	100
1800-1849						4.76	9.52	19.05	9.52	14.29	19.05	14.29	9.52	100
1850-1899			2.04	4.08	8.16	6.12	22.45	10.20	18.37	12.24	6.12	8.16	2.04	100
1900-1949	5.56	5.56	5.56		5.56	16.67		16.67	11.11	22.22	5.56	5.56		100
1950-2000	14.29		14.29	42.86			28.57							100

c. Older colleges and universities tend to have higher graduation rates.

55. a.

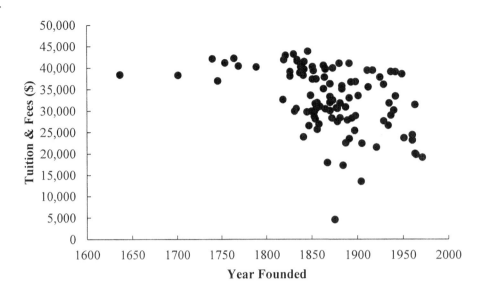

b. Older colleges and universities tend to be more expensive.

56. a.

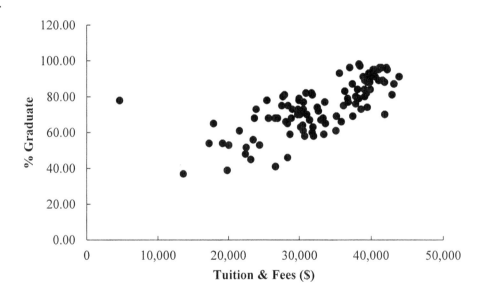

b. There appears to be a strong positive relationship between Tuition & Fees and % Graduation.

57. a.

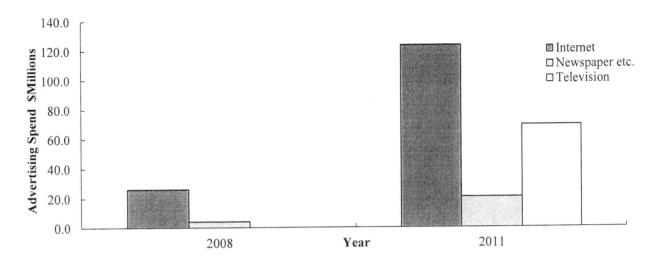

b.

	2008	2011
Internet	86.7%	57.8%
Newspaper etc.	13.3%	9.7%
Television	0.0%	32.5%
Total	100.0%	100.0%

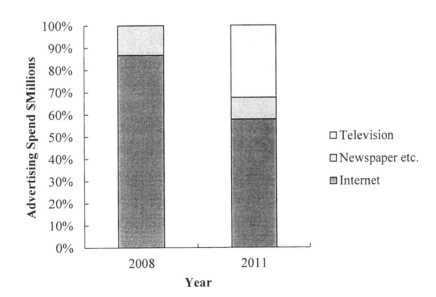

c. The graph is part a is more insightful because is shows the allocation of the budget across media, but also dramatic increase in the size of the budget.

58. a.

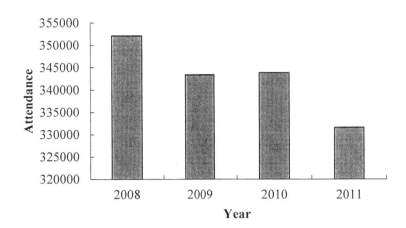

Zoo attendance appears to be dropping over time.

b.

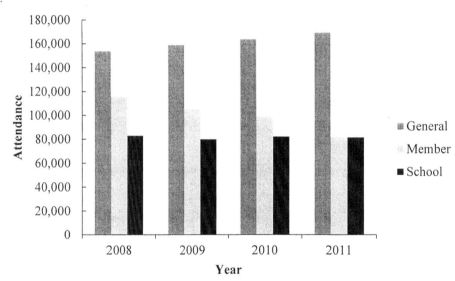

c. General attendance is increasing, but not enough to offset the decrease in member attendance. School membership appears fairly stable.

Chapter 3
Descriptive Statistics: Numerical Measures

Learning Objectives

1. Understand the purpose of measures of location.

2. Be able to compute the mean, weighted mean, geometric mean, median, mode, quartiles, and various percentiles.

3. Understand the purpose of measures of variability.

4. Be able to compute the range, interquartile range, variance, standard deviation, and coefficient of variation.

5. Understand skewness as a measure of the shape of a data distribution. Learn how to recognize when a data distribution is negatively skewed, roughly symmetric, and positively skewed.

6. Understand how z scores are computed and how they are used as a measure of relative location of a data value.

7. Know how Chebyshev's theorem and the empirical rule can be used to determine the percentage of the data within a specified number of standard deviations from the mean.

8. Learn how to construct a 5–number summary and a box plot.

9. Be able to compute and interpret covariance and correlation as measures of association between two variables.

10. Understand the role of summary measures in data dashboards.

Solutions:

1. $$\bar{x} = \frac{\Sigma x_i}{n} = \frac{75}{5} = 15$$

    10, 12, 16, 17, 20

    Median = 16 (middle value)

2. $$\bar{x} = \frac{\Sigma x_i}{n} = \frac{96}{6} = 16$$

    10, 12, 16, 17, 20, 21

    $$\text{Median} = \frac{16+17}{2} = 16.5$$

3. a. $$\bar{x} = \frac{\Sigma w_i x_i}{\Sigma w_i} = \frac{6(3.2)+3(2)+2(2.5)+8(5)}{6+3+2+8} = \frac{70.2}{19} = 3.69$$

    b. $$\frac{3.2+2+2.5+5}{4} = \frac{12.7}{4} = 3.175$$

4.

Period	Rate of Return (%)
1	-6.0
2	-8.0
3	-4.0
4	2.0
5	5.4

The mean growth factor over the five periods is:

$$\bar{x}_g = \sqrt[n]{(x_1)(x_2)\cdots(x_5)} = \sqrt[5]{(0.940)(0.920)(0.960)(1.020)(1.054)} = \sqrt[5]{0.8925} = 0.9775$$

So the mean growth rate $(0.9775 - 1)100\% = -2.25\%$.

5. 15, 20, 25, 25, 27, 28, 30, 34

    $$i = \frac{20}{100}(8) = 1.6 \qquad \text{2nd position} = 20$$

    $$i = \frac{25}{100}(8) = 2 \qquad \frac{20+25}{2} = 22.5$$

    $$i = \frac{65}{100}(8) = 5.2 \qquad \text{6th position} = 28$$

    $$i = \frac{75}{100}(8) = 6 \qquad \frac{28+30}{2} = 29$$

6.   Mean $= \dfrac{\Sigma x_i}{n} = \dfrac{657}{11} = 59.73$

Median $= 57$ 6th item

Mode $= 53$ It appears 3 times

7.   a.   The mean commute time is 26.9 minutes.

b.   The median commute time is 25.95 minutes.

c.   The data are bimodal. The modes are 23.4 and 24.8.

d.   The index for the third quartile is $i = \dfrac{75}{100} 48 = 36$, so the third quartile is the mean of the values of the 36th and 37th observations in the sorted data, or $\dfrac{28.5 + 28.5}{2} = 28.5$.

8.   a. $\bar{x} = \dfrac{\Sigma x_i}{n} = \dfrac{350}{19} = 18.42$

b. $\bar{x} = \dfrac{\Sigma x_i}{n} = \dfrac{120}{19} = 6.32$

c. $\dfrac{120}{350}(100) = 34.3\%$ of 3-point shots were made from the 20 feet, 9 inch line during the 19 games.

d.   Moving the 3-point line back to 20 feet, 9 inches has reduced the number of 3-point shots taken per game from 19.07 to 18.42, or $19.07 - 18.42 = .65$ shots per game. The percentage of 3-points made per game has been reduced from 35.2% to 34.3%, or only .9%. The move has reduced both the number of shots taken per game and the percentage of shots made per game, but the differences are small. The data support the Associated Press Sports conclusion that the move has not changed the game dramatically.

The 2008-09 sample data shows 120 3-point baskets in the 19 games. Thus, the mean number of points scored from the 3-point line is 120(3)/19 = 18.95 points per game. With the previous 3-point line at 19 feet, 9 inches, 19.07 shots per game and a 35.2% success rate indicate that the mean number of points scored from the 3-point line was 19.07(.352)(3) = 20.14 points per game. There is only a mean of 20.14 – 18.95 = 1.19 points per game less being scored from the 20 feet, 9 inch 3-point line.

9.   a. $\bar{x} = \dfrac{\Sigma x_i}{n} = \dfrac{148}{10} = 14.8$

b.   Order the data from low 6.7 to high 36.6

Median $i = \left(\dfrac{50}{100}\right) 10 = 5$ Use 5th and 6th positions.

Median $= \dfrac{10.1 + 16.1}{2} = 13.1$

c. Mode = 7.2 (occurs 2 times)

d. $i = \left(\dfrac{25}{100}\right)10 = 2.5$ Use 3rd position. $Q_1 = 7.2$

$i = \left(\dfrac{75}{100}\right)10 = 7.5$ Use 8th position. $Q_3 = 17.2$

e. $\Sigma x_i = \$148$ billion

The percentage of total endowments held by these 2.3% of colleges and universities is $(148/413)(100) = 35.8\%$.

f. A decline of 23% would be a decline of $.23(148) = \$34$ billion for these 10 colleges and universities. With this decline, administrators might consider budget cutting strategies such as

- Hiring freezes for faculty and staff
- Delaying or eliminating construction projects
- Raising tuition
- Increasing enrollments

10. a. $\bar{x} = \dfrac{\sum x_i}{n} = \dfrac{1318}{20} = 65.9$

Order the data from the lowest rating (42) to the highest rating (83)

Position	Rating	Position	Rating
1	42	11	67
2	53	12	67
3	54	13	68
4	61	14	69
5	61	15	71
6	61	16	71
7	62	17	76
8	63	18	78
9	64	19	81
10	66	20	83

$i = \dfrac{p}{100}(n) = \dfrac{50}{100}(20) = 10$ 10th value $= 66$, 11th value $= 67$

Median or 50th percentile $= (66 + 67)/2 = 66.5$

The mode is 67 (it occurs three times).

b. $i = \dfrac{p}{100}(n) = \dfrac{25}{100}(20) = 5$ 5th value = 61, 6th value = 61

First quartile or 25th percentile $Q_1 = (61 + 61) / 2 = 61$

$i = \dfrac{p}{100}(n) = \dfrac{75}{100}(20) = 15$ 15th value = 71, 16th value = 71

Third quartile or 75th percentile $Q_3 = (71 + 71) / 2 = 71$

c. $i = \dfrac{p}{100}(n) = \dfrac{90}{100}(20) = 18$ 18th value = 78, 19th value = 81

90th percentile = $(78 + 81) / 2 = 79.5$

At least 90% of the ratings are 79.5 or less; at least 10% of the ratings are 79.5 or greater.

11. a. The median number of hours worked per week for high school science teachers is 54.

    b. The median number of hours worked per week for high school English teachers is 47.

    c. The median number of hours worked per week for high school science teachers is greater than the median number of hours worked per week for high school English teachers; the difference is 54 – 47 = 7 hours.

12. a. The minimum number of viewers that watched a new episode is 13.3 million, and the maximum number is 16.5 million.

    b. The mean number of viewers that watched a new episode is 15.04 million or approximately 15.0 million; the median also 15.0 million. The data is multimodal (13.6, 14.0, 16.1, and 16.2 million); in such cases the mode is usually not reported.

    c. The data are first arranged in ascending order. The index for the first quartile is $i = \left(\dfrac{25}{100} \right) 21 = 5.25$, so the first quartile is the value of the 6th observation in the sorted data, or 14.1. The index for the third quartile is $i = \dfrac{75}{100} 21 = 15.75$, so the third quartile is the value of the 16th observation in the sorted data, or 16.0.

    d. A graph showing the viewership data over the air dates follows. Period 1 corresponds to the first episode of the season; period 2 corresponds to the second episode, and so on.

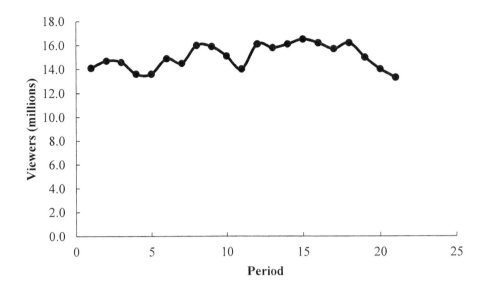

This graph shows that viewership of *The Big Bang Theory* has been relatively stable over the 2011–2012 television season.

13.   Using the mean we get $\bar{x}_{city} = 15.58$, $\bar{x}_{highway} = 18.92$

For the samples we see that the mean mileage is better on the highway than in the city.

City

13.2 14.4 15.2 15.3 15.3 15.3 15.9 16 16.1 16.2 16.2 16.7 16.8

↑

Median

Mode: 15.3

Highway

17.2 17.4 18.3 18.5 18.6 18.6 18.7 19.0 19.2 19.4 19.4 20.6 21.1

↑

Median

Mode: 18.6, 19.4

The median and modal mileages are also better on the highway than in the city.

14.   For March 2011:

The index for the first quartile is $i = \left(\dfrac{25}{100}\right)50 = 12.50$, so the first quartile is the value of the 13th observation in the sorted data, or 6.8.

The index for the median is $i = \dfrac{50}{100}50 = 25.0$, so the median (or second quartile) is the average of the values of the 25th and 26th observations in the sorted data, or 8.0.

The index for the third quartile is $i = \dfrac{75}{100} 50 = 37.50$, so the third quartile is the value of the 38th observation in the sorted data, or 9.4.

For March 2012:

The minimum is 3.0

The index for the first quartile is $i = \left(\dfrac{25}{100} \right) 50 = 12.50$, so the first quartile is the value of the 13th observation in the sorted data, or 6.8.

The index for the median is $i = \dfrac{50}{100} 50 = 25.0$, so the median (or second quartile) is the average of the values of the 25th and 26th observations in the sorted data, or 7.35.

The index for the third quartile is $i = \dfrac{75}{100} 50 = 37.50$, so the third quartile is the value of the 38th observation in the sorted data, or 8.6.

It may be easier to compare these results if we place them in a table.

	March 2011	March 2012
First Quartile	6.8	6.8
Median	8.0	7.35
Third Quartile	9.4	8.6

The results show that in March 2012 approximately 25% of the states had an unemployment rate of 6.8% or less, the same as in March 2011. However, the median of 7.35% and the third quartile of 8.6% in March 2012 are both less than the corresponding values in March 2011, indicating that unemployment rates across the states are decreasing.

15. To calculate the average sales price we must compute a weighted mean. The weighted mean is

$$\frac{501(34.99) + 1425(38.99) + 294(36.00) + 882(33.59) + 715(40.99) + 1088(38.59) + 1644(39.59) + 819(37.99)}{501 + 1425 + 294 + 882 + 715 + 1088 + 1644 + 819}$$

$$= 38.11$$

Thus, the average sales price per case is $38.11.

16. a.

Grade x_i	Weight W_i
4 (A)	9
3 (B)	15
2 (C)	33
1 (D)	3
0 (F)	0
	60 Credit Hours

$$\bar{x} = \frac{\Sigma w_i x_i}{\Sigma w_i} = \frac{9(4) + 15(3) + 33(2) + 3(1)}{9 + 15 + 33 + 3} = \frac{150}{60} = 2.50$$

b. Yes; satisfies the 2.5 grade point average requirement

17. a. $\bar{x} = \dfrac{\Sigma f_i M_i}{N} = \dfrac{9191(4.65) + 2621(18.15) + 1419(11.36) + 2900(6.75)}{9191 + 2621 + 1419 + 2900}$

$= \dfrac{126,004.14}{16,131} = 7.81$

The weighted average total return for the Morningstar funds is 7.81%.

b. If the amount invested in each fund was available, it would be better to use those amounts as weights. The weighted return computed in part (a) will be a good approximation, if the amount invested in the various funds is approximately equal.

c. Portfolio Return $= \dfrac{2000(4.65) + 4000(18.15) + 3000(11.36) + 1000(6.75)}{2000 + 4000 + 3000 + 1000}$

$= \dfrac{122,730}{10,000} = 12.27$

The portfolio return would be 12.27%.

18.

Assessment	Deans	$f_i M_i$	Recruiters	$f_i M_i$
5	44	220	31	155
4	66	264	34	136
3	60	180	43	129
2	10	20	12	24
1	0	0	0	0
Total	180	684	120	444

Deans: $\quad \bar{x} = \dfrac{\Sigma f_i M_i}{n} = \dfrac{684}{180} = 3.8$

Recruiters: $\bar{x} = \dfrac{\Sigma f_i M_i}{n} = \dfrac{444}{120} = 3.7$

19. To calculate the mean growth rate we must first compute the geometric mean of the five growth factors:

Year	% Growth	Growth Factor x_i
2007	5.5	1.055
2008	1.1	1.011
2009	-3.5	0.965
2010	-1.1	0.989
2011	1.8	1.018

$\bar{x}_g = \sqrt[n]{(x_1)(x_2)\cdots(x_5)} = \sqrt[5]{(1.055)(1.011)(0.965)(0.989)(1.018)} = \sqrt[5]{1.036275} = 1.007152$

The mean annual growth rate is $(1.007152 - 1)100 = 0.7152\%$.

20.

	Stivers		Trippi	
Year	End of Year Value	Growth Factor	End of Year Value	Growth Factor
2004	$11,000	1.100	$5,600	1.120
2005	$12,000	1.091	$6,300	1.125
2006	$13,000	1.083	$6,900	1.095
2007	$14,000	1.077	$7,600	1.101
2008	$15,000	1.071	$8,500	1.118
2009	$16,000	1.067	$9,200	1.082
2010	$17,000	1.063	$9,900	1.076
2011	$18,000	1.059	$10,600	1.071

For the Stivers mutual fund we have:

$$18000=10000\left[(x_1)(x_2)\cdots(x_8)\right], \text{ so } \left[(x_1)(x_2)\cdots(x_8)\right]=1.8 \text{ and}$$

$$\overline{x}_g = \sqrt[n]{(x_1)(x_2)\cdots(x_8)} = \sqrt[8]{1.80} = 1.07624$$

So the mean annual return for the Stivers mutual fund is $(1.07624 - 1)100 = 7.624\%$

For the Trippi mutual fund we have:

$$10600=5000\left[(x_1)(x_2)\cdots(x_8)\right], \text{ so } \left[(x_1)(x_2)\cdots(x_8)\right]=2.12 \text{ and}$$

$$\overline{x}_g = \sqrt[n]{(x_1)(x_2)\cdots(x_8)} = \sqrt[8]{2.12} = 1.09848$$

So the mean annual return for the Trippi mutual fund is $(1.09848 - 1)100 = 9.848\%$.

While the Stivers mutual fund has generated a nice annual return of 7.6%, the annual return of 9.8% earned by the Trippi mutual fund is far superior.

21. $$5000=3500\left[(x_1)(x_2)\cdots(x_9)\right], \text{ so } \left[(x_1)(x_2)\cdots(x_9)\right]=1.428571, \text{ and so}$$

$$\overline{x}_g = \sqrt[n]{(x_1)(x_2)\cdots(x_9)} = \sqrt[9]{1.428571} = 1.040426$$

So the mean annual growth rate is $(1.040426 - 1)100 = 4.0404\%$

22. $$25,000,000=10,000,000\left[(x_1)(x_2)\cdots(x_6)\right], \text{ so } \left[(x_1)(x_2)\cdots(x_6)\right]=2.50, \text{ and so}$$

$$\overline{x}_g = \sqrt[n]{(x_1)(x_2)\cdots(x_6)} = \sqrt[6]{2.50} = 1.165$$

So the mean annual growth rate is $(1.165 - 1)100 = 16.5\%$

23.   Range 20 - 10 = 10

10, 12, 16, 17, 20

$$i = \frac{25}{100}(5) = 1.25$$

Q_1 (2nd position) = 12

$$i = \frac{75}{100}(5) = 3.75$$

Q_3 (4th position) = 17

IQR = $Q_3 - Q_1$ = 17 - 12 = 5

24. $$\bar{x} = \frac{\Sigma x_i}{n} = \frac{75}{5} = 15$$

$$s^2 = \frac{\Sigma(x_i - \bar{x})^2}{n-1} = \frac{64}{4} = 16$$

$$s = \sqrt{16} = 4$$

25.   15, 20, 25, 25, 27, 28, 30, 34   Range = 34 - 15 = 19

$$i = \frac{25}{100}(8) = 2 \qquad Q_1 = \frac{20+25}{2} = 22.5$$

$$i = \frac{75}{100}(8) = 6 \qquad Q_3 = \frac{28+30}{2} = 29$$

IQR = $Q_3 - Q_1$ = 29 - 22.5 = 6.5

$$\bar{x} = \frac{\Sigma x_i}{n} = \frac{204}{8} = 25.5$$

$$s^2 = \frac{\Sigma(x_i - \bar{x})^2}{n-1} = \frac{242}{7} = 34.57$$

$$s = \sqrt{34.57} = 5.88$$

26. a.   Range = 190 - 168 = 22

b. $\Sigma(x_i - \bar{x})^2 = 376$

$$s^2 = \frac{376}{5} = 75.2$$

c. $s = \sqrt{75.2} = 8.67$

d.   Coefficient of Variation $= \left(\dfrac{8.67}{178}\right)100\% = 4.87\%$

27. a.   The mean price for a round–trip flight into Atlanta is \$356.73, and the mean price for a round–trip flight into Salt Lake City is \$400.95. Flights into Atlanta are less expensive than flights into Salt Lake City. This possibly could be explained by the locations of these two cities relative to the 14 departure cities; Atlanta is generally closer than Salt Lake City to the departure cities.

   b.   For flights into Atlanta, the range is \$290.0, the variance is 5517.41, and the standard Deviation is \$74.28. For flights into Salt Lake City, the range is \$458.8, the variance is 18933.32, and the standard deviation is \$137.60.

   The prices for round–trip flights into Atlanta are less variable than prices for round–trip flights into Salt Lake City. This could also be explained by Atlanta's relative nearness to the 14 departure cities.

28. a.   The mean serve speed is 180.95, the variance is 21.42, and the standard deviation is 4.63.

   b.   Although the mean serve speed for the twenty Women's Singles serve speed leaders for the 2011 Wimbledon tournament is slightly higher, the difference is very small. Furthermore, given the variation in the twenty Women's Singles serve speed leaders from the 2012 Australian Open and the twenty Women's Singles serve speed leaders from the 2011 Wimbledon tournament, the difference in the mean serve speeds is most likely due to random variation in the players' performances.

29. a.   Range = 60 – 28 = 32

   IQR = $Q_3 - Q_1$ = 55 – 45 = 10

   b. $\bar{x} = \dfrac{435}{9} = 48.33$

   $\Sigma(x_i - \bar{x})^2 = 742$

   $s^2 = \dfrac{\Sigma(x_i - \bar{x})^2}{n-1} = \dfrac{742}{8} = 92.75$

   $s = \sqrt{92.75} = 9.63$

   c.   The average air quality is about the same. But, the variability is greater in Anaheim.

30.   Dawson Supply: Range = 11 – 9 = 2

   $s = \sqrt{\dfrac{4.1}{9}} = 0.67$

   J.C. Clark: Range = 15 – 7 = 8

   $s = \sqrt{\dfrac{60.1}{9}} = 2.58$

31. a.

	18–34	**35–44**	**45+**
mean	1368.0	1330.1	1070.4
median	1423.0	1382.5	1163.5
standard deviation	540.8	431.7	334.5

b. The 45+ group appears to spend less on coffee than the other two groups, and the 18–34 and 35–44 groups spend similar amounts of coffee.

32. a. Automotive : $\bar{x} = \dfrac{\sum x_i}{n} = \dfrac{39201}{20} = 1960.05$

Department store: $\bar{x} = \dfrac{\sum x_i}{n} = \dfrac{13857}{20} = 692.85$

b. Automotive : $s = \sqrt{\dfrac{\sum (x_i - \bar{x})^2}{(n-1)}} = \sqrt{\dfrac{4,407,720.95}{19}} = 481.65$

Department store: $s = \sqrt{\dfrac{\sum (x_i - \bar{x})^2}{(n-1)}} = \sqrt{\dfrac{456804.55}{19}} = 155.06$

c. Automotive: $2901 - 598 = 2303$
Department Store: $1011 - 448 = 563$

d. Order the data for each variable from the lowest to highest.

	Automotive	**Department Store**
1	598	448
2	1512	472
3	1573	474
4	1642	573
5	1714	589
6	1720	597
7	1781	598
8	1798	622
9	1813	629
10	2008	669
11	2014	706
12	2024	714
13	2058	746
14	2166	760
15	2202	782
16	2254	824
17	2366	840
18	2526	856
19	2531	947
20	2901	1011

$$i = \frac{p}{100}(n) = \frac{25}{100}(20) = 5$$

Automotive:	First quartile $Q_1 = (1714 + 1720)/2 = 1717$
Department Store:	First quartile $Q_1 = (589 + 597)/2 = 593$

$$i = \frac{p}{100}(n) = \frac{75}{100}(20) = 15$$

Automotive:	Third quartile $Q_3 = (2202 + 2254)/2 = 2228$
Department Store:	Third quartile $Q_3 = (782 + 824)/2 = 803$

Automotive: IQR = 2228 – 1717 = 511
Department Store: IQR = 803 – 593 = 210

 e. Automotive spends more on average, has a larger standard deviation, larger max and min, and larger range than Department Store. Autos have all new model years and may spend more heavily on advertising.

33. a. For 2011

$$\bar{x} = \frac{\Sigma x_i}{n} = \frac{608}{8} = 76$$

$$s = \sqrt{\frac{\Sigma(x_i - \bar{x})^2}{n-1}} = \sqrt{\frac{30}{7}} = 2.07$$

For 2012

$$\bar{x} = \frac{\Sigma x_i}{n} = \frac{608}{8} = 76$$

$$s = \sqrt{\frac{\Sigma(x_i - \bar{x})^2}{n-1}} = \sqrt{\frac{194}{7}} = 5.26$$

 b. The mean score is 76 for both years, but there is an increase in the standard deviation for the scores in 2012. The golfer is not as consistent in 2012 and shows a sizeable increase in the variation with golf scores ranging from 71 to 85. The increase in variation might be explained by the golfer trying to change or modify the golf swing. In general, a loss of consistency and an increase in the standard deviation could be viewed as a poorer performance in 2012. The optimism in 2012 is that three of the eight scores were better than any score reported for 2011. If the golfer can work for consistency, eliminate the high score rounds, and reduce the standard deviation, golf scores should show improvement.

34. <u>Quarter milers</u>

$s = 0.0564$

Coefficient of Variation $= (s/\bar{x})100\% = (0.0564/0.966)100\% = 5.8\%$

Milers

$s = 0.1295$

Coefficient of Variation $= (s/\bar{x})100\% = (0.1295/4.534)100\% = 2.9\%$

Yes; the coefficient of variation shows that as a percentage of the mean the quarter milers' times show more variability.

35.
$$\bar{x} = \frac{\Sigma x_i}{n} = \frac{75}{5} = 15$$

$$s^2 = \sqrt{\frac{\Sigma(x_i - \bar{x})^2}{n-1}} = \sqrt{\frac{64}{4}} = 4$$

10    $z = \dfrac{10-15}{4} = -1.25$

20    $z = \dfrac{20-15}{4} = +1.25$

12    $z = \dfrac{12-15}{4} = -.75$

17    $z = \dfrac{17-15}{4} = +.50$

16    $z = \dfrac{16-15}{4} = +.25$

36.
$$z = \frac{520-500}{100} = +.20$$

$$z = \frac{650-500}{100} = +1.50$$

$$z = \frac{500-500}{100} = 0.00$$

$$z = \frac{450-500}{100} = -.50$$

$$z = \frac{280-500}{100} = -2.20$$

37. a. $z = \dfrac{20-30}{5} = -2,\ z = \dfrac{40-30}{5} = 2$ $1 - \dfrac{1}{2^2} = .75$ At least 75%

b. $z = \dfrac{15-30}{5} = -3,\ z = \dfrac{45-30}{5} = 3$ $1 - \dfrac{1}{3^2} = .89$ At least 89%

3 - 14

c. $z = \dfrac{22-30}{5} = -1.6, \; z = \dfrac{38-30}{5} = 1.6$ $\qquad 1 - \dfrac{1}{1.6^2} = .61$ At least 61%

d. $z = \dfrac{18-30}{5} = -2.4, \; z = \dfrac{42-30}{5} = 2.4$ $\qquad 1 - \dfrac{1}{2.4^2} = .83$ At least 83%

e. $z = \dfrac{12-30}{5} = -3.6, \; z = \dfrac{48-30}{5} = 3.6$ $\qquad 1 - \dfrac{1}{3.6^2} = .92$ At least 92%

38. a. Approximately 95%

  b. Almost all

  c. Approximately 68%

39. a. This is from 2 standard deviations below the mean to 2 standard deviations above the mean.

  With $z = 2$, Chebyshev's theorem gives:

  $$1 - \frac{1}{z^2} = 1 - \frac{1}{2^2} = 1 - \frac{1}{4} = \frac{3}{4}$$

  Therefore, at least 75% of adults sleep between 4.5 and 9.3 hours per day.

  b. This is from 2.5 standard deviations below the mean to 2.5 standard deviations above the mean.

  With $z = 2.5$, Chebyshev's theorem gives:

  $$1 - \frac{1}{z^2} = 1 - \frac{1}{2.5^2} = 1 - \frac{1}{6.25} = .84$$

  Therefore, at least 84% of adults sleep between 3.9 and 9.9 hours per day.

  c. With $z = 2$, the empirical rule suggests that 95% of adults sleep between 4.5 and 9.3 hours per day. The percentage obtained using the empirical rule is greater than the percentage obtained using Chebyshev's theorem.

40. a. $3.33 is one standard deviation below the mean and $3.53 is one standard deviation above the mean. The empirical rule says that approximately 68% of gasoline sales are in this price range.

  b. Part (a) shows that approximately 68% of the gasoline sales are between $3.33 and $3.53. Since the bell-shaped distribution is symmetric, approximately half of 68%, or 34%, of the gasoline sales should be between $3.33 and the mean price of $3.43. $3.63 is two standard deviations above the mean price of $3.43. The empirical rule says that approximately 95% of the gasoline sales should be within two standard deviations of the mean. Thus, approximately half of 95%, or 47.5%, of the gasoline sales should be between the mean price of $3.43 and $3.63. The percentage of gasoline sales between $3.33 and $3.63 should be approximately 34% + 47.5% = 81.5%.

  c. $3.63 is two standard deviations above the mean and the empirical rule says that approximately 95% of the gasoline sales should be within two standard deviations of the mean. Thus, $1 - 95\% = 5\%$ of the gasoline sales should be more than two standard deviations from the mean. Since the bell-shaped distribution is symmetric, we expected half of 5%, or 2.5%, would be more than $3.63.

41. a. 615 is one standard deviation above the mean. Approximately 68% of the scores are between 415 and 615 with half of 68%, or 34%, of the scores between the mean of 515 and 615. Also, since the distribution is symmetric, 50% of the scores are above the mean of 515. With 50% of the scores above 515 and with 34% of the scores between 515 and 615, 50% – 34% = 16% of the scores are above 615.

    b. 715 is two standard deviations above the mean. Approximately 95% of the scores are between 315 and 715 with half of 95%, or 47.5%, of the scores between the mean of 515 and 715. Also, since the distribution is symmetric, 50% of the scores are above the mean of 515. With 50% of the scores above 515 and with 47.5% of the scores between 515 and 715, 50%– 47.5% = 2.5% of the scores are above 715.

    c. Approximately 68% of the scores are between 415 and 615 with half of 68%, or 34%, of the scores between 415 and the mean of 515.

    d. Approximately 95% of the scores are between 315 and 715 with half of 95%, or 47.5%, of the scores between 315 and the mean of 515. Approximately 68% of the scores are between 415 and 615 with half of 68%, or 34%, of the scores between the mean of 515 and 615. Thus, 47.5% + 34% = 81.5% of the scores are between 315 and 615.

42. a. $z = \dfrac{x - \mu}{\sigma} = \dfrac{2300 - 3100}{1200} = -.67$

    b. $z = \dfrac{x - \mu}{\sigma} = \dfrac{4900 - 3100}{1200} = 1.50$

    c. $2300 is .67 standard deviations below the mean. $4900 is 1.50 standard deviations above the mean. Neither is an outlier.

    d. $z = \dfrac{x - \mu}{\sigma} = \dfrac{13000 - 3100}{1200} = 8.25$

        $13,000 is 8.25 standard deviations above the mean. This cost is an outlier.

43. a. $\bar{x} = \dfrac{\Sigma x_i}{n} = \dfrac{64}{7} = 9.14$ days

        Median: with $n = 7$, use 4th position

        2, 3, 8, 8, 12, 13, 18

            Median = 8 days

        Mode: 8 days (occurred twice)

    b. Range = Largest value – Smallest value
             = 18 – 2 = 16

$$s = \sqrt{\frac{\Sigma(x_i - \bar{x})^2}{n-1}}$$

$$\begin{aligned}\Sigma(x_i - \bar{x})^2 &= (13-9.14)^2 + (12-9.14)^2 + (8-9.14)^2 + (3-9.14)^2 \\ &\quad + (8-9.14)^2 + (2-9.14)^2 + (18-9.14)^2 \\ &= 192.86\end{aligned}$$

$$s = \sqrt{\frac{192.86}{6}} = 5.67$$

c. $z = \dfrac{x-\bar{x}}{s} = \dfrac{18-9.14}{5.67} = 1.56$

The 18 days required to restore service after hurricane Wilma is not an outlier.

d. Yes, FP&L should consider ways to improve its emergency repair procedures. The mean, median and mode show repairs requiring an average of 8 to 9 days can be expected if similar hurricanes are encountered in the future. The 18 days required to restore service after hurricane Wilma should not be considered unusual if FP&L continues to use its current emergency repair procedures. With the number of customers affected running into the millions, plans to shorten the number of days to restore service should be undertaken by the company.

44. a. $\bar{x} = \dfrac{\Sigma x_i}{n} = \dfrac{765}{10} = 76.5$

$$s = \sqrt{\frac{\Sigma(x_i - \bar{x})^2}{n-1}} = \sqrt{\frac{442.5}{10-1}} = 7$$

b. $z = \dfrac{x-\bar{x}}{s} = \dfrac{84-76.5}{7} = 1.07$

Approximately one standard deviation above the mean. Approximately 68% of the scores are within one standard deviation. Thus, half of (100–68), or 16%, of the games should have a winning score of 84 or more points.

$$z = \frac{x-\bar{x}}{s} = \frac{90-76.5}{7} = 1.93$$

Approximately two standard deviations above the mean. Approximately 95% of the scores are within two standard deviations. Thus, half of (100–95), or 2.5%, of the games should have a winning score of more than 90 points.

c. $\bar{x} = \dfrac{\Sigma x_i}{n} = \dfrac{122}{10} = 12.2$

$$s = \sqrt{\frac{\Sigma(x_i - \bar{x})^2}{n-1}} = \sqrt{\frac{559.6}{10-1}} = 7.89$$

Largest margin 24: $z = \dfrac{x - \bar{x}}{s} = \dfrac{24 - 12.2}{7.89} = 1.50$. No outliers.

45. a. $\bar{x} = \dfrac{\sum x_i}{n} = \dfrac{1050}{14} = 75$

    b. $75.00 – $72.20 = $2.80

    $2.80/$72.20 = .0388   Ticket price increased 3.88% during the one-year period.

    c. 7th position – Green Bay Packers   63

    8th position – Pittsburgh Steelers   67

    $$\text{Median} = \frac{63 + 67}{2} = 65$$

    d. $i = .25(14) = 3.5$ Use 4th position

    $Q_1 = 61$ (Tennessee Titans)

    $i = .75(14) = 10.5$ Use 11th position

    $Q_3 = 83$ (Indianapolis Colts)

    e. $s = \sqrt{\dfrac{\Sigma(x_i - \bar{x})^2}{n-1}} = \sqrt{\dfrac{9504}{13}} = 27.04$

    f. Dallas Cowboys: $z = \dfrac{x - \mu}{\sigma} = \dfrac{160 - 75}{27.04} = 3.14$

    With $z > 3$, this is an outlier. The Dallas Cowboys have an unusually high ticket price compared to the other NFL teams.

46.   15, 20, 25, 25, 27, 28, 30, 34

    Smallest = 15

    $i = \dfrac{25}{100}(8) = 2$ $Q_1 = \dfrac{20 + 25}{2} = 22.5$

    $\text{Median} = \dfrac{25 + 27}{2} = 26$

    $i = \dfrac{75}{100}(8) = 8$ $Q_3 = \dfrac{28 + 30}{2} = 29$

    Largest = 34

47.

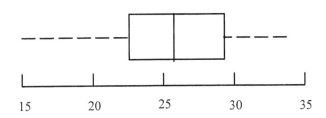

48.   5, 6, 8, 10, 10, 12, 15, 16, 18

Smallest = 5

$i = \dfrac{25}{100}(9) = 2.25$ $Q_1 = 8$ (3rd position)

Median = 10

$i = \dfrac{75}{100}(9) = 6.75$ $Q_3 = 15$ (7th position)

Largest = 18

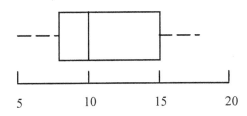

49.   IQR = 50 − 42 = 8

Lower Limit: $Q_1 − 1.5$ IQR $= 42 − 12 = 30$

Upper Limit: $Q_3 + 1.5$ IQR $= 50 + 12 = 62$

65 is an outlier

50. a.   The first place runner in the men's group finished $109.03 − 65.30 = 43.73$ minutes ahead of the first place runner in the women's group. Lauren Wald would have finished in 11th place for the combined groups.

   b.   Men: $i = \left(\dfrac{50}{100}\right)22 = .50(22) = 11$. Use the 11th and 12th place finishes.

   Median $= \dfrac{109.05 + 110.23}{2} = 109.64$

   Women: $i = \left(\dfrac{50}{100}\right)31 = .50(31) = 15.5$. Use the 16th place finish. Median $= 131.67$.

   Using the median finish times, the men's group finished $131.67 − 109.64 = 22.03$ minutes ahead of the women's group.

Also note that the fastest time for a woman runner, 109.03 minutes, is approximately equal to the median time of 109.64 minutes for the men's group.

c. Men: Lowest time = 65.30; Highest time = 148.70

Q_1: $\qquad i = \left(\dfrac{25}{100}\right) n = .25(22) = 5.5$ Use 6th position. $Q_1 = 87.18$

Q_3: $\qquad i = \left(\dfrac{75}{100}\right) n = .75(22) = 16.5$ Use 17th position. $Q_3 = 128.40$

Five number summary for men: 65.30, 87.18, 109.64, 128.40, 148.70

Women: Lowest time = 109.03; Highest time = 189.28

Q_1: $\qquad i = \left(\dfrac{25}{100}\right) n = .25(31) = 7.75$ Use 8th position. $Q_1 = 122.08$

Q_3: $\qquad i = \left(\dfrac{75}{100}\right) n = .75(31) = 23.25$ Use 24th position. $Q_3 = 147.18$

Five number summary for women: 109.03, 122.08, 131.67, 147.18, 189.28

d. Men: IQR = $128.40 - 87.18 = 41.22$

Lower Limit = $Q_1 - 1.5(IQR) = 87.18 - 1.5(41.22) = 25.35$

Upper Limit = $Q_3 + 1.5(IQR) = 128.40 + 1.5(41.22) = 190.23$

There are no outliers in the men's group.

Women: IQR = $147.18 - 122.08 = 25.10$

Lower Limit = $Q_1 - 1.5(IQR) = 122.08 - 1.5(25.10) = 84.43$

Upper Limit = $Q_3 + 1.5(IQR) = 147.18 + 1.5(25.10) = 184.83$

The two slowest women runners with times of 189.27 and 189.28 minutes are outliers in the women's group.

e.

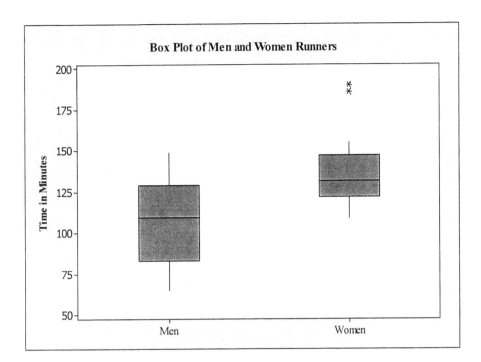

The box plots show the men runners with the faster or lower finish times. However, the box plots show the women runners with the lower variation in finish times. The interquartile ranges of 41.22 minutes for men and 25.10 minutes for women support this conclusion.

51. a. Median (11th position) = 4019

$$i = \frac{25}{100}(21) = 5.25$$

Q_1 (6th position) = 1872

$$i = \frac{75}{100}(21) = 15.75$$

Q_3 (16th position) = 8305

608, 1872, 4019, 8305, 14138

b. Limits:

IQR = $Q_3 - Q_1$ = 8305 – 1872 = 6433

Lower Limit: $Q_1 - 1.5$ (IQR) = –7777

Upper Limit: $Q_3 + 1.5$ (IQR) = 17955

c. There are no outliers, all data are within the limits.

d. Yes, if the first two digits in Johnson and Johnson's sales were transposed to 41,138, sales would have shown up as an outlier. A review of the data would have enabled the correction of the data.

3 - 21

e.

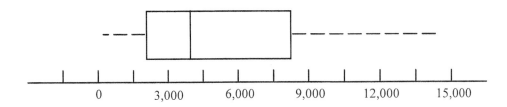

52. a. Median $n = 20$;   10th and 11th positions

   Median $= \dfrac{73 + 74}{2} = 73.5$

   b. Smallest 68

   Q_1: $i = \left(\dfrac{25}{100}\right) 20 = 5$; 5th and 6th positions

   $Q_1 = \dfrac{71 + 72}{2} = 71.5$

   Q_3: $i = \left(\dfrac{75}{100}\right) 20 = 15$; 15th and 16th positions

   $Q_3 = \dfrac{74 + 75}{2} = 74.5$

   Largest 77

   5- number summary: 68, 71.5, 73.5, 74.5, 77

   c. IQR $= Q_3 - Q_1 = 74.5 - 71.5 = 3$

   Lower Limit $= Q_1 - 1.5(\text{IQR})$

   $= 71.5 - 1.5(3) = 67$

   Upper Limit $= Q_3 + 1.5(\text{IQR})$

   $= 74.5 + 1.5(3) = 79$

   All ratings are between 67 and 79. There are no outliers for the T-Mobile service.

   d. Using the solution procedures shown in parts a, b, and c, the five number summaries and outlier limits for the other three cell-phone services are as follows.

AT&T 66, 68, 71, 73, 75	Limits: 60.5 and 80.5
Sprint 63, 65, 66, 67.5, 69	Limits: 61.25 and 71.25
Verizon 75, 77, 78.5, 79.5, 81	Limits: 73.25 and 83.25

There are no outliers for any of the cell-phone services.

e.

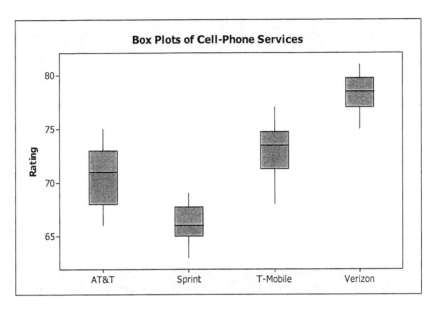

The box plots show that Verizon is the best cell-phone service provider in terms of overall customer satisfaction. Verizon's lowest rating is better than the highest AT&T and Sprint ratings and is better than 75% of the T-Mobile ratings. Sprint shows the lowest customer satisfaction ratings among the four services.

53. a. Total Salary for the Philadelphia Phillies = $96,870,000

Median $n = 28$; 14th and 15th positions

$$\text{Median} = \frac{900 + 1700}{2} = 1300$$

Smallest 390

Q_1: $i = \left(\frac{25}{100}\right) 28 = 7$; 7th and 8th positions

$$Q_1 = \frac{425 + 440}{2} = 432.5$$

Q_3: $i = \left(\frac{75}{100}\right) 28 = 21$; 21st and 22nd positions

$$Q_3 = \frac{6000 + 6350}{2} = 6175$$

Largest 14250

5– number summary for the Philadelphia Phillies: 390, 432.5, 1300, 6175, 14250

Using the 5-number summary, the lower quartile shows salaries closely bunched between 390 and 432.5. The median is 1300. The most variation is in the upper quartile where the salaries are spread between 6175 and 14250, or between \$6,175,000 and \$14,250,000.

b.　　$IQR = Q_3 - Q_1 = 6175 - 432.5 = 5742.5$

Lower Limit = $Q_1 - 1.5(IQR)$

$$= 432.5 - 1.5(5742.5) = -8181.25; \quad \text{Use } 0$$

Upper Limit = $Q_3 + 1.5(IQR)$

$$= 6175 + 1.5(5742.5) = 14788.75$$

All salaries are between 0 and 14788.75. There are no salary outliers for the Philadelphia Phillies.

c.　　Using the solution procedures shown in parts a and b, the total salary, the five-number summaries, and the outlier limits for the other teams are as follows.

Los Angeles Dodgers　　　　\$136,373,000
　　　390, 403, 857.5, 9125, 19000　　　　Limits:　0 and 22208

Tampa Bay Rays　　　　\$ 42,334,000
　　　390, 399, 415, 2350, 6000　　　　Limits:　0 and 5276.5

Boston Red Sox　　　　\$120,460,000
　　　396, 439.5, 2500, 8166.5, 14000　　　　Limits:　0 and 19757

The Los Angeles Dodgers had the highest payroll while the Tampa Bay Rays clearly had the lowest payroll among the four teams. With the lower salaries, the Rays had two outlier salaries compared to other salaries on the team. But these top two salaries are substantially below the top salaries for the other three teams. There are no outliers for the Phillies, Dodgers and Red Sox.

d.

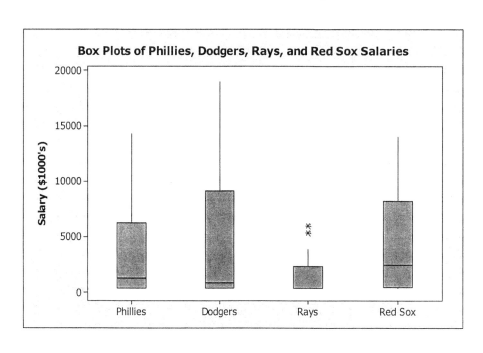

3 - 24

The box plots show that the lowest salaries for the four teams are very similar. The Red Sox have the highest median salary. Of the four teams the Dodgers have the highest upper end salaries and highest total payroll, while the Rays are clearly the lowest paid team.

For this data, we would conclude that paying higher salaries do not always bring championships. In the National League Championship, the lower paid Phillies beat the higher paid Dodgers. In the American League Championship, the lower paid Rays beat the higher paid Red Sox. The biggest surprise was how the Tampa Bay Rays over achieved based on their salaries and made it to the World Series. Teams with the highest salaries do not always win the championships.

54. a. $\bar{x} = \dfrac{\sum x_i}{n} = \dfrac{8862}{50} = 173.24$

$i = \dfrac{p}{100}(n) = \dfrac{50}{100}(50) = 25$

Median = (89 + 90) / 2 = 89.5

b. $i = \dfrac{p}{100}(n) = \dfrac{25}{100}(50) = 12.5$ (13th position) $Q_1 = 40$

$i = \dfrac{p}{100}(n) = \dfrac{75}{100}(50) = 37.5$ (38th position) $Q_3 = 228$

c. Smallest   21

Q_1 40

Median   89.5

Q_3 228

Largest   995

d. IQR = 228 − 40 = 188

LL = Q_1 − 1.5 IQR = 40 − 1.5(188) = −242

UL = Q_3 + 1.5 IQR = 228 + 1.5(188) = 510

There are three outliers: 707, 807, and 995.

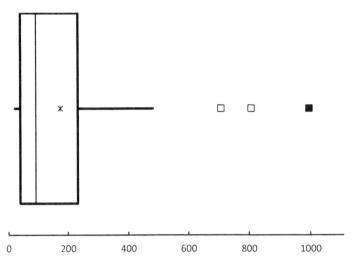

The box plot shows the distribution of number of personal vehicle crossings is skewed to the right (positive). Three ports of entry are considered outliers:

NY: Buffalo-Niagara Falls   707

TX: El Paso   807

CA: San Ysidro   995

55. a.

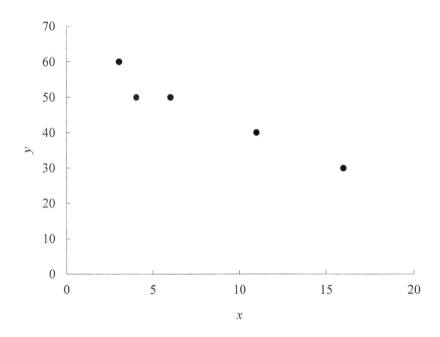

b. Negative relationship

c/d. $\Sigma x_i = 40$ $\bar{x} = \dfrac{40}{5} = 8$ $\Sigma y_i = 230$ $\bar{y} = \dfrac{230}{5} = 46$

3 - 26

$$\Sigma(x_i - \bar{x})(y_i - \bar{y}) = -240 \quad \Sigma(x_i - \bar{x})^2 = 118 \quad \Sigma(y_i - \bar{y})^2 = 520$$

$$s_{xy} = \frac{\Sigma(x_i - \bar{x})(y_i - \bar{y})}{n-1} = \frac{-240}{5-1} = -60$$

$$s_x = \sqrt{\frac{\Sigma(x_i - \bar{x})^2}{n-1}} = \sqrt{\frac{118}{5-1}} = 5.4314$$

$$s_y = \sqrt{\frac{\Sigma(y_i - \bar{y})^2}{n-1}} = \sqrt{\frac{520}{5-1}} = 11.4018$$

$$r_{xy} = \frac{s_{xy}}{s_x s_y} = \frac{-60}{(5.4314)(11.4018)} = -.969$$

There is a strong negative linear relationship.

56. a.

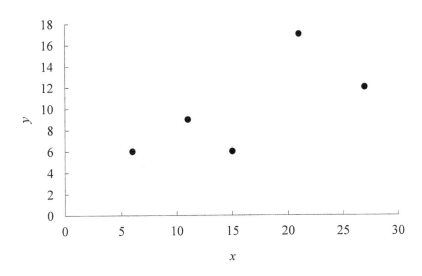

b. Positive relationship

c/d. $\Sigma x_i = 80 \quad \bar{x} = \dfrac{80}{5} = 16 \quad \Sigma y_i = 50 \quad \bar{y} = \dfrac{50}{5} = 10$

$$\Sigma(x_i - \bar{x})(y_i - \bar{y}) = 106 \quad \Sigma(x_i - \bar{x})^2 = 272 \quad \Sigma(y_i - \bar{y})^2 = 86$$

$$s_{xy} = \frac{\Sigma(x_i - \bar{x})(y_i - \bar{y})}{n-1} = \frac{106}{5-1} = 26.5$$

$$s_x = \sqrt{\frac{\Sigma(x_i - \bar{x})^2}{n-1}} = \sqrt{\frac{272}{5-1}} = 8.2462$$

$$s_y = \sqrt{\frac{\Sigma(y_i - \bar{y})^2}{n-1}} = \sqrt{\frac{86}{5-1}} = 4.6368$$

$$r_{xy} = \frac{s_{xy}}{s_x s_y} = \frac{26.5}{(8.2462)(4.6368)} = .693$$

A positive linear relationship

57. a.

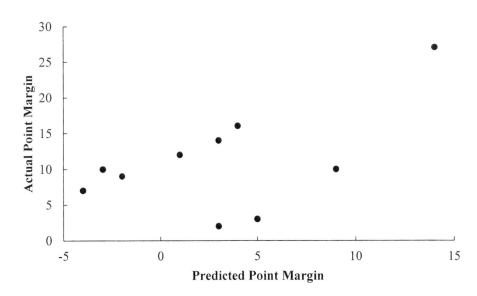

b.   The scatter diagram shows a positive relationship with higher predicted point margins associated with higher actual point margins.

c.   Let x = predicted point margin and y = actual point margin

$$\Sigma x_i = 30 \quad \bar{x} = \frac{30}{10} = 3 \quad \Sigma y_i = 110 \quad \bar{y} = \frac{110}{10} = 11$$

$$\Sigma(x_i - \bar{x})(y_i - \bar{y}) = 201 \quad \Sigma(x_i - \bar{x})^2 = 276 \quad \Sigma(y_i - \bar{y})^2 = 458$$

$$s_{xy} = \frac{\Sigma(x_i - \bar{x})(y_i - \bar{y})}{n-1} = \frac{201}{10-1} = 22.3333$$

A positive covariance shows a positive relationship between predicted point margins and actual point margins.

d.

$$s_x = \sqrt{\frac{\Sigma(x_i - \bar{x})^2}{n-1}} = \sqrt{\frac{276}{10-1}} = 5.5377$$

$$s_y = \sqrt{\frac{\Sigma(y_i - \bar{y})^2}{n-1}} = \sqrt{\frac{458}{10-1}} = 7.1336$$

$$r_{xy} = \frac{s_{xy}}{s_x s_y} = \frac{22.3333}{(5.5377)(7.1336)} = .565$$

The modest positive correlation shows that the Las Vegas predicted point margin is a general, but not a perfect, indicator of the actual point margin in college football bowl games.

Note: The Las Vegas odds makers set the point margins so that someone betting on a favored team has to have the team *win by more than the point margin* to win the bet. For example, someone betting on Auburn to win the Outback Bowl would have to have Auburn win by more than five points to win the bet. Since Auburn beat Northwestern by only three points, the person betting on Auburn would have lost the bet.

A review of the predicted and actual point margins shows that the favorites won by more than the predicted point margin in five bowl games: Gator, Sugar, Cotton, Alamo, and the Championship bowl game. The underdog either won its game or kept the actual point margin less than the predicted point margin in the other five bowl games. In this case, betting on the underdog would have provided winners in the Outback, Capital One, Rose, Fiesta and Orange bowls. In this example, the Las Vegas odds point margins made betting on the favored team a 50-50 probability of winning the bet.

58.　Let x = miles per hour and y = miles per gallon

$$\Sigma x_i = 420 \quad \bar{x} = \frac{420}{10} = 42 \quad \Sigma y_i = 270 \quad \bar{y} = \frac{270}{10} = 27$$

$$\Sigma(x_i - \bar{x})(y_i - \bar{y}) = -475 \quad \Sigma(x_i - \bar{x})^2 = 1660 \quad \Sigma(y_i - \bar{y})^2 = 164$$

$$s_{xy} = \frac{\Sigma(x_i - \bar{x})(y_i - \bar{y})}{n-1} = \frac{-475}{10-1} = -52.7778$$

$$s_x = \sqrt{\frac{\Sigma(x_i - \bar{x})^2}{n-1}} = \sqrt{\frac{1660}{10-1}} = 13.5810$$

$$s_y = \sqrt{\frac{\Sigma(y_i - \bar{y})^2}{n-1}} = \sqrt{\frac{164}{10-1}} = 4.2687$$

$$r_{xy} = \frac{s_{xy}}{s_x s_y} = \frac{-52.7778}{(13.5810)(4.2687)} = -.91$$

A strong negative linear relationship exists. For driving speeds between 25 and 60 miles per hour, higher speeds are associated with lower miles per gallon.

59. a. $\bar{x} = \dfrac{\Sigma x_i}{n} = \dfrac{184}{27} = 6.81$ $\bar{y} = \dfrac{\Sigma y_i}{n} = \dfrac{170.93}{27} = 6.33$

x_i	y_i	$(x_i - \bar{x})$	$(y_i - \bar{y})$	$(x_i - \bar{x})^2$	$(y_i - \bar{y})^2$	$(x_i - \bar{x})(y_i - \bar{y})$
7.1	7.02	0.2852	0.6893	0.0813	0.4751	0.1966
5.2	5.31	-1.6148	-1.0207	2.6076	1.0419	1.6483
7.8	5.38	0.9852	-0.9507	0.9706	0.9039	-0.9367
7.8	5.40	0.9852	-0.9307	0.9706	0.8663	-0.9170
5.8	5.00	-1.0148	-1.3307	1.0298	1.7709	1.3505
5.8	4.07	-1.0148	-2.2607	1.0298	5.1109	2.2942
9.3	6.53	2.4852	0.1993	6.1761	0.0397	0.4952
5.7	5.57	-1.1148	-0.7607	1.2428	0.5787	0.8481
7.3	6.99	0.4852	0.6593	0.2354	0.4346	0.3199
7.6	11.12	0.7852	4.7893	0.6165	22.9370	3.7605
8.2	7.56	1.3852	1.2293	1.9187	1.5111	1.7028
7.1	12.11	0.2852	5.7793	0.0813	33.3998	1.6482
6.3	4.39	-0.5148	-1.9407	0.2650	3.7665	0.9991
6.6	4.78	-0.2148	-1.5507	0.0461	2.4048	0.3331
6.2	5.78	-0.6148	-0.5507	0.3780	0.3033	0.3386
6.3	6.08	-0.5148	-0.2507	0.2650	0.0629	0.1291
7.0	10.05	0.1852	3.7193	0.0343	13.8329	0.6888
6.2	4.75	-0.6148	-1.5807	0.3780	2.4987	0.9719
5.5	7.22	-1.3148	0.8893	1.7287	0.7908	-1.1692
6.5	3.79	-0.3148	-2.5407	0.0991	6.4554	0.7999
6.0	3.62	-0.8148	-2.7107	0.6639	7.3481	2.2088
8.3	9.24	1.4852	2.9093	2.2058	8.4638	4.3208
7.5	4.40	0.6852	-1.9307	0.4695	3.7278	-1.3229
7.1	6.91	0.2852	0.5793	0.0813	0.3355	0.1652
6.8	5.57	-0.0148	-0.7607	0.0002	0.5787	0.0113
5.5	3.87	-1.3148	-2.4607	1.7287	6.0552	3.2354
7.5	8.42	0.6852	2.0893	0.4695	4.3650	1.4315
			Total	25.77407	130.0594	25.5517

$$s_{xy} = \frac{\Sigma(x_i - \bar{x})(y_i - \bar{y})}{n-1} = \frac{25.5517}{26} = .9828$$

$$s_x = \sqrt{\frac{\Sigma(x_i - \bar{x})^2}{n-1}} = \sqrt{\frac{25.7741}{26}} = .9956$$

$$s_y = \sqrt{\frac{\Sigma(y_i - \bar{y})^2}{n-1}} = \sqrt{\frac{130.0594}{26}} = 2.2366$$

$$r_{xy} = \frac{s_{xy}}{s_x s_y} = \frac{.9828}{(.9956)(2.2366)} = .4413$$

There is evidence of a modest positive linear association between the jobless rate and the delinquent housing loan percentage. If the jobless rate were to increase, it is likely that an increase in the percentage of delinquent housing loans would also occur.

b.

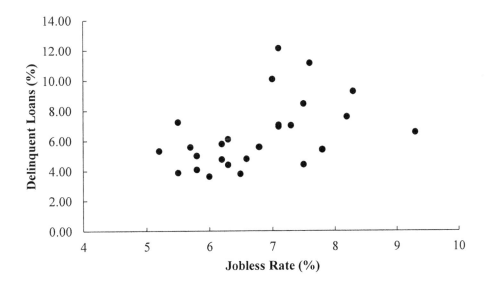

60. a.

% Return ofDJIA versus Russell 1000

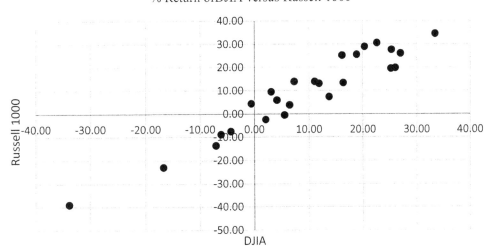

b. DJIA : $\quad \overline{x} = \dfrac{\sum x_i}{n} = \dfrac{227.57}{25} = 9.10 \qquad s = \sqrt{\dfrac{\sum (x_i - \overline{x})^2}{(n-1)}} = \sqrt{\dfrac{5672.61}{24}} = 15.37$

Russell 1000: $\overline{x} = \dfrac{\sum x_i}{n} = \dfrac{227.29}{25} = 9.09 \qquad s = \sqrt{\dfrac{\sum (x_i - \overline{x})^2}{(n-1)}} = \sqrt{\dfrac{7679.81}{24}} = 17.89$

c. $r_{xy} = \dfrac{s_{xy}}{s_x s_y} = \dfrac{263.611}{(15.37)(17.89)} = .959$

d. Based on this sample, the two indexes are very similar. They have a strong positive correlation. The variance of the Russell 1000 is slightly larger than that of the DJIA.

3 - 31

61. a. $\bar{x} = \dfrac{\Sigma x_i}{n} = \dfrac{945}{14} = 67.5$

    b. $\bar{y} = \dfrac{\Sigma y_i}{n} = \dfrac{706}{14} = 50.4286 \approx 50.4$

    c.

x_i	y_i	$(x_i - \bar{x})$	$(y_i - \bar{y})$	$(x_i - \bar{x})^2$	$(y_i - \bar{y})^2$	$(x_i - \bar{x})(y_i - \bar{y})$
68	50	.5	-.4286	.25	.1837	-.2143
70	49	2.5	-1.4286	6.25	2.0408	-3.5714
65	44	-2.5	-6.4286	6.25	41.3265	16.0714
96	64	28.5	13.5714	812.25	184.1837	386.7857
57	46	-10.5	-4.4286	110.25	19.6122	46.5000
70	45	2.5	-5.4286	6.25	29.4694	-13.5714
80	73	12.5	22.5714	156.25	509.4694	282.1429
67	45	-.5	-5.4286	.25	29.4694	2.7143
44	29	-23.5	-21.4286	552.25	459.1837	503.5714
69	44	1.5	-6.4286	2.25	41.3265	-9.6429
76	69	8.5	18.5714	72.25	344.8980	157.8571
69	51	1.5	.5714	2.25	.3265	.8571
70	58	2.5	7.5714	6.25	57.3265	18.9286
44	39	-23.5	-11.4286	552.25	130.6122	268.5714
			Total	2285.5	1849.4286	1657.0000

$s_{xy} = \dfrac{\Sigma(x_i - \bar{x})(y_i - \bar{y})}{n-1} = \dfrac{1657}{14-1} = 127.4615$

$s_x = \sqrt{\dfrac{\Sigma(x_i - \bar{x})^2}{n-1}} = \sqrt{\dfrac{2285.5}{14-1}} = 13.2592$

$s_y = \sqrt{\dfrac{\Sigma(y_i - \bar{y})^2}{n-1}} = \sqrt{\dfrac{1849.4286}{14-1}} = 11.9274$

$r_{xy} = \dfrac{s_{xy}}{s_x s_y} = \dfrac{127.4615}{13.2592(11.9274)} = +.806$

High positive correlation as should be expected.

62. a. The mean is 2.95 and the median is 3.0.

    b. The index for the first quartile is $i = \left(\dfrac{25}{100}\right)20 = 5$, so the first quartile is the mean of the values of the 5th and 6th observations in the sorted data, or $\dfrac{1+1}{2} = 1$.

The index for the third quartile is $i = \dfrac{75}{100} 20 = 15$, so the third quartile is mean of the values of the 15th and 16th observations in the sorted data, or $\dfrac{4+5}{2} = 4.5$.

c. The range is 7 and the interquartile range is $4.5 - 1 = 3.5$.

d. The variance is 4.37 and standard deviation is 2.09.

e. Because most people dine out a relatively few times per week and a few families dine out very frequently, we would expect the data to be positively skewed. The skewness measure of 0.34 indicates the data are somewhat skewed to the right.

f. The lower limit is –4.25 and the upper limit is 9.75. No values in the data are less than the lower limit or greater than the upper limit, so the Minitab boxplot indicates there are no outliers.

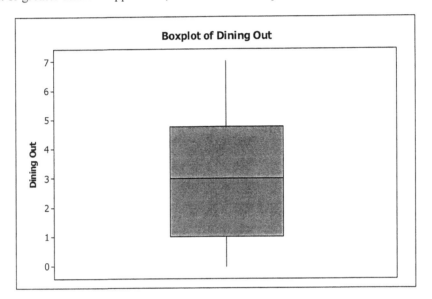

63. a. $i = \dfrac{p}{100}(n) = \dfrac{50}{100}(23) = 11.5$ (12th position)

Previous Coach Median = 850,000

New Coach Median = 1,150,000

b. Range: Previous Coach Base: $3,500,000 - 267,800 = 3,232,200$

              New Coach Base: $3,200,000 - 280,000 = 2,290,000$

c. Standard Deviation:

Previous Coach Base: $s = \sqrt{\dfrac{\sum (x_i - \bar{x})^2}{n-1}} = \sqrt{\dfrac{2.2209\,x\,10^{13}}{22}} = 1,004,740$

New Coach Base: $\quad s = \sqrt{\dfrac{\sum (x_i - \bar{x})^2}{n-1}} = \sqrt{\dfrac{1.7894 \, x \, 10^{13}}{22}} = 901,873$

d. The new coaches have a higher median annual salary, but a smaller range and standard deviation.

64. a. The mean and median patient wait times for offices with a wait tracking system are 17.2 and 13.5, respectively. The mean and median patient wait times for offices without a wait tracking system are 29.1 and 23.5, respectively.

b. The variance and standard deviation of patient wait times for offices with a wait tracking system are 86.2 and 9.3, respectively. The variance and standard deviation of patient wait times for offices without a wait tracking system are 275.7 and 16.6, respectively.

c. Offices with a wait tracking system have substantially shorter patient wait times than offices without a wait tracking system.

d. $\quad z = \dfrac{37 - 29.1}{16.6} = 0.48$

e. $\quad z = \dfrac{37 - 17.2}{9.3} = 2.13$

As indicated by the positive z–scores, both patients had wait times that exceeded the means of their respective samples. Even though the patients had the same wait time, the z–score for the sixth patient in the sample who visited an office with a wait tracking system is much larger because that patient is part of a sample with a smaller mean and a smaller standard deviation.

f. The z–scores for all patients follow.

Without Wait Tracking System	With Wait Tracking System
-0.31	1.49
2.28	-0.67
-0.73	-0.34
-0.55	0.09
0.11	-0.56
0.90	2.13
-1.03	-0.88
-0.37	-0.45
-0.79	-0.56
0.48	-0.24

The z–scores do not indicate the existence of any outliers in either sample.

65. a. $\quad \bar{x} = \dfrac{\sum x_i}{n} = \dfrac{148}{20} = 7.4$

b. $\quad s^2 = \dfrac{\sum (x_i - \bar{x})^2}{(n-1)} = \dfrac{58.8}{19} = 3.09 \qquad s = \sqrt{3.09} = 1.76$

3 - 34

66. a. $\bar{x} = \dfrac{\sum x_i}{n} = \dfrac{20665}{50} = 413.3$ This is slightly higher than the mean for the study.

   b. $s = \sqrt{\dfrac{\sum (x_i - \bar{x})^2}{(n-1)}} = \sqrt{\dfrac{69424.5}{49}} = 37.64$

   c. $i = \dfrac{p}{100}(n) = \dfrac{25}{100}(50) = 12.5$ (13th position) $Q_1 = 384$

   $i = \dfrac{p}{100}(n) = \dfrac{75}{100}(50) = 37.5$ (38th position) $Q_3 = 445$

   IQR = 445 − 384 = 61

   LL = Q_1 − 1.5 IQR = 384 − 1.5(61) = 292.5

   UL = Q_3 + 1.5 IQR = 445 + 1.5(61) = 536.5

   There are no outliers.

67. a. Public Transportation: $\bar{x} = \dfrac{320}{10} = 32$

   Automobile: $\bar{x} = \dfrac{320}{10} = 32$

   b. Public Transportation: $s = 4.64$

   Automobile: $s = 1.83$

   c. Prefer the automobile. The mean times are the same, but the auto has less variability.

   d. Data in ascending order:

   Public: 25 28 29 29 32 32 33 34 37 41

   Auto: 29 30 31 31 32 32 33 33 34 35

   Five number Summaries

   Public: 25 29 32 34 41

   Auto: 29 31 32 33 35

Box Plots:

Public:

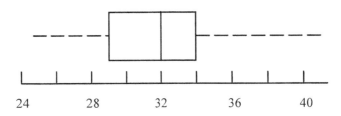

Auto:

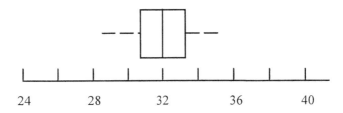

The box plots do show lower variability with automobile transportation and support the conclusion in part c.

68. a. $i = \dfrac{p}{100}(n) = \dfrac{50}{100}(25) = 12.5$ (13th position) Median = 79,649

b. $i = \dfrac{p}{100}(n) = \dfrac{25}{100}(25) = 6.25$ (7th position) $Q_1 = 59,423$

$i = \dfrac{p}{100}(n) = \dfrac{75}{100}(25) = 18.75$ (19th position) $Q_3 = 122,231$

Smallest	18,927
Q_1	59,423
Median	79,649
Q_3	122,231
Largest	148,782

c. $\bar{x} = \dfrac{\sum x_i}{n} = \dfrac{2,234,409}{25} = 89,376.4$

d. IQR = 122,231 – 59,423 = 62,808

LL = Q_1 – 1.5 IQR = 59,423 – 1.5(62,808) = –34,789

UL = Q_3 + 1.5 IQR = 122,231 + 1.5(62,808) = 216443

There are no outliers.

e. Even though there are no outliers, the median is preferred as it indicates the middle of the data and is not influenced by overly large or small values.

69. a. Median for $n = 50$; Use 25th and 26th positions

25th – South Dakota 16.8

26th – Pennsylvania 16.9

$$\text{Median} = \frac{16.8 + 16.9}{2} = 16.85\%$$

b. Q_1: $\quad i = \left(\frac{25}{100}\right)50 = 12.5$

13th position: $Q_1 = 13.7\%$ (Iowa)

Q_3: $\quad i = \left(\frac{75}{100}\right)50 = 37.5$

38th position: $Q_3 = 20.2\%$ (North Carolina & Georgia)

25% of the states have a poverty level less than or equal to 13.7% and 25% of the states have a poverty level greater than or equal to 20.2%

c. IQR $= Q_3 - Q_1 = 20.2 - 13.7 = 6.5$

Upper Limit $= Q_3 + 1.5(\text{IQR})$

$= 20.2 + 1.5(6.5) = 29.95$

Lower Limit $= Q_1 - 1.5(\text{IQR})$

$= 13.7 - 1.5(6.5) = 3.95$

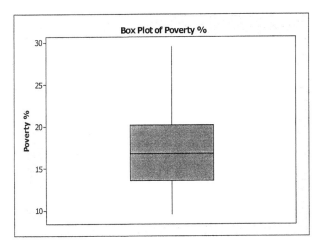

The Minitab box plot shows the distribution of poverty levels is skewed to the right (positive). There are no states considered outliers. Mississippi with 29.5% is closest to being an outlier on the high poverty rate side. New Hampshire has the lowest poverty level with 9.6%. The five-number summary is 9.6, 13.7, 16.85, 20.2 and 29.95.

d. The states in the lower quartile are the states with the lowest percentage of children who have lived below the poverty level in the last 12 months. These states are as follows.

State	Region	Poverty %
New Hampshire	NE	9.6
Maryland	NE	9.7
Connecticut	NE	11.0
Hawaii	W	11.4
New Jersey	NE	11.8
Utah	W	11.9
Wyoming	W	12.0
Minnesota	MW	12.2
Virginia	SE	12.2
Massachusetts	NE	12.4
North Dakota	MW	13.0
Vermont	NE	13.2

Generally, these states are the states with better economic conditions and less poverty. The Northeast region with 6 of the 12 states in this quartile appears to be the best economic region of the country. The West region was second with 3 of the 12 states in this group.

70. a. $\bar{x} = \dfrac{\Sigma x_i}{n} = \dfrac{4368}{12} = 364$ rooms

b. $\bar{y} = \dfrac{\Sigma y_i}{n} = \dfrac{5484}{12} = \$457$

c.

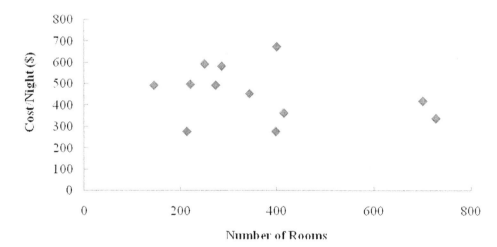

3 - 38

It is difficult to see much of a relationship. When the number of rooms becomes larger, there is no indication that the cost per night increases. The cost per night may even decrease slightly.

d.

x_i	y_i	$(x_i - \bar{x})$	$(y_i - \bar{y})$	$(x_i - \bar{x})^2$	$(y_i - \bar{y})^2$	$(x_i - \bar{x})(y_i - \bar{y})$
	499	-144	42	20.736	1,764	-6,048
727	340	363	-117	131,769	13,689	-42,471
285	585	-79	128	6,241	16,384	-10,112
273	495	-91	38	8,281	1,444	-3,458
145	495	-219	38	47,961	1,444	-8,322
213	279	-151	-178	22,801	31,684	26,878
398	279	34	-178	1,156	31,684	-6,052
343	455	-21	-2	441	4	42
250	595	-114	138	12,996	19,044	-15,732
414	367	50	-90	2,500	8,100	-4,500
400	675	36	218	1,296	47,524	7,848
700	420	336	-37	112,896	1,369	-12,432
			Total	69,074	174,134	-74,359

$$s_{xy} = \frac{\Sigma(x_i - \bar{x})(y_i - \bar{y})}{n-1} = \frac{-74,350}{11} = -6759.91$$

$$s_x = \sqrt{\frac{\Sigma(x_i - \bar{x})^2}{n-1}} = \sqrt{\frac{369,074}{11}} = 183.17$$

$$s_y = \sqrt{\frac{\Sigma(y_i - \bar{y})^2}{n-1}} = \sqrt{\frac{174,134}{11}} = 125.82$$

$$r_{xy} = \frac{s_{xy}}{s_x s_y} = \frac{-6759.91}{(183.17)(125.82)} = -.293$$

There is evidence of a slightly negative linear association between the number of rooms and the cost per night for a double room. Although this is not a strong relationship, it suggests that the higher room rates tend to be associated with the smaller hotels.

This tends to make sense when you think about the economies of scale for the larger hotels. Many of the amenities in terms of pools, equipment, spas, restaurants, and so on exist for all hotels in the *Travel + Leisure* top 50 hotels in the world. The smaller hotels tend to charge more for the rooms. The larger hotels can spread their fixed costs over many room and may actually be able to charge less per night and still achieve and nice profit. The larger hotels may also charge slightly less in an effort to obtain a higher occupancy rate. In any case, it appears that there is a slightly negative linear association between the number of rooms and the cost per night for a double room at the top hotels.

71. a. The scatter diagram is shown below.

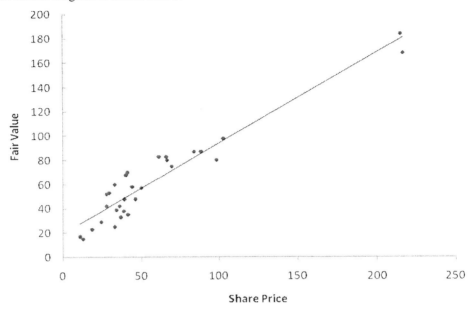

The sample correlation coefficient is .954. This indicates a strong positive linear relationship between Morningstar's Fair Value estimate per share and the most recent price per share for the stock.

b. The scatter diagram is shown below:

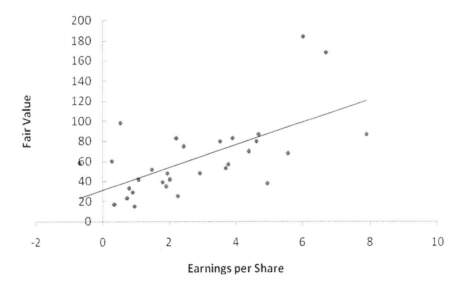

The sample correlation coefficient is .624. While not a strong of a relationship as shown in part a, this indicates a positive linear relationship between Morningstar's Fair Value estimate per share and the earnings per share for the stock.

72. a.

x_i	y_i	$(x_i - \bar{x})$	$(y_i - \bar{y})$	$(x_i - \bar{x})^2$	$(y_i - \bar{y})^2$	$(x_i - \bar{x})(y_i - \bar{y})$
.407	.422	-.1458	-.0881	.0213	.0078	.0128
.429	.586	-.1238	.0759	.0153	.0058	-.0094
.417	.546	-.1358	.0359	.0184	.0013	-.0049
.569	.500	.0162	-.0101	.0003	.0001	-.0002
.569	.457	.0162	-.0531	.0003	.0028	-.0009
.533	.463	-.0198	-.0471	.0004	.0022	.0009
.724	.617	.1712	.1069	.0293	.0114	.0183
.500	.540	-.0528	.0299	.0028	.0009	-.0016
.577	.549	.0242	.0389	.0006	.0015	.0009
.692	.466	.1392	-.0441	.0194	.0019	-.0061
.500	.377	-.0528	-.1331	.0028	.0177	.0070
.731	.599	.1782	.0889	.0318	.0079	.0158
.643	.488	.0902	-.0221	.0081	.0005	-.0020
.448	.531	-.1048	.0209	.0110	.0004	-.0022
			Total	.1617	.0623	.0287

$$s_{xy} = \frac{\Sigma(x_i - \bar{x})(y_i - \bar{y})}{n-1} = \frac{.0287}{14-1} = .0022$$

$$s_x = \sqrt{\frac{\Sigma(x_i - \bar{x})^2}{n-1}} = \sqrt{\frac{.1617}{14-1}} = .1115$$

$$s_y = \sqrt{\frac{\Sigma(y_i - \bar{y})^2}{n-1}} = \sqrt{\frac{.0623}{14-1}} = .0692$$

$$r_{xy} = \frac{s_{xy}}{s_x s_y} = \frac{.0022}{.1115(.0692)} = +.286$$

b. There is a low positive correlation between a major league baseball team's winning percentage during spring training and its winning percentage during the regular season. The spring training record should not be expected to be a good indicator of how a team will play during the regular season.

Spring training consists of practice games between teams with the outcome as to who wins or who loses not counting in the regular season standings or affecting the chances of making the playoffs. Teams use spring training to help players regain their timing and evaluate new players. Substitutions are frequent with the regular or better players rarely playing an entire spring training game. Winning is not the primary goal in spring training games. A low correlation between spring training winning percentage and regular season winning percentage should be anticipated.

73. $$\bar{x} = \frac{\Sigma w_i x_i}{\Sigma w_i} = \frac{20(20) + 30(12) + 10(7) + 15(5) + 10(6)}{20 + 30 + 10 + 15 + 10} = \frac{965}{85} = 11.4 \text{ days}$$

74.

f_i	M_i	$f_i M_i$	$M_i - \bar{x}$	$(M_i - \bar{x})^2$	$f_i(M_i - \bar{x})^2$
10	47	470	-13.68	187.1424	1871.42
40	52	2080	-8.68	75.3424	3013.70
150	57	8550	-3.68	13..5424	2031.36
175	62	10850	+1.32	1.7424	304.92
75	67	5025	+6.32	39.9424	2995.68
15	72	1080	+11.32	128.1424	1922.14
10	77	770	+16.32	266.3424	2663.42
475		28,825			14,802.64

a. $\bar{x} = \dfrac{28,825}{475} = 60.68$

b. $s^2 = \dfrac{14,802.64}{474} = 31.23$

$s = \sqrt{31.23} = 5.59$

75. a.

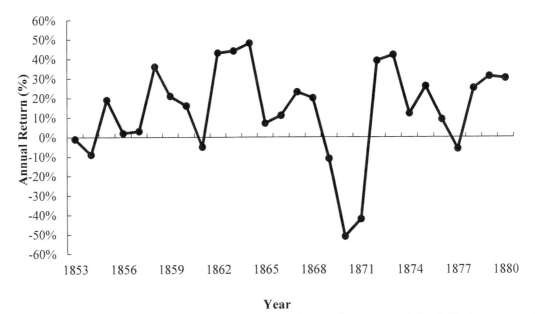

It appears the Panama Railroad Company outperformed the New York Stock Exchange annual average return of 8.4%, but the large drop in returns in 1870-71 makes it difficult to be certain.

b. The geometric mean is

$$\bar{x}_g = \sqrt[28]{(x_1)(x_2)\cdots(x_{28})} = \sqrt[28]{16.769} = 1.106$$

So the mean annual return on Panama Railroad Company stock is 10.6%. During the period of 1853–1880, the Panama Railroad Company stock yielded a return superior to the 8.4% earned by the New York Stock Exchange.

Note that we could also calculate the geometric mean with Excel. If the growth factors for the individual years are in cells C2:C30, then typing =GEOMEAN(C2:C30) into an empty cell will yield the geometric mean.

Chapter 4
Introduction to Probability

Learning Objectives

1. Obtain an appreciation of the role probability information plays in the decision making process.

2. Understand probability as a numerical measure of the likelihood of occurrence.

3. Know the three methods commonly used for assigning probabilities and understand when they should be used.

4. Know how to use the laws that are available for computing the probabilities of events.

5. Understand how new information can be used to revise initial (prior) probability estimates using Bayes' theorem.

Solutions:

1.   Number of experimental Outcomes = (3)(2)(4) = 24

2. $\binom{6}{3} = \dfrac{6!}{3!3!} = \dfrac{6 \cdot 5 \cdot 4 \cdot 3 \cdot 2 \cdot 1}{(3 \cdot 2 \cdot 1)(3 \cdot 2 \cdot 1)} = 20$

ABC	ACE	BCD	BEF
ABD	ACF	BCE	CDE
ABE	ADE	BCF	CDF
ABF	ADF	BDE	CEF
ACD	AEF	BDF	DEF

3. $P_3^6 = \dfrac{6!}{(6-3)!} = (6)(5)(4) = 120$

   BDF BFD DBF DFB FBD FDB

4.   a.

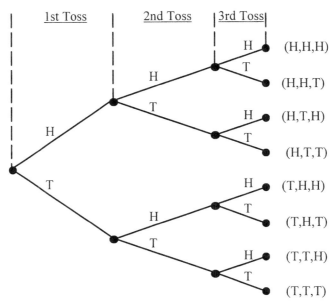

	1st Toss	2nd Toss	3rd Toss	

   b.   Let: H be head and T be tail

   (H,H,H) (T,H,H)
   (H,H,T) (T,H,T)
   (H,T,H) (T,T,H)
   (H,T,T) (T,T,T)

   c.   The outcomes are equally likely, so the probability of each outcome is 1/8.

5. $P(E_i) = 1/5$ for i = 1, 2, 3, 4, 5

   $P(E_i) \geq 0$ for i = 1, 2, 3, 4, 5

   $P(E_1) + P(E_2) + P(E_3) + P(E_4) + P(E_5) = 1/5 + 1/5 + 1/5 + 1/5 + 1/5 = 1$

   The classical method was used.

6. $P(E_1) = .40$, $P(E_2) = .26$, $P(E_3) = .34$

       The relative frequency method was used.

7.   No. Requirement (4.4) is not satisfied; the probabilities do not sum to 1. $P(E_1) + P(E_2) + P(E_3) + P(E_4) = .10 + .15 + .40 + .20 = .85$

8. a. There are four outcomes possible for this 2-step experiment; planning commission positive - council approves; planning commission positive - council disapproves; planning commission negative - council approves; planning commission negative - council disapproves.

    b. Let p = positive, n = negative, a = approves, and d = disapproves

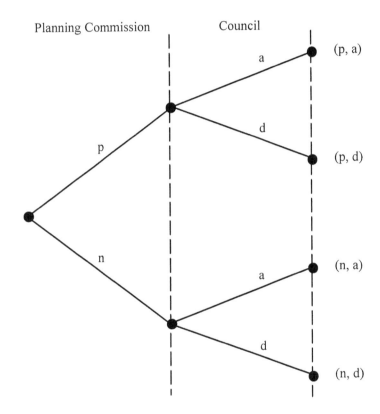

9. $\dbinom{50}{4} = \dfrac{50!}{4!46!} = \dfrac{50 \cdot 49 \cdot 48 \cdot 47}{4 \cdot 3 \cdot 2 \cdot 1} = 230,300$

10. a. Using the table provided, 94% of students graduating from Morehouse College have debt.

        $P(\text{Debt}) = .94$

    b. Five of the 8 institutions have over 60% of their graduates with debt.

        $P(\text{over } 60\%) = 5/8 = .625$

    c. Two of the 8 institutions have graduates with debt who have an average debt more than $30,000.

        $P(\text{more than } \$30,000) = 2/8 = .25$

d. $P(\text{No debt}) = 1 - P(\text{Debt}) = 1 - .72 = .28$

e. This is a weighted average calculation. 72% graduate with an average debt of $32,980 and 28% graduate with a debt of $0.

$$\text{Average debt per graduate} = \frac{.72(\$32,980) + .28(\$0)}{.72 + .28} = \$23,746$$

11. a. Total motorcyclists = 350 + 170 = 520

$$P(\text{DOT-Compliant Helmet}) = \frac{350}{520} = .6731$$

b. Yes, the overall probability has been increasing from .48 five years ago, to .63 one year ago, and is now approximately .67. The probability that a motorcyclist wears a DOT-compliant helmet appears to be increasing.

c. Northeast: $\dfrac{96}{158} = .6076$

   Midwest: $\dfrac{86}{129} = .6667$

   South: $\dfrac{92}{141} = .6525$

   West: $\dfrac{76}{92} = .8261$

   The West region shows the highest probability (.8261) of DOT-compliant helmet use.

12. a. Step 1: Use the counting rule for combinations:

$$\binom{59}{5} = \frac{59!}{5!(59-5)!} = \frac{(59)(58)(57)(56)(55)}{(5)(4)(3)(2)(1)} = 5,006,386$$

   Step 2: There are 35 ways to select the red Powerball from digits 1 to 35

   Total number of Powerball lottery outcomes: (5,006,386) x (35) = 175,223,510

b. Probability of winning the lottery: 1 chance in 175,223,510

$$= 1/(175,223,510) = .000000005707$$

13. Initially a probability of .20 would be assigned if selection is equally likely. Data does not appear to confirm the belief of equal consumer preference. For example using the relative frequency method we would assign a probability of 5/100 = .05 to the design 1 outcome, .15 to design 2, .30 to design 3, .40 to design 4, and .10 to design 5.

14. a. $P(E_2) = 1/4$

    b. P(any 2 outcomes) = 1/4 + 1/4 = 1/2

    c. P(any 3 outcomes) = 1/4 + 1/4 + 1/4 = 3/4

15. a. S = {ace of clubs, ace of diamonds, ace of hearts, ace of spades}

    b. S = {2 of clubs, 3 of clubs, . . . , 10 of clubs, J of clubs, Q of clubs, K of clubs, A of clubs}

    c. There are 12; jack, queen, or king in each of the four suits.

    d. For a: 4/52 = 1/13 = .08

       For b: 13/52 = 1/4 = .25

       For c: 12/52 = .23

16. a. (6)(6) = 36 sample points

    b.

    Die 2

		1	2	3	4	5	6
	1	2	3	4	5	6	7
	2	3	4	5	6	7	8	← Total for Both
	3	4	5	6	7	8	9
Die 1	4	5	6	7	8	9	10
	5	6	7	8	9	10	11
	6	7	8	9	10	11	12

    c. 6/36 = 1/6

    d. 10/36 = 5/18

    e. No. P(odd) = 18/36 = P(even) = 18/36 or 1/2 for both.

    f. Classical. A probability of 1/36 is assigned to each experimental outcome.

17. a. (4,6), (4,7), (4,8)

    b. .05 + .10 + .15 = .30

c.   (2,8), (3,8), (4,8)

d. $.05 + .05 + .15 = .25$

e.   .15

18. a.   Let C = corporate headquarters located in California

$P(C) = 53/500 = .106$

b.   Let N = corporate headquarters located in New York
T = corporate headquarters located in Texas

$P(N) = 50/500 = .100$
$P(T) = 52/500 = .104$

Located in California, New York, or Texas

$P(C) + P(N) + P(T) = .106 + .100 + .104 = .31$

c.   Let A = corporate headquarters located in one of the eight states

Total number of companies with corporate headquarters in the eight states = 283

$P(A) = 283/500 = .566$

Over half the Fortune 500 companies have corporate headquartered located in these eight states.

19. a.   A summary of the data provided in the exercise follows:

Response	United States	Great Britain	Total
Yes	187	197	384
No	334	411	745
Unsure	256	213	469
Total	777	821	1598

Probability = $334/777 = .4299$

b.   Probability = $(411 + 213)/821 = .76$

c.   Probability = $(334 + 411)/1598 = .4662$

d.   The probability that an investor in the United States thinks the government is adequately protecting investors is $187/777 = .2407$; for investors in Great Britain the probability is $197/821 = .24$. The two probabilities are almost identical; thus, there does not appear to be a difference between the perceptions of investors in these two countries with regard to the "Yes" response.

However, in part (a) we showed that the probability that an investor in the United States does not think the government is adequately protecting investors is .4299, or approximately .43; for investors in Great Britain the probability is $411/821 = .5006$ or approximately .50. These results show a slightly higher probability that an investor in Great Britain will say that the government is not protecting investors adequately.

20. a.

Experimental Outcome	Age Financially Independent	Number of Responses	Probability
E_1	16 to 20	191	$191/944 = .2023$
E_2	21 to 24	467	$467/944 = .4947$
E_3	25 to 27	244	$244/944 = .2585$
E_4	28 or older	42	$42/944 = .0445$
		944	

   b. $P(\text{Age} <25) = P(E_1) + P(E_2) = .2023 + .4947 = .6970$

   c. $P(\text{Age} >24) = P(E_3) + P(E_4) = .2585 + .0445 = .3030$

   e.   The probability of being financially independent before the age of 25, .6970, seems high given the general economic conditions. It appears that the teenagers who responded to this survey may have unrealistic expectations about becoming financially independent at a relatively young age.

21. a. $P(\text{Fall}) = \dfrac{645}{4535} = .1422$

   b. $P(\text{Transportation Incident}) = \dfrac{1795}{4535} = .3958$

   c.   The cause of fatality that is least likely to occur is Fires and Explosions with a probability of

   $P(\text{Fires and Explosions}) = \dfrac{113}{4535} = .0249$

22. a. $P(A) = .40$, $P(B) = .40$, $P(C) = .60$

   b. $P(A \cup B) = P(E_1, E_2, E_3, E_4) = .80$.   Yes $P(A \cup B) = P(A) + P(B)$.

   c. $A^c = \{E_3, E_4, E_5\}$ $C^c = \{E_1, E_4\}$ $P(A^c) = .60$ $P(C^c) = .40$

   d. $A \cup B^c = \{E_1, E_2, E_5\}$ $P(A \cup B^c) = .60$

   e. $P(B \cup C) = P(E_2, E_3, E_4, E_5) = .80$

23. a. $P(A) = P(E_1) + P(E_4) + P(E_6) = .05 + .25 + .10 = .40$

   $P(B) = P(E_2) + P(E_4) + P(E_7) = .20 + .25 + .05 = .50$

   $P(C) = P(E_2) + P(E_3) + P(E_5) + P(E_7) = .20 + .20 + .15 + .05 = .60$

   b. $A \cup B = \{E_1, E_2, E_4, E_6, E_7\}$

   $P(A \cup B) = P(E_1) + P(E_2) + P(E_4) + P(E_6) + P(E_7)$
   $= .05 + .20 + .25 + .10 + .05 = .65$

   c. $A \cap B = \{E_4\}$ $P(A \cap B) = P(E_4) = .25$

d. Yes, they are mutually exclusive.

e. $B^c = \{E_1, E_3, E_5, E_6\}$; $P(B^c)$ $= P(E_1) + P(E_3) + P(E_5) + P(E_6)$
$= .05 + .20 + .15 + .10 = .50$

24. Let E = experience exceeded expectations
M = experience met expectations

a. Percentage of respondents that said their experience exceeded expectations
$= 100 - (4 + 26 + 65) = 5\%$

$P(E) = .05$

b. $P(M \cup E) = P(M) + P(E) = .65 + .05 = .70$

25. Let W = person feels guilty about wasting food
L = person feels guilty about leaving lights on when not in a room

a. $P(W \cup L) = P(W) + P(L) - P(W \cap L)$
$= .39 + .27 - .12 = .54$

b. $1 - P(W \cup L) = 1 - .54 = .46$

26. a. Let D = Domestic Equity Fund

$P(D) = 16/25 = .64$

b. Let A = 4- or 5-star rating

13 funds were rated 3-star of less; thus, $25 - 13 = 12$ funds must be 4-star or 5-star.

$P(A) = 12/25 = .48$

c. 7 Domestic Equity funds were rated 4-star and 2 were rated 5-star. Thus, 9 funds were Domestic Equity funds and were rated 4-star or 5-star

$P(D \cap A) = 9/25 = .36$

d. $P(D \cup A) = P(D) + P(A) - P(D \cap A)$

$= .64 + .48 - .36 = .76$

27. Let A = the event the ACC has a team in the championship game
S = the event the SEC has a team in the championship game

a. $P(A) = \dfrac{10}{20} = .50$

b. $P(S) = \dfrac{8}{20} = .40$

c. $P(A \cap S) = \dfrac{1}{20} = .05$

There is a low probability that teams from both the ACC and SEC will be in the championship game.

d. $P(A \cup S) = P(A) + P(S) - P(A \cap S) = .50 + .40 - .05 = .85$

There is a high probability that a team from the ACC or SEC will be in the championship game.

e. $P(\text{Neither conference}) = 1 - P(A \cup S) = 1 - .85 = .15$

In this case, teams will most likely come from the Big Ten (6), Big East (4), Pac-10 (4), or Big 12 (3). Numbers shown are the number of times teams from these conferences have played in the national championship game over the previous 20 years.

28. Let: B = rented a car for business reasons
          P = rented a car for personal reasons

a. $P(B \cup P) = P(B) + P(P) - P(B \cap P)$
    $= .54 + .458 - .30 = .698$

b. $P(\text{Neither}) = 1 - .698 = .302$

29. a. $P(E) = \dfrac{1033}{2851} = .3623$

$P(R) = \dfrac{854}{2851} = .2995$

$P(D) = \dfrac{964}{2851} = .3381$

b. Yes; $P(E \cap D) = 0$

c. Probability $= \dfrac{1033}{2375} = .4349$

d. Let F denote the event that a student who applies for early admission is deferred and later admitted during the regular admission process.

Events E and F are mutually exclusive and the addition law applies.

$P(E \cup F) = P(E) + P(F)$

$P(E) = .3623$ from part (a)

Of the 964 early applicants who were deferred, we expect 18%, or .18(964) students, to be admitted during the regular admission process. Thus, for the total of 2851 early admission applicants

$P(F) = \dfrac{.18(964)}{2851} = .0609$

$P(E \cup F) = P(E) + P(F) = .3623 + .0609 = .4232$

4 - 9

Note: .18(964) = 173.52. Some students may round this to 174 students. If rounding is done, the answer becomes .4233. Either approach is acceptable.

30. a. $P(A|B) = \dfrac{P(A \cap B)}{P(B)} = \dfrac{.40}{.60} = .6667$

    b. $P(B|A) = \dfrac{P(A \cap B)}{P(A)} = \dfrac{.40}{.50} = .80$

    c. No because $P(A \mid B) \neq P(A)$

31. a. $P(A \cap B) = 0$

    b. $P(A|B) = \dfrac{P(A \cap B)}{P(B)} = \dfrac{0}{.4} = 0$

    c. No. $P(A \mid B) \neq P(A)$; $\therefore$ the events, although mutually exclusive, are not independent.

    d. Mutually exclusive events are dependent.

32. a. Row and column sums are shown.

	Car	Light Truck	Total
U.S.	87.4	193.1	280.5
Non U.S.	228.5	148.0	376.5
Total	315.9	341.1	657.0

    A total of 657.0 thousand vehicles were sold.

    Dividing each entry in the table by 657.0 provides the following joint probability table.

	Car	Light Truck	Total
U.S.	.1330	.2939	.4269
Non U.S.	.3478	.2253	.5731
Total	.4808	.5192	1.0000

    b. Let U = U. S. manufacturer
           N = Non U.S. manufacturer
           C = Car
           L = Light Truck

    Marginal probabilities: $P(U) = .4269$ $P(B) = .5731$

    There is a higher probability that the vehicle was not manufactured by a U. S. auto maker. In terms of market share, non U.S. auto makers lead with a 57.3% share of vehicle sales.

    Marginal probabilities: $P(C) = .4808$ $P(L) = .5192$

    The light truck category which includes pickup, minivans, SUVs and crossover models has a slightly higher probability. But the types of vehicles are fairly even split.

c. $P(C|U) = \dfrac{P(C \cap U)}{P(U)} = \dfrac{.1330}{.4269} = .3115$ $\qquad$ $P(L|U) = \dfrac{P(L \cap U)}{P(L)} = \dfrac{.2939}{.4269} = .6885$

If a vehicle was manufactured by one of the U.S. auto makers, there is a higher probability it will be in the light truck category.

d. $P(C|N) = \dfrac{P(C \cap N)}{P(N)} = \dfrac{.3478}{.5731} = .6069$ $\qquad$ $P(L|N) = \dfrac{P(L \cap N)}{P(L)} = \dfrac{.2253}{.5731} = .3931$

If a vehicle was not manufactured by one of the U.S. auto makers, there is a higher probability it will be a car.

e. $P(U|L) = \dfrac{P(U \cap L)}{P(L)} = \dfrac{.2939}{.5192} = .5661$

If a vehicle was a light truck, there is better than a 50-50 chance that it was manufactured by one of the U.S. auto makers.

f. There is a higher probability, and thus a larger market share for non U.S. auto makers. However, the U. S. auto makers are leaders in sales for the light truck category.

33. a.

		Business	Engineering	Other	Totals
			Undergraduate Major		
Intended Enrollment Status	Full-Time	.2697	.1510	.1923	.6130
	Part-Time	.1149	.1234	.1487	.3870
	Totals	.3847	.2743	.3410	1.0000

b. Let B = undergraduate major in business
E = undergraduate major in engineering
O = other undergraduate major
F = full-time enrollment

$P(B) = .3847$, $P(E) = .2743$, and $P(O) = .3410$, so business is the undergraduate major that produces the most potential MBA students.

c. $P(E | F) = \dfrac{P(E \cap F)}{P(F)} = \dfrac{.1510}{.6130} = .2463$

d. $P(F | B) = \dfrac{P(F \cap B)}{P(B)} = \dfrac{.2697}{.3847} = .7012$

e. For independence, we must have $P(F)P(B) = P(F \cap B)$

$P(F) = .6130$ and $P(B) = .3847$

$$P(F)P(B) = (.6130)(.3847) = .4299$$

But $P(F \cap B) = .2697$ as shown in the joint probability table

Thus $P(F)P(B) \neq P(F \cap B)$; the events are not independent.

34. a. Let O = flight arrives on time
L = flight arrives late
J = Jet Blue flight
N = United flight
U = US Airways flight

Given: $P(O \mid J) = .768$ $P(O \mid N) = .715$ $P(O \mid U) = .822$

$P(J) = .30$ $P(N) = .32$ $P(U) = .38$

Joint probabilities using the multiplication law

$$P(J \cap O) = P(J)P(O \mid J) = (.30)(.768) = .2304$$

$$P(N \cap O) = P(N)P(O \mid N) = (.32)(.715) = .2288$$

$$P(U \cap O) = P(U)P(O \mid U) = (.38)(.822) = .3124$$

With the marginal probabilities $P(J) = .30$, $P(N) = .32$, and $P(U) = .38$ given, the joint probability table can then be shown as follows.

	On time	Late	Total
Jet Blue	.2304	.0696	.30
United	.2288	.0912	.32
US Airways	.3124	.0676	.38
Total	.7716	.2284	1.00

b. Using the joint probability table, the probability of an on-time flight is the marginal probability

$$P(O) = .2304 + .2288 + .3124 = .7716$$

c. Since US Airways has the highest percentage of flights into terminal C, US Airways with $P(U) = .38$ is the most likely airline for Flight 1382.

d. From the joint probability table, $P(L) = .2284$

$$P(J \mid L) = \frac{P(J \cap L)}{P(L)} = \frac{.0696}{.2284} = .3047$$

$$P(N \mid L) = \frac{P(N \cap L)}{P(L)} = \frac{.0912}{.2284} = .3992$$

$$P(U \mid L) = \frac{P(U \cap L)}{P(L)} = \frac{.0676}{.2284} = .2961$$

Most likely airline for Flight 1382 is now United with a probability of .3992. US Airways is now the least likely airline for this flight with a probability of .2961.

35. a. The total sample size is 200. Dividing each entry by 200 provides the following joint probability table.

		Pay Rent		
		Yes	No	
Buy a Car	Yes	.28	.26	.54
	No	.07	.39	.46
		.35	.65	

b. Let   C = the event of financial assistance to buy a car
   R = the event of financial assistance to pay rent

Using the marginal probabilities, $P(C) = .54$ and $P(R) = .35$. Parents are more likely to provide their adult children with financial assistance to buy a car. The probability of financial assistance to buy a car is .54 and the probability of financial assistance to pay rent is .35.

c. $P(R|C) = \dfrac{P(R \cap C)}{P(C)} = \dfrac{.28}{.54} = .5185$

d. $P(R|C^{C}) = \dfrac{P(R \cap C^{C})}{P(C^{C})} = \dfrac{.07}{.46} = .1522$

e. Financial assistance to buy a car is not independent of financial assistance to pay rent, $P(R|C) \neq P(R)$.

If there is financial assistance to buy a car, the probability of financial assistance to pay rent increases from .35 to .5185. However, if there is no financial assistance to buy a car, the probability of financial assistance to pay rent decreases from .35 to .1522.

f. $P(C \cup R) = P(C) + P(R) - P(R \cap C) = .54 + .35 - .28 = .61$

36. a. Let A = makes 1st free throw
   B = makes 2nd free throw

Assuming independence, $P(A \cap B) = P(A)P(B) = (.93)(.93) = .8649$

b. At least one shot

$P(A \cup B) = P(A) + P(B) - P(A \cap B) = (.93) + (.93) - .8649 = .9951$

c. Miss both $1 - P(A \cup B) = 1 - .9951 = .0049$

d. For the Portland Trail Blazers' center with $P(A) = P(B) = .58$

$P(A \cap B) = P(A)P(B) = (.58)(.58) = .3346$

$P(A \cup B) = P(A) + P(B) - P(A \cap B) = (.58) + (.58) - .3364 = .8236$

Miss both $1 - P(A \cup B) = 1 - .8236 = .1764$

Intentionally fouling the Portland Trail Blazers' center is a better strategy than intentionally fouling Jamal Crawford.

37. Let S = worker would select the same career
D = worker would select a different career
E = worker plans to retire early

a. $P(S) = 1 - P(D) = 1 - .59 = .41$ as shown as the marginal probability in the table

b. $P(E \mid S) = \dfrac{P(E \cap S)}{P(S)} = \dfrac{.20}{.41} = .4878$

c. $P(E \mid D) = \dfrac{P(E \cap D)}{P(D)} = \dfrac{.13}{.59} = .2203$

d. The probability the worker plans to retire early is greater for the worker who would choose the same career. This suggests that one of the reasons the worker would select the same career is that there is a greater probability of being able to retire early. On the other hand, the worker who would choose a different career may feel stuck with a smaller probability of being able to retire early.

38. Let Y = has a college degree
N = does not have a college degree
D = a delinquent student loan

a. From the table, $P(Y) = .42$

b. From the table, $P(N) = .58$

c. $P(D \mid Y) = \dfrac{P(D \cap Y)}{P(Y)} = \dfrac{.16}{.42} = .3810$

d. $P(D \mid N) = \dfrac{P(D \cap N)}{P(N)} = \dfrac{.34}{.58} = .5862$

e. Individuals who obtained a college degree have a .3810 probability of a delinquent student loan while individuals who dropped out without obtaining a college degree have a .5862 probability of a delinquent student loan. Not obtaining a college degree will lead to a greater probability of struggling to payback the student loan and will likely lead to financial problems in the future.

39. a. Yes, since $P(A_1 \cap A_2) = 0$

b. $P(A_1 \cap B) = P(A_1)P(B \mid A_1) = .40(.20) = .08$

$P(A_2 \cap B) = P(A_2)P(B \mid A_2) = .60(.05) = .03$

c. $P(B) = P(A_1 \cap B) + P(A_2 \cap B) = .08 + .03 = .11$

d. $P(A_1|B) = \dfrac{.08}{.11} = .7273$

$P(A_2|B) = \dfrac{.03}{.11} = .2727$

40. a. $P(B \cap A_1) = P(A_1)P(B \mid A_1) = (.20)(.50) = .10$

$P(B \cap A_2) = P(A_2)P(B \mid A_2) = (.50)(.40) = .20$

$P(B \cap A_3) = P(A_3)P(B \mid A_3) = (.30)(.30) = .09$

b. $P(A_2|B) = \dfrac{.20}{.10 + .20 + .09} = .51$

c.

Events	$P(A_i)$	$P(B \mid A_i)$	$P(A_i \cap B)$	$P(A_i \mid B)$
A_1	.20	.50	.10	.26
A_2	.50	.40	.20	.51
A_3	.30	.30	.09	.23
	1.00		.39	1.00

41. S_1 = successful, S_2 = not successful and B = request received for additional information.

a. $P(S_1) = .50$

b. $P(B \mid S_1) = .75$

c. $P(S_1|B) = \dfrac{(.50)(.75)}{(.50)(.75) + (.50)(.40)} = \dfrac{.375}{.575} = .65$

42. M = missed payment
D$_1$ = customer defaults
D$_2$ = customer does not default

$P(D_1) = .05 \quad P(D_2) = .95 \quad P(M \mid D_2) = .2 \quad P(M \mid D_1) = 1$

a. $P(D_1|M) = \dfrac{P(D_1)P(M|D_1)}{P(D_1)P(M|D_1) + P(D_2)P(M|D_2)} = \dfrac{(.05)(1)}{(.05)(1) + (.95)(.2)} = \dfrac{.05}{.24} = .21$

b. Yes, the probability of default is greater than .20.

43. a. Let H = event Isaac becomes a hurricane by the time it reaches the Gulf of Mexico
T = event Isaac does not become a hurricane and remains a tropical storm when it reaches the Gulf of Mexico

$P(H) = .69$
$P(T) = P(H^C) = 1 - P(H) = 1 - .69 = .31$

b. Let C = event that Isaac passes over Cuba

$P(C \mid H) = .08$

$P(C \mid T) = .20$

$$P(H \mid C) = \frac{P(H)P(C \mid H)}{P(H)P(C \mid H) + P(T)P(C \mid T)} = \frac{(.69)(.08)}{(.69)(.08) + (.31)(.20)} = .4710$$

c. Passing over a landmass such as Cuba tends to slow down and break up a tropical storm. As this exercise shows, the probability that tropical storm Isaac would become a hurricane by the time it reached the Gulf of Mexico dropped from .69 to .4710 when it was learned that the projected path of Isaac was over Cuba.

For the record, Isaac passed over Cuba and reached the Gulf of Mexico as a tropical storm. But once in the warm waters of the Gulf of Mexico it gained strength once again, eventually became a category 1 hurricane before reaching landfall in Louisiana on August 28, 2012.

44. M = the current visitor to the ParFore website is a male
F = the current visitor to the Parfore website is a female
D = a visitor to the ParFore website previously visited the Dillard website

a. Using past history, $P(F) = .40$.

b. $P(M) = .60$, $P(D \mid F) = .30$, and $P(D \mid M) = .10$

$$P(F \mid D) = \frac{P(F)P(D \mid F)}{P(F)P(D \mid F) + P(M)P(D \mid M)} = \frac{(.40)(.30)}{(.40)(.30) + (.60)(.10)} = .6667$$

The revised probability that the current visitor is a female is .6667.

ParFore should display the special offer that appeals to female visitors.

45. a. Let M = event that a putt is made

$P(M) = 983,764/1,613,234 = .6098$

Note: The probability that a putt is missed is $P(M^C) = 1 - P(M) = 1 - .6098 = .3902$

b. Let A = event that a PGA Tour player has a par putt

$P(A \mid M) = .640$

$P(A \mid M^C) = .203$

$$P(M \mid A) = \frac{P(M)P(A \mid M)}{P(M)P(A \mid M) + P(M^C)P(A \mid M^C)} = \frac{(.6098)(.640)}{(.6098)(.640) + (.3902)(.203)} = .8313$$

c. Let B = event that a PGA Tour player has a birdie putt

$P(B|M) = .188$

$P(B|M^C) = .734$

$$P(M \mid B) = \frac{P(M)P(B|M)}{P(M)P(B|M) + P(M^C)P(B|M^C)} = \frac{(.6098)(.188)}{(.6098)(.188) + (.3902)(.734)} = .2859$$

d. These probabilities indicate that there is a much higher probability of making a par putt than making a birdie putt. One reason is that par putts have an extra stroke than birdie putts. Because of the extra stroke, par putts tend to be closer to the hole than birdie putts and there is thus a higher probability of making a par putt. For example, the average length of all putts made is slightly less than 5 feet while the average length of birdie putts made is 21 feet.

In addition, the authors of the article referenced in this exercise conclude that PGA Tour players tend to view missing a par as a loss and making a birdie as a gain. Thus, to avoid the loss of missing out on a par, the golfers are more conservative when they have a birdie putt. As a result, even with par and birdie putts of the same length, players tend to miss more birdies to insure that they will be close enough to have a very high probability of making a par.

46. a. $422 + 181 + 80 + 121 + 201 = 1005$ respondents

b. Most frequent response a day or less; Probability = $422/1005 = .4199$

c. $201/1005 = .20$

d. Responses of 2 days, 3 days, and 4 or more days = $181 + 80 + 121 = 382$

Probability = $382/1005 = .3801$

47. a.   (2)(2) = 4

  b.   Let   S = successful
        U = unsuccessful

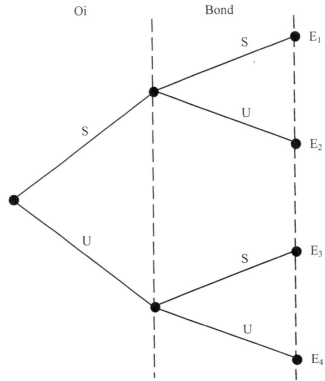

  c.   O = {E₁, E₂}

      M = {E₁, E₃}

  d.   O ∪ M = {E₁, E₂, E₃}

  e.   O ∩ M = {E₁}

  f.   No; since O ∩ M has a sample point.

48. a.   There are a total of 1364 responses. Dividing each entry by 1364 provides the following joint probability table.

	A	B	Total
Female	.2896	.2133	.5029
Male	.2368	.2603	.4971
Total	.5264	.4736	1.0000

  b.   The marginal probability of a female is .5029 from above.

  c.   Let A = uses social media and other websites to voice opinions about television programs
        F = female respondent

$$P(A \mid F) = \frac{P(A \cap F)}{P(F)} = \frac{.2896}{.5029} = .5758$$

d. $P(F \cap A) = .2896$ from the joint probability table

$P(F)P(A) = (.5029)(.5264) = .2647$

$P(F \cap A) \neq P(F)P(A)$; the events are not independent

49.   Let   I = treatment-caused injury
D = death from injury
N = injury caused by negligence
M = malpractice claim filed
$ = payment made in claim

We are given $P(I) = .04$, $P(N \mid I) = .25$, $P(D \mid I) = 1/7$, $P(M \mid N) = 1/7.5 = .1333$, and $P(\$ \mid M) = .50$

a. $P(N) = P(N \mid I)\, P(I) + P(N \mid I^c)\, P(I^c)$
$= (.25)(.04) + (0)(.96) = .01$

b. $P(D) = P(D \mid I)\, P(I) + P(D \mid I^c)\, P(I^c)$
$= (1/7)(.04) + (0)(.96) = .006$

c. $P(M) = P(M \mid N)\, P(N) + P(M \mid N^c)\, P(N^c)$
$= (.1333)(.01) + (0)(.99) = .001333$

$P(\$) = P(\$ \mid M)\, P(M) + P(\$ \mid M^c)\, P(M^c)$
$= (.5)(.001333) + (0)(.9987) = .00067$

50. a.   Probability of the event $= P(\text{average}) + P(\text{above average}) + P(\text{excellent})$

$$= \frac{11}{50} + \frac{14}{50} + \frac{13}{50} = .22 + .28 + .26 = .76$$

b.   Probability of the event $= P(\text{poor}) + P(\text{below average})$

$$= \frac{4}{50} + \frac{8}{50} = .24$$

51. a.

Education Level	Household Income ($1000)					Total
	Under 25	25-49.9	50-74.9	75-99.9	100 or More	
Not H.S. Graduate	.0571	.0469	.0188	.0073	.0050	.1351
H.S. Graduate	.0667	.0929	.0682	.0358	.0362	.2997
Some College	.0381	.0713	.0634	.0441	.0553	.2721
Bachelor's Degree	.0120	.0284	.0386	.0350	.0729	.1870
Beyond Bach. Degree	.0039	.0112	.0173	.0168	.0568	.1061
Total	.1777	.2508	.2064	.1390	.2262	1.0000

b.   This is a marginal probability.

$P(\text{Not H.S. graduate}) = .1351$

c.   This is the sum of 2 marginal probabilities.

$$P(\text{Bachelor's Degree} \cup \text{Beyond Bachelor's Degree}) = .1870 + .1061 = .2931$$

d. This is a conditional probability.

$$P(100 \text{ or More} | BD) = \frac{P(100 \text{ or More} \cap BD)}{P(BD)} = \frac{.0729}{.1870} = .3898$$

e. This is a marginal probability.

$$P(\text{Under 25}) = .1777$$

f. This is a conditional probability.

$$P(\text{Under 25} | BD) = \frac{P(\text{Under 25} \cap BD)}{P(BD)} = \frac{.0120}{.1870} = .0642$$

g. No. $P(100 \text{ or More} | BD) = .3898$ which is not equal to $P(100 \text{ or More}) = .2262$. This is also shown by comparing the probabilities in parts (e) and (f). Household income is not independent of education level. Individuals with a Bachelor's Degree have a higher probability of having a higher household income.

52. a.

Age Group	More Than One		Total
	Yes	No	
23 and Under	.1026	.0996	.2022
24 – 26	.1482	.1878	.3360
27 – 30	.0917	.1328	.2245
31 – 25	.0327	.0956	.1283
36 and Over	.0253	.0837	.1090
Total	.4005	.5995	1.0000

b. Marginal probability .2022

c. $.2245 + .1283 + .1090 = .4618$

d. Marginal probability .4005

53. a. $P(24 \text{ to } 26 \,|\, \text{Yes}) = .1482/.4005 = .3700$

b. $P(\text{Yes} \,|\, 36 \text{ and over}) = .0253/.1090 = .2321$

c. $.1026 + .1482 + .1878 + .0917 + .0327 + .0253 = .5883$

d. $P(31 \text{ or more} \,|\, \text{No}) = (.0956 + .0837)/.5995 = .2991$

e. No, because the conditional probabilities do not all equal the marginal probabilities. For instance,

$$P(24 \text{ to } 26 \,|\, \text{Yes}) = .3700 \neq P(24 \text{ to } 26) = .3360$$

54. a. $P(\text{Not Okay}) = .1485 + .2273 + .4008 = .7768$

b. $P(30-49) = .2273 + .0907 = .3180$

$$P(\text{Okay}|30-49) = \frac{P(\text{Okay} \cap 30-49)}{P(30-49)} = \frac{.0907}{.3180} = .2852$$

c. $P(50+|\text{Not Okay}) = \dfrac{P(50+ \cap \text{Not Okay})}{P(\text{Not Okay})} = \dfrac{.4008}{.7766} = .5161$

d. The attitude about this practice is not independent of the age of the respondent. One way to show this follows.

$P(\text{Okay}) = 1 - P(\text{Not Okay}) = 1 - .7766 = .2234$

$P\left(\text{Okay}|30-49\right) = .2852$

Since $P(\text{Okay}|30-49) \neq P(\text{Okay})$, attitude is not independent of the age of the respondent.

e. $P\left(\text{Not Okay}|50+\right) = \dfrac{P\left(\text{Not Okay} \cap 50+\right)}{P\left(50+\right)} = \dfrac{.4008}{.4731} = .8472$

$P\left(\text{Not Okay}|18\text{-}29\right) = \dfrac{P\left(\text{Not Okay} \cap 18\text{-}29\right)}{P\left(18\text{-}29\right)} = \dfrac{.1485}{.2089} = .7109$

There is a higher probability the 50+ year olds will not be okay with this practice.

55. a. $P(\text{B}|\text{S}) = \dfrac{P(\text{B} \cap S)}{P(S)} = \dfrac{.12}{.40} = .30$

We have $P(\text{B} | \text{S}) > P(\text{B})$.

Yes, continue the ad since it increases the probability of a purchase.

b. Estimate the company's market share at 20%. Continuing the advertisement should increase the market share since $P(\text{B} | \text{S}) = .30$.

c. $P(\text{B}|\text{S}) = \dfrac{P(\text{B} \cap S)}{P(S)} = \dfrac{.10}{.30} = .333$

The second ad has a bigger effect.

56. a. $P(A) = 200/800 = .25$

b. $P(B) = 100/800 = .125$

c. $P(A \cap B) = 10/800 = .0125$

d. $P(A | B) = P(A \cap B)/P(B) = .0125/.125 = .10$

e.   No, $P(A \mid B) \neq P(A) = .25$

57.   Let A = lost time accident in current year
         B = lost time accident previous year

   Given: $P(B) = .06$, $P(A) = .05$, $P(A \mid B) = .15$

a. $P(A \cap B) = P(A \mid B)P(B) = .15(.06) = .009$

b. $P(A \cup B) = P(A) + P(B) - P(A \cap B) = .06 + .05 - .009 = .101$ or 10.1%

58.   a.   Let A_1 = student studied abroad

         A_2 = student did not study abroad
         F = female student
         M = male student

   $P(A_1) = .095$

   $P(A_2) = 1 - P(A_1) = 1 - .095 = .905$

   $P(F \mid A_1) = .60$

   $P(F \mid A_2) = .49$

   Tabular computations

Events	$P(A_i)$	$P(F|A_i)$	$P(A_i \cap F)$	$P(A_i|F)$
A_1	.095	.60	.0570	.1139
A_2	.905	.49	.4435	.8861
			$P(F) = .5005$	

   $P(A_1|F) = .1139$

b.

Events	$P(A_i)$	$P(M|A_i)$	$P(A_i \cap M)$	$P(A_i|M)$
A_1	.095	.40	.0380	.0761
A_2	.905	.51	.4615	.9239
			$P(M) = .4995$	

   $P(A_1|M) = .0761$

c.   From above, $P(F) = .5005$ and $P(M) = .4995$, so almost 50/50 female and male full-time students.

59.   a. $P(\text{Oil}) = .50 + .20 = .70$

b.   Let S = Soil test results

Events	$P(A_i)$	$P(S \mid A_i)$	$P(A_i \cap S)$	$P(A_i \mid S)$
High Quality (A_1)	.50	.20	.10	.31
Medium Quality (A_2)	.20	.80	.16	.50
No Oil (A_3)	.30	.20	.06	.19
	1.00		$P(S) = .32$	1.00

$P(\text{Oil}) = .81$ which is good; however, probabilities now favor medium quality rather than high quality oil.

60. a.

$$P\left(\text{spam}|shipping!\right) = \frac{P\left(\text{spam}\right)P\left(shipping!|\text{spam}\right)}{P\left(\text{spam}\right)P\left(shipping!|\text{spam}\right) + P\left(\text{ham}\right)P\left(shipping!|\text{ham}\right)}$$

$$= \frac{\left(.10\right)\left(.051\right)}{\left(.10\right)\left(.051\right) + \left(.90\right)\left(.0015\right)} = .7907$$

$$P\left(\text{ham}|shipping!\right) = \frac{P\left(\text{ham}\right)P\left(shipping!|\text{ham}\right)}{P\left(\text{ham}\right)P\left(shipping!|\text{ham}\right) + P\left(\text{spam}\right)P\left(shipping!|\text{ham}\right)}$$

$$= \frac{\left(.90\right)\left(.0015\right)}{\left(.90\right)\left(.0015\right) + \left(.10\right)\left(.051\right)} = .2093$$

If a message includes the word *shipping!*, the probability the message is spam is high (.7910), and so the message should be flagged as spam.

b.

$$P\left(\text{spam}|today!\right) = \frac{P\left(\text{spam}\right)P\left(today!|\text{spam}\right)}{P\left(\text{spam}\right)P\left(today!|\text{spam}\right) + P\left(\text{ham}\right)P\left(today!|\text{ham}\right)}$$

$$= \frac{\left(.10\right)\left(.045\right)}{\left(.10\right)\left(.045\right) + \left(.90\right)\left(.0022\right)} = .6944$$

$$P\left(\text{spam}|here!\right) = \frac{P\left(\text{spam}\right)P\left(here!|\text{spam}\right)}{P\left(\text{spam}\right)P\left(here!|\text{spam}\right) + P\left(\text{ham}\right)P\left(here!|\text{ham}\right)}$$

$$= \frac{\left(.10\right)\left(.034\right)}{\left(.10\right)\left(.034\right) + \left(.90\right)\left(.0022\right)} = .6320$$

A message that includes the word *today!* is more likely to be spam. This is because $P(today!|\text{spam})$ is larger than $P(here!|\text{spam})$. Because *today!* occurs more often in unwanted messages (spam), it is easier to distinguish spam from ham in messages that include *today!*.

c.

$$P\left(\text{spam}|available!\right) = \frac{P\left(\text{spam}\right)P\left(available!|\text{spam}\right)}{P\left(\text{spam}\right)P\left(available!|\text{spam}\right) + P\left(\text{ham}\right)P\left(available!|\text{ham}\right)}$$

$$= \frac{\left(.10\right)\left(.014\right)}{\left(.10\right)\left(.014\right) + \left(.90\right)\left(.0041\right)} = .2750$$

$$P\left(\text{spam}|fingertips!\right) = \frac{P\left(\text{spam}\right)P\left(fingertips!|\text{spam}\right)}{P\left(\text{spam}\right)P\left(fingertips!|\text{spam}\right) + P\left(\text{ham}\right)P\left(fingertips!|\text{ham}\right)}$$

$$= \frac{\left(.10\right)\left(.014\right)}{\left(.10\right)\left(.014\right) + \left(.90\right)\left(.0011\right)} = .5858$$

A message that includes the word *fingertips!* is more likely to be spam.

d.   It is easier to distinguish spam from ham when a word occurs more often in unwanted messages (spam) and/or less often in legitimate messages (ham).

Chapter 5
Discrete Probability Distributions

Learning Objectives

1.   Understand the concepts of a random variable and a probability distribution.

2.   Be able to distinguish between discrete and continuous random variables.

3.   Be able to compute and interpret the expected value, variance, and standard deviation for a discrete random variable.

4.   Be able to compute and work with probabilities involving a binomial probability distribution.

5.   Be able to compute and work with probabilities involving a Poisson probability distribution.

6.   Know when and how to use the hypergeometric probability distribution.

Solutions:

1.   a.   Head, Head (H,H)
   Head, Tail (H,T)
   Tail, Head (T,H)
   Tail, Tail (T,T)

    b. x = number of heads on two coin tosses

    c.

Outcome	Values of x
(H,H)	2
(H,T)	1
(T,H)	1
(T,T)	0

    d.   Discrete. It may assume 3 values: 0, 1, and 2.

2.   a.   Let x = time (in minutes) to assemble the product.

    b.   It may assume any positive value: $x > 0$.

    c.   Continuous

3.   Let Y = position is offered
       N = position is not offered

    a. S = {(Y,Y,Y), (Y,Y,N), (Y,N,Y), (N,Y,Y), (Y,N,N), (N,Y,N), (N,N,Y), (N,N,N)}

    b.   Let N = number of offers made; N is a discrete random variable.

    c.

Experimental Outcome	(Y,Y,Y)	(Y,Y,N)	(Y,N,Y)	(N,Y,Y)	(Y,N,N)	(N,Y,N)	(N,N,Y)	(N,N,N)
Value of N	3	2	2	2	1	1	1	0

4.   0, 1, 2, 3, 4, 5, 6, 7, 8, 9

5.   a. S = {(1,1), (1,2), (1,3), (2,1), (2,2), (2,3)}

    b.

Experimental Outcome	(1,1)	(1,2)	(1,3)	(2,1)	(2,2)	(2,3)
Number of Steps Required	2	3	4	3	4	5

6.   a.   values: 0,1,2,...,20
                  discrete

    b.   values: 0,1,2,...
                  discrete

    c.   values: 0,1,2,...,50
                  discrete

    d.   values: $0 \leq x \leq 8$
                  continuous

e. values: $x > 0$
    continuous

7. a. $f(x) \geq 0$ for all values of x.

    $\Sigma f(x) = 1$ Therefore, it is a proper probability distribution.

    b. Probability $x = 30$ is $f(30) = .25$

    c. Probability $x \leq 25$ is $f(20) + f(25) = .20 + .15 = .35$

    d. Probability $x > 30$ is $f(35) = .40$

8. a.

x	$f(x)$
1	3/20 = .15
2	5/20 = .25
3	8/20 = .40
4	4/20 = .20
	Total 1.00

    b.

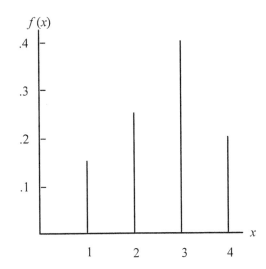

    c. $f(x) \geq 0$ for $x = 1,2,3,4$.

    $\Sigma f(x) = 1$

9. a. There are a total of 26,975 unemployed persons in the data set. Each probability $f(x)$ is computed by dividing the number of months of unemployment by 26,975. For example, $f(1) = 1029/26,975 = .0381$. The complete probability distribution is as follows.

x	$f(x)$
1	.0381
2	.0625
3	.0841
4	.0992
5	.1293
6	.1725
7	.1537
8	.1330
9	.0862
10	.0415

b. $f(x) \geq 0$ and $\sum f(x) = 1$

c. Probability 2 months or less $= f(1) + f(2) = .0381 + .0625 = .1006$

Probability more than 2 months $= 1 - .1006 = .8994$

d. Probability more than 6 months $= f(7) + f(8) + f(9) + f(10) = .1537 + .1330 + .0862 + .0415 = .4144$

10. a.

x	$f(x)$
1	0.05
2	0.09
3	0.03
4	0.42
5	0.41
	1.00

b.

x	$f(x)$
1	0.04
2	0.10
3	0.12
4	0.46
5	0.28
	1.00

c. $P(4 \text{ or } 5) = f(4) + f(5) = 0.42 + 0.41 = 0.83$

d. Probability of very satisfied: 0.28

e. Senior executives appear to be more satisfied than middle managers. 83% of senior executives have a score of 4 or 5 with 41% reporting a 5. Only 28% of middle managers report being very satisfied.

11. a.

Duration of Call

x	$f(x)$
1	0.25
2	0.25
3	0.25
4	0.25
	1.00

b.

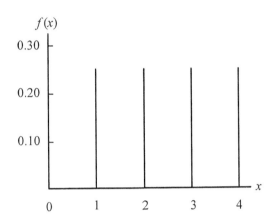

c. $f(x) \geq 0$ and $f(1) + f(2) + f(3) + f(4) = 0.25 + 0.25 + 0.25 + 0.25 = 1.00$

d. $f(3) = 0.25$

e. $P(\text{overtime}) = f(3) + f(4) = 0.25 + 0.25 = 0.50$

12. a. Yes; $f(x) \geq 0$. $\Sigma f(x) = 1$

b. $f(500,000) + f(600,000) = .10 + .05 = .15$

c. $f(100,000) = .10$

13. a. Yes, since $f(x) \geq 0$ for $x = 1,2,3$ and $\Sigma f(x) = f(1) + f(2) + f(3) = 1/6 + 2/6 + 3/6 = 1$

b. $f(2) = 2/6 = .333$

c. $f(2) + f(3) = 2/6 + 3/6 = .833$

14. a. $f(200) = 1 - f(-100) - f(0) - f(50) - f(100) - f(150)$

$= 1 - .95 = .05$

This is the probability MRA will have a $200,000 profit.

b. $P(\text{Profit}) = f(50) + f(100) + f(150) + f(200)$

$= .30 + .25 + .10 + .05 = .70$

c. $P(\text{at least } 100) = f(100) + f(150) + f(200)$

$= .25 + .10 + .05 = .40$

15. a.

x	$f(x)$	$x f(x)$
3	.25	.75
6	.50	3.00
9	.25	2.25
	1.00	6.00

$E(x) = \mu = 6$

b.

x	$x - \mu$	$(x - \mu)^2$	$f(x)$	$(x - \mu)^2 f(x)$
3	-3	9	.25	2.25
6	0	0	.50	0.00
9	3	9	.25	2.25
				4.50

$Var(x) = \sigma^2 = 4.5$

c. $\sigma = \sqrt{4.50} = 2.12$

16. a.

y	$f(y)$	$y f(y)$
2	.2	.4
4	.3	1.2
7	.4	2.8
8	.1	.8
	1.0	5.2

$E(y) = \mu = 5.2$

b.

y	$y - \mu$	$(y - \mu)^2$	$f(y)$	$(y - \mu)^2 f(y)$
2	-3.20	10.24	.20	2.048
4	-1.20	1.44	.30	.432
7	1.80	3.24	.40	1.296
8	2.80	7.84	.10	.784
				4.560

$Var(y) = 4.56$

$\sigma = \sqrt{4.56} = 2.14$

17. a.   Total Student = 1,518,859

$x = 1$ $f(1) = 721,769/1,518,859 = .4752$
$x = 2$ $f(2) = 601,325/1,518,859 = .3959$
$x = 3$ $f(3) = 166,736/1,518,859 = .1098$
$x = 4$ $f(4) = 22,299/1,518,859 = .0147$
$x = 5$ $f(5) = 6730/1,518,859 = .0044$

b. $P(x > 1) = 1 - f(1) = 1 - .4752 = .5248$

Over 50% of the students take the SAT more than 1 time.

c. $P(x \geq 3) = f(3) + f(4) + f(5) = .1098 + .0147 + .0044 = .1289$

d./e.

x	$f(x)$	$xf(x)$	$x - \mu$	$(x - \mu)^2$	$(x - \mu)^2 f(x)$
1	.4752	.4752	-.6772	.4586	.2179
2	.3959	.7918	.3228	.1042	.0412
3	.1098	.3293	1.3228	1.7497	.1921
4	.0147	.0587	2.3228	5.3953	.0792
5	.0044	.0222	3.3228	11.0408	.0489
		1.6772			.5794

$E(x) = \Sigma \, x f(x) = 1.6772$

The mean number of times a student takes the SAT is 1.6772, or approximately 1.7 times.

$\sigma^2 = \Sigma(x - \mu)^2 f(x) = .5794$

$\sigma = \sqrt{\sigma^2} = \sqrt{.5794} = .7612$

18. a/b/

x	$f(x)$	$xf(x)$	$x - \mu$	$(x - \mu)^2$	$(x - \mu)^2 f(x)$
0	.2188	.0000	-1.1825	1.3982	.3060
1	.5484	.5484	-.1825	.0333	.0183
2	.1241	.2483	.8175	.6684	.0830
3	.0489	.1466	1.8175	3.3035	.1614
4	.0598	.2393	2.8175	7.9386	.4749
Total	1.0000	1.1825			1.0435
		↑			↑
		$E(x)$			$Var(x)$

c/d.

y	$f(y)$	$yf(y)$	$y - \mu$	$(y - \mu)^2$	$(y - \mu)^2 f(y)$
0	.2497	.0000	-1.2180	1.4835	.3704
1	.4816	.4816	-.2180	.0475	.0229
2	.1401	.2801	.7820	.6115	.0856
3	.0583	.1749	1.7820	3.1755	.1851
4	.0703	.2814	2.7820	7.7395	.5444
Total	1.0000	1.2180			1.2085
		↑			↑
		$E(y)$			$Var(y)$

e.   The expected number of times that owner-occupied units have a water supply stoppage lasting 6 or more hours in the past 3 months is 1.1825, slightly less than the expected value of 1.2180 for renter-occupied units. And, the variability is somewhat less for owner-occupied units (1.0435) as compared to renter-occupied units (1.2085).

19. a. $f(x) \geq 0$ for all values of x.

$\Sigma f(x) = 1$ Therefore, it is a valid probability distribution.

b.   Probability $x > 30$ is $f(40) + f(50) + f(60) = .20 + .35 + .20 = .75$

c. Probability $x < 20 = f(10) = .05$

d. Expected value and variance computations follow.

x	$f(x)$	$xf(x)$	$x - \mu$	$(x - \mu)^2$	$(x - \mu)^2 f(x)$
10	.05	.5	-33.0	1089.0	54.45
20	.10	2.0	-23.0	529.0	52.90
30	.10	3.0	-13.0	169.0	16.90
40	.20	8.0	-3.0	9.0	1.80
50	.35	17.5	7.0	49.0	17.15
60	.20	12.0	17.0	289.0	57.80
Total	1.00	43.0			201.00
		↑			↑
		$E(x)$			$Var(x)$

20. a.

x	$f(x)$	$xf(x)$
0	.85	0
500	.04	20
1000	.04	40
3000	.03	90
5000	.02	100
8000	.01	80
10000	.01	100
Total	1.00	430

The expected value of the insurance claim is $430. If the company charges $430 for this type of collision coverage, it would break even.

b. From the point of view of the policyholder, the expected gain is as follows:

Expected Gain = Expected claim payout – Cost of insurance coverage
= $430 - $520 = -$90

The policyholder is concerned that an accident will result in a big repair bill if there is no insurance coverage. So even though the policyholder has an expected annual loss of $90, the insurance is protecting against a large loss.

21. a. $E(x) = \Sigma x f(x) = 0.05(1) + 0.09(2) + 0.03(3) + 0.42(4) + 0.41(5) = 4.05$

b. $E(x) = \Sigma x f(x) = 0.04(1) + 0.10(2) + 0.12(3) + 0.46(4) + 0.28(5) = 3.84$

c. Executives: $\sigma^2 = \Sigma (x - \mu)^2 f(x) = 1.25$

Middle Managers: $\sigma^2 = \Sigma (x - \mu)^2 f(x) = 1.13$

d. Executives: $\sigma = 1.12$

Middle Managers: $\sigma = 1.07$

e. The senior executives have a higher average score: 4.05 vs. 3.84 for the middle managers. The executives also have a slightly higher standard deviation.

22. a. $E(x) = \Sigma x f(x) = 300\ (.20) + 400\ (.30) + 500\ (.35) + 600\ (.15) = 445$

    The monthly order quantity should be 445 units.

    b. Cost: 445 @ \$50 = \$22,250
       Revenue: 300 @ \$70 = <u>21,000</u>
       \$ 1,250 Loss

23. a., b. and c. follow.

    The total number of responses is 1014, so $f(0) = 365/1014 = .3600$; $f(1) = 264/1014 = .2604$; and so on.

x	$f(x)$	$xf(x)$	$x - \mu$	$(x - \mu)^2$	$(x - \mu)^2 f(x)$
0	0.3600	0.0000	-1.3087	1.7126	0.6165
1	0.2604	0.2604	-0.3087	0.0953	0.0248
2	0.1903	0.3807	0.6913	0.4779	0.0910
3	0.0897	0.2692	1.6913	2.8606	0.2567
4	<u>0.0996</u>	<u>0.3984</u>	2.6913	7.2432	<u>0.7215</u>
Total	1.0000	1.3087			1.7104

    $E(x) = 1.3087$ and $Var(x) = 1.7104$

    d. The possible values of y are 1, 2, 3, and 4. The total number of responses is 649, so $f(1) = 264/649 = .41$; $f(2) = 193/649 = .30$; and so on.

y	$f(y)$	$yf(y)$
1	.4068	.4068
2	.2974	.5948
3	.1402	.4206
4	<u>.1556</u>	<u>.6225</u>
Total	1.0000	2.0447

    $E(y) = 2.0447$. The expected value or mean number of cups per day for adults that drink at least one cup of coffee on an average day is 2.0447 or approximately a mean of 2 cups per day. As expected, the mean is somewhat higher when we only take into account adults that drink at least one cup of coffee per day.

24. a. Medium $E(x) = \Sigma x f(x)$

    $= 50\ (.20) + 150\ (.50) + 200\ (.30) = 145$

    Large: $E(x) = \Sigma x f(x)$

    $= 0\ (.20) + 100\ (.50) + 300\ (.30) = 140$

    Medium preferred.

b. Medium

x	$f(x)$	$x - \mu$	$(x - \mu)^2$	$(x - \mu)^2 f(x)$
50	.20	-95	9025	1805.0
150	.50	5	25	12.5
200	.30	55	3025	907.5
				$\sigma^2 = 2725.0$

Large

y	$f(y)$	$y - \mu$	$(y - \mu)^2$	$(y - \mu)^2 f(y)$
0	.20	-140	19600	3920
100	.50	-40	1600	800
300	.30	160	25600	7680
				$\sigma^2 = 12{,}400$

Medium preferred due to less variance.

25. a. $E(x) = .2(50) + .5(30) + .3(40) = 37$

$E(y) = .2(80) + .5(50) + .3(60) = 59$

$Var(x) = .2(50 - 37)^2 + .5(30 - 37)^2 + .3(40 - 37)^2 = 61$

$Var(y) = .2(80 - 59)^2 + .5(50 - 59)^2 + .3(60 - 59)^2 = 129$

b.

$x + y$	$f(x + y)$
130	.2
80	.5
100	.3

c.

$x + y$	$f(x + y)$	$(x + y)f(x + y)$	$x + y - E(x + y)$	$[x + y - E(x + y)]^2$	$[x + y - E(x + y)]^2 f(x + y)$
130	.2	26	34	1156	231.2
80	.5	40	-16	256	128.0
100	.3	30	4	16	4.8
		$(x + y) = 96$			$Var(x + y) = 364$

d. $\sigma_{xy} = [Var(x + y) - Var(x) - Var(y)] / 2 = (364 - 61 - 129) / 2 = 87$

$Var(x) = 61$ and $Var(y) = 129$ were computed in part (a), so

$\sigma_x = \sqrt{61} = 7.8102$ $\qquad$ $\sigma_y = \sqrt{129} = 11.3578$

$\rho_{xy} = \dfrac{\sigma_{xy}}{\sigma_x \sigma_y} = \dfrac{87}{(7.8102)(11.3578)} = .98$

The random variables x and y are positively related. Both the covariance and correlation coefficient are positive. Indeed, they are very highly correlated; the correlation coefficient is almost equal to 1.

e. $Var(x+y) = Var(x) + Var(y) + 2\sigma_{xy} = 61 + 129 + 2(87) = 364$

$Var(x) + Var(y) = 61 + 129 = 190$

The variance of the sum of x and y is greater than the sum of the variances by two times the covariance: $2(87) = 174$. The reason it is positive is that, in this case the variables are positively related. Whenever two random variables are positively related, the variance of the sum of the randomly variables will be greater than the sum of the variances of the individual random variables.

26. a. The standard deviation for these two stocks is the square root of the variance.

$\sigma_x = \sqrt{Var(x)} = \sqrt{25} = 5\%$ $\sigma_y = \sqrt{Var(y)} = \sqrt{1} = 1\%$

Investments in Stock 1 would be considered riskier than investments in Stock 2 because the standard deviation is higher. Note that if the return for Stock 1 falls $8.45/5 = 1.69$ or more standard deviation below its expected value, an investor in that stock will experience a loss. The return for Stock 2 would have to fall 3.2 standard deviations below its expected value before an investor in that stock would experience a loss.

b. Since x represents the percent return for investing in Stock 1, the expected return for investing $100 in Stock 1 is $8.45 and the standard deviation is $5.00. So to get the expected return and standard deviation for a $500 investment we just multiply by 5.

Expected return ($500 investment) = 5($8.45) = $42.25

Standard deviation ($500 investment) = 5($5.00) = $25.00

c. Since x represents the percent return for investing in Stock 1 and y represents the percent return for investing in Stock 2, we want to compute the expected value and variance for $.5x + .5y$.

$E(.5x + .5y) = .5E(x) + .5E(y) = .5(8.45) + .5(3.2) = 4.225 + 1.6 = 5.825$

$Var(.5x + .5y) = .5^2 Var(x) + .5^2 Var(y) + 2(.5)(.5)\sigma_{xy}$

$= (.5)^2(25) + (.5)^2(1) + 2(.5)(.5)(-3)$

$= 6.25 + .25 - 1.50 = 5$

$\sigma_{.5x+.5y} = \sqrt{5} = 2.236$

d. Since x represents the percent return for investing in Stock 1 and y represents the percent return for investing in Stock 2, we want to compute the expected value and variance for $.7x + .3y$.

$E(.7x + .3y) = .7E(x) + .3E(y) = .7(8.45) + .3(3.2) = 5.915 + .96 = 6.875$

$Var(.7x + .3y) = .7^2 Var(x) + .3^2 Var(y) + 2(.7)(.3)\sigma_{xy}$

$= .7^2(25) + .3^2(1) + 2(.7)(.3)(-3)$

$= 12.25 + .09 - 1.26 = 11.08$

$$\sigma_{.7x+.3y} = \sqrt{11.08} = 3.329$$

e. The standard deviations of x and y were computed in part (a). The correlation coefficient is given by

$$\rho_{xy} = \frac{\sigma_{xy}}{\sigma_x \sigma_y} = \frac{-3}{(5)(1)} = -.6$$

There is a fairly strong negative relationship between the variables.

27. a. Dividing each of the frequencies in the table by the total number of restaurants provides the joint probability table below. The bivariate probability for each pair of quality and meal price is shown in the body of the table. This is the bivariate probability distribution. For instance, the probability of a rating of 2 on quality and a rating of 3 on meal price is given by $f(2, 3) = .18$. The marginal probability distribution for quality, x, is in the rightmost column. The marginal probability for meal price, y, is in the bottom row.

	Meal Price (y)			
Quality (x)	1	2	3	Total
1	0.14	0.13	0.01	0.28
2	0.11	0.21	0.18	0.50
3	0.01	0.05	0.16	0.22
Total	0.26	0.39	0.35	1.00

b. $E(x) = 1(.28) + 2(.50) + 3(.22) = 1.94$

$Var(x) = .28(1 - 1.94)^2 + .50(2 - 1.94)^2 + .22(3 - 1.94)^2 = .4964$

c. $E(y) = 1(.26) + 2(.39) + 3(.35) = 2.09$

$Var(y) = .26(1 - 2.09)^2 + .39(2 - 2.09)^2 + .35(3 - 2.09)^2 = .6019$

d. $\sigma_{xy} = [Var(x + y) - Var(x) - Var(y)] / 2 = [1.6691 - .4964 - .6019] / 2 = .2854$

Since, the covariance $\sigma_{xy} = .2854$ is positive we can conclude that as the quality rating goes up, the meal price goes up. This is as we would expect.

e. $\rho_{xy} = \frac{\sigma_{xy}}{\sigma_x \sigma_y} = \frac{.2854}{\sqrt{.4964}\sqrt{.6019}} = .5221$

With a correlation coefficient of .5221 we would call this a moderately positive relationship. It is not likely to find a low cost restaurant that is also high quality. But, it is possible. There are 3 of them leading to $f(3,1) = .01$.

28. a. Yes. Since the teenagers are selected randomly, p is the same from trial to trial and the trials are independent. The two outcomes per trial are use Pandora Media Inc.'s online radio service or do not use Pandora Media Inc.'s online radio service.

Binomial $n = 10$ and $p = .35$

$$f(x) = \frac{10!}{x!(10-x)!}(.35)^x(1-.35)^{10-x}$$

b. $f(0) = \frac{10!}{0!(10-0)!}(.35)^0(.65)^{10-0} = .0135$

c. $f(4) = \frac{10!}{4!(10-4)!}(.35)^4(.65)^{10-4} = .2377$

d. Probability $(x \geq 2) = 1 - f(0) - f(1)$

From part (b), $f(0) = .0135$

$$f(1) = \frac{10!}{1!(10-1)!}(.35)^1(.65)^{10-1} = .0725$$

Probability $(x \geq 2) = 1 - f(0) - f(1) = 1 - (.0135 + .0725) = .9140$

29. a. Binomial $n = 10$ and $p = .40$

$$f(x) = \frac{10!}{x!(10-x)!}(.40)^x(1-.40)^{10-x}$$

$$f(0) = \frac{10!}{0!(10-0)!}(.40)^0(.60)^{10-0} = .0060$$

b. $f(1) = \frac{10!}{1!(10-1)!}(.40)^1(.60)^{10-1} = .0403$

c. Probability $(x \geq 2) = 1 - f(0) - f(1)$

Using the results from parts (a) and (b)

Probability $(x \geq 2) = 1 - f(0) - f(1) = 1 - (.0060 + .0403) = .9537$

d. Probability more than half $= f(6) - f(7) + f(8) + f(9) + f(10)$

Using the binomial probability table:

Probability more than half $= .1115 + .0425 + .0106 + .0016 + .0001 = .1663$

30. a. Probability of a defective part being produced must be .03 for each part selected; parts must be selected independently.

b. Let: D = defective
G = not defective

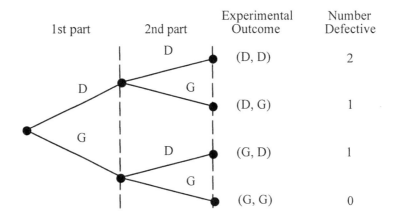

c. 2 outcomes result in exactly one defect.

d. $P(\text{no defects}) = (.97)(.97) = .9409$

$P(1\text{ defect}) = 2(.03)(.97) = .0582$

$P(2\text{ defects}) = (.03)(.03) = .0009$

31. a. Yes. Since the employees are selected randomly, p is the same from trial to trial and the trials are independent. The two outcomes per trial are loyal and not loyal.

   Binomial $n = 10$ and $p = .25$

   $$f(x) = \frac{10!}{x!(10-x)!}(.25)^x(1-.25)^{10-x}$$

   b. $f(0) = \dfrac{10!}{0!(10-0)!}(.25)^0(1-.25)^{10-0} = .0563$

   c. $f(4) = \dfrac{10!}{4!(10-4)!}(.25)^4(1-.25)^{10-4} = .1460$

   d. Probability $(x \geq 2) = 1 - f(0) - f(1)$

   From part (b), $f(0) = .0563$

   $$f(1) = \frac{10!}{1!(10-1)!}(.25)^1(1-.25)^{10-1} = .1877$$

   Probability $(x \geq 2) = 1 - f(0) - f(1) = 1 - (.0563 + .1877) = .7560$

32. a. .90

    b. $P(\text{at least } 1) = f(1) + f(2)$

    $$f(1) = \frac{2!}{1!\,1!}(.9)^1(.1)^1$$

    $$= 2(.9)(.1) = .18$$

    $$f(2) = \frac{2!}{2!\,0!}(.9)^1(.1)^0$$

    $$= 1(.81)(1) = .81$$

    $\therefore P(\text{at least } 1) = .18 + .81 = .99$

    Alternatively

    $P(\text{at least } 1) = 1 - f(0)$

    $$f(0) = \frac{2!}{0!\,2!}(.9)^0(.1)^2 = .01$$

    Therefore, $P(\text{at least } 1) = 1 - .01 = .99$

    c. $P(\text{at least } 1) = 1 - f(0)$

    $$f(0) = \frac{3!}{0!\,3!}(.9)^0(.1)^3 = .001$$

    Therefore, $P(\text{at least } 1) = 1 - .001 = .999$

    d. Yes; $P(\text{at least } 1)$ becomes very close to 1 with multiple systems and the inability to detect an attack would be catastrophic.

33. a. Using the 20 golfers in the Hazeltine PGA Championship, the probability that a PGA professional golfer uses a Titleist brand golf ball is $p = 14/20 = .6$

    For the sample of 15 PGA Tour players, use a binomial distribution with $n = 15$ and $p = .6$.

    $$f(10) = \frac{15!}{10!5!}(.6)^{10}(1-.6)^{15-10} = .1859$$

    Or, using the binomial tables, $f(10) = .1859$

    b. $P(x \geq 10) = f(11) + f(12) + f(13) + f(14) + f(15)$

    Using the binomial tables, we have

    $.1268 + .0634 + .0219 + .0047 + .0005 = .2173$

    c. $E(x) = np = 15(.6) = 9$

d. $Var(x) = \sigma^2 = np(1 - p) = 15(.6)(1 - .6) = 3.6$

$\sigma = \sqrt{3.6} = 1.8974$

34. a. Yes. Since the 18- to 34-year olds living with their parents are selected randomly, p is the same from trial to trial and the trials are independent. The two outcomes per trial are contribute to household expenses or do not contribute to household expenses.

Binomial $n = 15$ and $p = .75$

$$f(x) = \frac{15!}{x!(15-x)!}(.75)^x(1-.75)^{15-x}$$

b. The probability that none of the fifteen contribute to household expenses is

$$f(0) = \frac{15!}{0!(15-0)!}(.75)^0(1-.75)^{15-0} = .0000$$

Obtaining a sample result that shows that none of the fifteen contributed to household expenses is so unlikely you would have to question whether the 75% value reported by the Pew Research Center is accurate.

c. Probability of at least ten $= f(10) + f(11) + f(12) + f(13) + f(14) + f(15)$

Using binomial tables

Probability $= .1651 + .2252 + .2252 + .1559 + .0668 + .0134 = .8516$

35. a. $f(0) + f(1) + f(2) = .0115 + .0576 + .1369 = .2060$

b. $f(4) = .2182$

c. $1 - [f(0) + f(1) + f(2) + f(3)] = 1 - .2060 - .2054 = .5886$

d. $\mu = np = 20(.20) = 4$

36. a. $f(4) = \frac{20!}{4!(20-4)!}(.30)^4(.70)^{20-4} = .1304$

b. Probability $(x \geq 2) = 1 - f(0) - f(1)$

$$f(0) = \frac{20!}{0!(20-0)!}(.30)^0(.70)^{20-0} = .0008$$

$$f(1) = \frac{20!}{1!(20-1)!}(.30)^1(.70)^{20-1} = .0068$$

Probability $(x \geq 2) = 1 - f(0) - f(1) = 1 - (.0008 + .0068) = .9924$

c. $E(x) = np = 20(.30) = 6$

d. $Var(x) = n\,p\,(1 - p) = 20(.30)(1 - .30) = 4.2$

$\sigma = \sqrt{4.2} = 2.0499$

37. $E(x) = n\,p = 35(.23) = 8.05$ (8 automobiles)

$Var(x) = n\,p\,(1 - p) = 35(.23)(1 - .23) = 6.2$

$\sigma = \sqrt{6.2} = 2.49$

38. a. $f(x) = \dfrac{3^x e^{-3}}{x!}$

b. $f(2) = \dfrac{3^2 e^{-3}}{2!} = \dfrac{9(.0498)}{2} = .2241$

c. $f(1) = \dfrac{3^1 e^{-3}}{1!} = 3(.0498) = .1494$

d. $P(x \geq 2) = 1 - f(0) - f(1) = 1 - .0498 - .1494 = .8008$

39. a. $f(x) = \dfrac{2^x e^{-2}}{x!}$

b. $\mu = 6$ for 3 time periods

c. $f(x) = \dfrac{6^x e^{-6}}{x!}$

d. $f(2) = \dfrac{2^2 e^{-2}}{2!} = \dfrac{4(.1353)}{2} = .2706$

e. $f(6) = \dfrac{6^6 e^{-6}}{6!} = .1606$

f. $f(5) = \dfrac{4^5 e^{-4}}{5!} = .1563$

40. a. $\mu = 48\,(5/60) = 4$

$f(3) = \dfrac{4^3 e^{-4}}{3!} = \dfrac{(64)(.0183)}{6} = .1952$

b. $\mu = 48\,(15/60) = 12$

$f(10) = \dfrac{12^{10} e^{-12}}{10!} = .1048$

c. $\mu = 48\,(5/60) = 4$ I expect 4 callers to be waiting after 5 minutes.

$$f(0) = \frac{4^0 e^{-4}}{0\,!} = .0183$$

The probability none will be waiting after 5 minutes is .0183.

d. $\mu = 48\,(3/60) = 2.4$

$$f(0) - \frac{2.4^0 e^{-2.4}}{0\,!} = .0907$$

The probability of no interruptions in 3 minutes is .0907.

41. a. 30 per hour

b. $\mu = 1\,(5/2) = 5/2$

$$f(3) = \frac{(5/2)^3 e^{-(5/2)}}{3!} = .2138$$

c. $f(0) = \frac{(5/2)^0 e^{-(5/2)}}{0!} = e^{-(5/2)} = .0821$

42. a. For a 15-minute period the mean is $14.4/4 = 3.6$

$$f(0) = \frac{3.6^0 e^{-3.6}}{0!} = e^{-3.6} = .0273$$

b. probability $= 1 - f(0) = 1 - .2073 = .9727$

c. probability $= 1 - [f(0) + f(1) + f(2) + f(3)]$

$$= 1 - [..0273 + .0984 + .1771 + .2125] = .4847$$

Note: The value of $f(0)$ was computed in part (a) and the Poisson tables were used to compute the probabilities for $f(1)$, $f(2)$, and $f(3)$.

43. a. $f(0) = \frac{10^0 e^{-10}}{0!} = e^{-10} = .000045$

b. $f(0) + f(1) + f(2) + f(3)$

$f(0) = .000045$ (part a)

$$f(1) = \frac{10^1 e^{-10}}{1!} = .00045$$

Similarly, $f(2) = .002267$, $f(3) = .007567$

and $f(0) + f(1) + f(2) + f(3) = .010329$

c. 2.5 arrivals / 15 sec. period Use $\mu = 2.5$

$$f(0) = \frac{2.5^0 e^{-2.5}}{0!} = .0821$$

d. $1 - f(0) = 1 - .0821 = .9179$

44. a. $\mu = 18/30 = .6$ per day during June

b. $f(0) = \frac{.6^0 e^{-.6}}{0!} = .5488$

c. $f(1) = \frac{.6^1 e^{-.6}}{1!} = .3293$

d. $P(\text{More than } 1) = 1 - f(0) - f(1) = 1 - .5488 - .3293 = .1219$

45. a. $f(x) = \frac{\mu^x e^{-\mu}}{x!}$

$$f(0) = \frac{3^0 e^{-3}}{0!} = e^{-3} = .0498$$

b. $P(x \geq 2) = 1 - f(0) - f(1)$

$$f(1) = \frac{3^1 e^{-3}}{1!} = .1494$$

$P(x \geq 2) = 1 - .0498 - .1494 = .8008$

c. $\mu = 3$ per year

$\mu = 3/2 = 1.5$ per 6 months

d. $f(0) = \frac{1.5^0 e^{-1.5}}{0!} = .2231$

46. a. $f(1) = \frac{\binom{3}{1}\binom{10-3}{4-1}}{\binom{10}{4}} = \frac{\left(\frac{3!}{1!2!}\right)\left(\frac{7!}{3!4!}\right)}{\frac{10!}{4!6!}} = \frac{(3)(35)}{210} = .50$

b. $f(2) = \frac{\binom{3}{2}\binom{10-3}{2-2}}{\binom{10}{2}} = \frac{(3)(1)}{45} = .067$

c. $f(0) = \dfrac{\dbinom{3}{0}\dbinom{10-3}{2-0}}{\dbinom{10}{2}} = \dfrac{(1)(21)}{45} = .4667$

d. $f(2) = \dfrac{\dbinom{3}{2}\dbinom{10-3}{4-2}}{\dbinom{10}{4}} = \dfrac{(3)(21)}{210} = .30$

e. Note $x = 4$ is *greater than* $r = 3$. It is not possible to have $x = 4$ successes when there are only 3 successes in the population. Thus, $f(4) = 0$. In this exercise, n is greater than r. Thus, the number of successes x can only take on values up to and including $r = 3$. Thus, $x = 0, 1, 2, 3$.

47. $f(3) = \dfrac{\dbinom{4}{3}\dbinom{15-4}{10-3}}{\dbinom{15}{10}} = \dfrac{(4)(330)}{3003} = .4396$

48.   Hypergeometric Distribution with $N = 10$ and $r = 7$

a. $f(2) = \dfrac{\dbinom{7}{2}\dbinom{3}{1}}{\dbinom{10}{3}} = \dfrac{(21)(3)}{120} = .5250$

b.   Compute the probability that 3 prefer shopping online.

$f(3) = \dfrac{\dbinom{7}{3}\dbinom{3}{0}}{\dbinom{10}{3}} = \dfrac{(35)(1)}{120} = .2917$

$P(\text{majority prefer shopping online}) = f(2) + f(3) = .5250 + .2917 = .8167$

49.   Parts a, b & c involve the hypergeometric distribution with $N = 52$ and $n = 2$

a. $r = 20, x = 2$

$f(2) = \dfrac{\dbinom{20}{2}\dbinom{32}{0}}{\dbinom{52}{2}} = \dfrac{(190)(1)}{1326} = .1433$

b. $r = 4, x = 2$

$$f(2) = \frac{\binom{4}{2}\binom{48}{0}}{\binom{52}{2}} = \frac{(6)(1)}{1326} = .0045$$

c. $r = 16, x = 2$

$$f(2) = \frac{\binom{16}{2}\binom{36}{0}}{\binom{52}{2}} = \frac{(120)(1)}{1326} = .0905$$

d. Part (a) provides the probability of blackjack plus the probability of 2 aces plus the probability of two 10s. To find the probability of blackjack we subtract the probabilities in (b) and (c) from the probability in (a).

$P(\text{blackjack}) = .1433 - .0045 - .0905 = .0483$

50. $N = 60 \quad n = 10$

a. $r = 20 \quad x = 0$

$$f(0) = \frac{\binom{20}{0}\binom{40}{10}}{\binom{60}{10}} = \frac{(1)\left(\dfrac{40!}{10!30!}\right)}{\dfrac{60!}{10!50!}} = \left(\frac{40!}{10!30!}\right)\left(\frac{10!50!}{60!}\right)$$

$$= \frac{40 \cdot 39 \cdot 38 \cdot 37 \cdot 36 \cdot 35 \cdot 34 \cdot 33 \cdot 32 \cdot 31}{60 \cdot 59 \cdot 58 \cdot 57 \cdot 56 \cdot 55 \cdot 54 \cdot 53 \cdot 52 \cdot 51} \approx .0112$$

b. $r = 20 \quad x = 1$

$$f(1) = \frac{\binom{20}{1}\binom{40}{9}}{\binom{60}{10}} = 20\left(\frac{40!}{9!31!}\right)\left(\frac{10!50!}{60!}\right) \approx .0725$$

c. $1 - f(0) - f(1) = 1 - .0112 - .0725 = .9163$

d. Same as the probability one will be from Hawaii; .0725.

51. a. $f(0) = \dfrac{\binom{5}{0}\binom{10}{3}}{\binom{15}{3}} = \dfrac{(1)(120)}{455} = .2637$

5 - 21

b. $f(1) = \dfrac{\binom{5}{1}\binom{10}{2}}{\binom{15}{3}} = \dfrac{(5)(45)}{455} = .4945$

c. $f(2) = \dfrac{\binom{5}{2}\binom{10}{1}}{\binom{15}{3}} = \dfrac{(10)(10)}{455} = .2198$

d. $f(3) = \dfrac{\binom{5}{3}\binom{10}{0}}{\binom{15}{3}} = \dfrac{(10)(1)}{455} = .0220$

52. Hypergeometric with $N = 10$ and $r = 3$.

   a. $n = 3, x = 0$

   $$f(0) = \dfrac{\binom{3}{0}\binom{7}{3}}{\binom{10}{3}} = \dfrac{\left(\dfrac{3!}{0!3!}\right)\left(\dfrac{7!}{3!4!}\right)}{\dfrac{10!}{3!7!}} = \dfrac{(1)(35)}{120} = .2917$$

   This is the probability there will be no banks with increased lending in the study.

   b. $n = 3, x = 3$

   $$f(3) = \dfrac{\binom{3}{3}\binom{7}{0}}{\binom{10}{3}} = \dfrac{\left(\dfrac{3!}{3!0!}\right)\left(\dfrac{7!}{0!7!}\right)}{\dfrac{10!}{3!7!}} = \dfrac{(1)(1)}{120} = .0083$$

   This is the probability there all three banks with increased lending will be in the study. This has a very low probability of happening.

   c. $n = 3, x = 1$

   $$f(1) = \dfrac{\binom{3}{1}\binom{7}{2}}{\binom{10}{3}} = \dfrac{\left(\dfrac{3!}{1!2!}\right)\left(\dfrac{7!}{2!5!}\right)}{\dfrac{10!}{3!7!}} = \dfrac{(3)(21)}{120} = .5250$$

   $n = 3, x = 2$

$$f(2) = \frac{\binom{3}{2}\binom{7}{1}}{\binom{10}{3}} = \frac{\left(\frac{3!}{2!1!}\right)\left(\frac{7!}{1!6!}\right)}{\frac{10!}{3!7!}} = \frac{(3)(7)}{120} = .1750$$

x	f(x)
0	0.2917
1	0.5250
2	0.1750
3	0.0083
Total	1.0000

$f(1) = .5250$ has the highest probability showing that there is over a .50 chance that there will be exactly one bank that had increased lending in the study.

d. $P(x \geq 1) = 1 - f(0) = 1 - .2917 = .7083$

There is a reasonably high probability of .7083 that there will be at least one bank that had increased lending in the study.

e. $E(x) = n\left(\frac{r}{N}\right) = 3\left(\frac{3}{10}\right) = .90$

$$\sigma^2 = n\left(\frac{r}{N}\right)\left(1 - \frac{r}{N}\right)\left(\frac{N-n}{N-1}\right) = 3\left(\frac{3}{10}\right)\left(1 - \frac{3}{10}\right)\left(\frac{10-3}{10-1}\right) = .49$$

$$\sigma = \sqrt{\sigma^2} = \sqrt{.49} = .70$$

53. a. The probability distribution for x follows.

x	f(x)
0	.0960
1	.5700
2	.2380
3	.0770
4	.0190
Total	1.0000

b. and c follow.

x	$f(x)$	$xf(x)$	$x - \mu$	$(x - \mu)^2$	$(x - \mu)^2 f(x)$
0	.0960	.0000	-1.3530	1.8306	.1757
1	.5700	.5700	-.3530	.1246	.0710
2	.2380	.4760	.6470	.4186	.0996
3	.0770	.2310	1.6470	2.7126	.2089
4	.0190	.0760	2.6470	7.0066	.1331
Total	1.0000	1.3530			0.6884

$E(x) = 1.353$, $Var(x) = .6884$, $\sigma = \sqrt{.6884} = .8297$

d. The expected value of 1.353 indicates that the mean wind condition when an accident occurred is slightly greater than light wind conditions.

54. a.

x	$f(x)$
1	.150
2	.050
3	.075
4	.050
5	.125
6	.050
7	.100
8	.125
9	.125
10	.150
Total	1.000

b. Probability of outstanding service is $.125 + .150 = .275$

c.

x	$f(x)$	$xf(x)$	$x - \mu$	$(x - \mu)^2$	$(x - \mu)^2 f(x)$
1	.150	.150	-4.925	24.2556	3.6383
2	.050	.100	-3.925	15.4056	.7703
3	.075	.225	-2.925	8.5556	.6417
4	.050	.200	-1.925	3.7056	.1853
5	.125	.625	-.925	.8556	.1070
6	.050	.300	.075	.0056	.0003
7	.100	.700	1.075	1.1556	.1156
8	.125	1.000	2.075	4.3056	.5382
9	.125	1.125	3.075	9.4556	1.1820
10	.150	1.500	4.075	16.6056	2.4908
Total	1.000	5.925			9.6694

$E(x) = 5.925$ and $Var(x) = 9.6694$

d. The probability of a new car dealership receiving an outstanding wait-time rating is $2/7 = .2857$. For the remaining $40 - 7 = 33$ service providers, 9 received and outstanding rating; this corresponds to a probability of $9/33 = .2727$. For these results, there does not appear to be much difference between the probability that a new car dealership is rated outstanding compared to the same probability for other types of service providers.

55. a.

x	$f(x)$
9	.30
10	.20
11	.25
12	.05
13	.20

b. $E(x) = \Sigma x f(x)$

$= 9(.30) + 10(.20) + 11(.25) + 12(.05) + 13(.20) = 10.65$

Expected value of expenses: $10.65 million

c. $Var(x) = \Sigma(x - \mu)^2 f(x)$

$= (9 - 10.65)^2 (.30) + (10 - 10.65)^2 (.20) + (11 - 10.65)^2 (.25)$

$+ (12 - 10.65)^2 (.05) + (13 - 10.65)^2 (.20) = 2.13$

d. Looks Good: $E(\text{Profit}) = 12 - 10.65 = 1.35$ million

However, there is a .20 probability that expenses will equal $13 million and the college will run a deficit.

56. a. $n = 20$ and $x = 3$

$$f(3) = \binom{20}{3}(.05)^3(.95)^{17} = .0596$$

b. $n = 20$ and $x = 0$

$$f(0) = \binom{20}{0}(.05)^0(.95)^{20} = .3585$$

c. $E(x) = n p = 2000(.05) = 100$

The expected number of employees is 100.

d. $\sigma^2 = np(1 - p) = 2000(.05)(.95) = 95$

$\sigma = \sqrt{95} = 9.75$

57. a.   We must have $E(x) = np \geq 25$

For the 18-34 age group, $p = .16$.
$$n(.16) \geq 25$$
$$n \geq 156.25$$

For the 18-34 age group you need to sample at least 157 people to have an expected number of at least 25.

b.   For the 35-44 age group, $p = .12$.
$$n(.12) > 25$$
$$n \geq 208.3$$

For the 35-44 age group you need to sample at least 209 people to have an expected number of at least 25.

c.   For the 65 and over age group, $p = .02$.
$$n(.02) \geq 25$$
$$n \geq 1250$$

For the 65 and over age group you need to sample at least 1250 people to have an expected number of at least 25.

d. $\sigma = \sqrt{np(1-p)} = \sqrt{157(.16)(.84)} = 4.59$

d. $\sigma = \sqrt{np(1-p)} = \sqrt{209(.12)(.88)} = 22.07$

58.   Since the shipment is large we can assume that the probabilities do not change from trial to trial and use the binomial probability distribution.

a. $n = 5$

$$f(0) = \binom{5}{0}(0.01)^0 (0.99)^5 = .9510$$

b. $f(1) = \binom{5}{1}(0.01)^1 (0.99)^4 = .0480$

c. $1 - f(0) = 1 - .9510 = .0490$

d.   No, the probability of finding one or more items in the sample defective when only 1% of the items in the population are defective is small (only .0490). I would consider it likely that more than 1% of the items are defective.

59. a. $E(x) = np = 100(.041) = 4.1$

b. $Var(x) = np(1 - p) = 100(.041)(.959) = 3.93$

$$\sigma = \sqrt{3.93} = 1.98$$

60. a. $E(x) = 200(.235) = 47$

    b. $\sigma = \sqrt{np(1-p)} = \sqrt{200(.235)(.765)} = 5.9962$

    c. For this situation $p = .765$ and $(1-p) = .235$; but the answer is the same as in part (b). For a binomial probability distribution, the variance for the number of successes is the same as the variance for the number of failures. Of course, this also holds true for the standard deviation.

61. $\mu = 15$

    $P(20 \text{ or more arrivals}) = f(20) + f(21) + \cdots$

    $\qquad = .0418 + .0299 + .0204 + .0133 + .0083 + .0050 + .0029$
    $\qquad\quad + .0016 + .0009 + .0004 + .0002 + .0001 + .0001 = .1249$

62. $\mu = 1.5$

    $P(3 \text{ or more breakdowns}) = 1 - [f(0) + f(1) + f(2)]$.

    $1 - [f(0) + f(1) + f(2)]$

    $\quad = 1 - [.2231 + .3347 + .2510]$

    $\quad = 1 - .8088 = .1912$

63. $\mu = 10 \quad f(4) = .0189$

64. a. $f(3) = \dfrac{3^3 e^{-3}}{3!} = .2240$

    b. $f(3) + f(4) + \cdots = 1 - [f(0) + f(1) + f(2)]$

    $f(0) = \dfrac{3^0 e^{-3}}{0!} = e^{-3} = .0498$

    Similarly, $f(1) = .1494, f(2) = .2240$

    $\therefore 1 - [.0498 + .1494 + .2241] = .5767$

65. Hypergeometric $N = 52, n = 5$ and $r = 4$.

    a. $\dfrac{\dbinom{4}{2}\dbinom{48}{3}}{\dbinom{52}{5}} = \dfrac{6(17296)}{2,598,960} = .0399$

    b. $\dfrac{\dbinom{4}{1}\dbinom{48}{4}}{\dbinom{52}{5}} = \dfrac{4(194580)}{2,598,960} = .2995$

c. $\dfrac{\dbinom{4}{0}\dbinom{48}{5}}{\dbinom{52}{5}} = \dfrac{1,712,304}{2,598,960} = .6588$

d. $1 - f(0) = 1 - .6588 = .3412$

66. a. Hypergeometric distribution with $N = 10$, $n = 2$, and $r = 7$.

$$f(1) = \frac{\dbinom{r}{x}\dbinom{N-r}{n-x}}{\dbinom{N}{n}} = \frac{\dbinom{7}{1}\dbinom{10-7}{2-1}}{\dbinom{10}{2}} = \frac{\dbinom{7}{1}\dbinom{3}{1}}{\dbinom{10}{2}} = \frac{(7)(3)}{45} = .4667$$

b. $f(2) = \dfrac{\dbinom{7}{2}\dbinom{3}{0}}{\dbinom{10}{2}} = \dfrac{(21)(1)}{45} = .4667$

c. $f(0) = \dfrac{\dbinom{7}{0}\dbinom{3}{2}}{\dbinom{10}{2}} = \dfrac{(1)(3)}{45} = .0667$

Chapter 6
Continuous Probability Distributions

Learning Objectives

1. Understand the difference between how probabilities are computed for discrete and continuous random variables.

2. Know how to compute probability values for a continuous uniform probability distribution and be able to compute the expected value and variance for such a distribution.

3. Be able to compute probabilities using a normal probability distribution. Understand the role of the standard normal distribution in this process.

4. Be able to use the normal distribution to approximate binomial probabilities.

5. Be able to compute probabilities using an exponential probability distribution.

6. Understand the relationship between the Poisson and exponential probability distributions.

Solutions:

1. a.

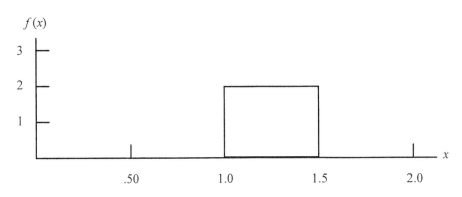

    b. $P(x = 1.25) = 0$. The probability of any single point is zero since the area under the curve above any single point is zero.

    c. $P(1.0 \le x \le 1.25) = 2(.25) = .50$

    d. $P(1.20 < x < 1.5) = 2(.30) = .60$

2. a.

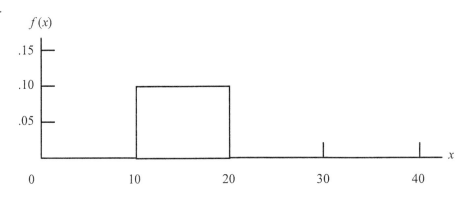

    b. $P(x < 15) = .10(5) = .50$

    c. $P(12 \le x \le 18) = .10(6) = .60$

    d. $E(x) = \dfrac{10 + 20}{2} = 15$

    e. $Var(x) = \dfrac{(20 - 10)^2}{12} = 8.33$

3. a.
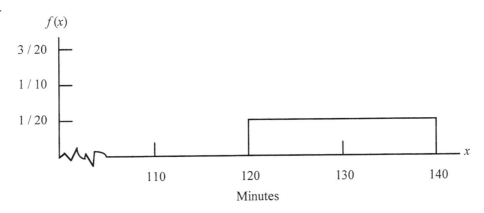

b. $P(x \le 130) = (1/20)(130 - 120) = 0.50$

c. $P(x > 135) = (1/20)(140 - 135) = 0.25$

d. $E(x) = \dfrac{120 + 140}{2} = 130$ minutes

4. a.
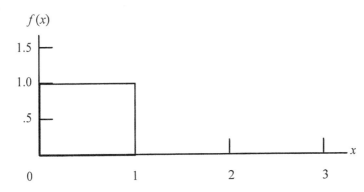

b. $P(.25 < x < .75) = 1(.50) = .50$

c. $P(x \le .30) = 1(.30) = .30$

d. $P(x > .60) = 1(.40) = .40$

5. a. Length of Interval $= 12 - 8.5 = 3.5$

$$f(x) = \begin{cases} \dfrac{1}{3.5} & \text{for } 8.5 \le x \le 12 \\ 0 & \text{elsewhere} \end{cases}$$

b. $P(x \le 10) = (10 - 8.5)(1/3.5) = 1.5/3.5 = .4286$

c. $P(x \ge 11) = (12 - 11)(1/3.5) = 1/3.5 = .2857$

d. $P(9.5 \le x \le 11.5) = (11.5 - 9.5)(1/3.5) = 2/3.5 = .5714$

e. $P(x \ge 9) = (12 - 9)(1/3.5) = 3/3.5 = .8571$

100 x (.8571) = 85.71 or rounding, 86 iPad Minis should have a battery life of at least 9 hours.

6. a. For a uniform probability density function $f(x) = \begin{cases} \dfrac{1}{b-a} & \text{for } a \leq x \leq b \\ 0 & \text{elsewhere} \end{cases}$

Thus, $\dfrac{1}{b-a} = .00625$.

Solving for $b - a$, we have $b - a = 1/.00625 = 160$

In a uniform probability distribution, ½ of this interval is below the mean and ½ of this interval is above the mean. Thus,

$a = 136 - \frac{1}{2}(160) = 56$ and $b = 136 + \frac{1}{2}(160) = 216$

b. $P(100 \leq x \leq 200) = (200 - 100)(.00625) = .6250$

c. $P(x \geq 150) = (216 - 150)(.00625) = .4125$

d. $P(x \leq 80) = (80 - 56)(.00625) = .1500$

7. a. $P(10,000 \leq x < 12,000) = 2000\,(1 / 5000) = .40$

The probability your competitor will bid lower than you, and you get the bid, is .40.

b. $P(10,000 \leq x < 14,000) = 4000\,(1 / 5000) = .80$

c. A bid of $15,000 gives a probability of 1 of getting the property.

d. Yes, the bid that maximizes expected profit is $13,000.

The probability of getting the property with a bid of $13,000 is

$P(10,000 \leq x < 13,000) = 3000\,(1 / 5000) = .60$.

The probability of not getting the property with a bid of $13,000 is .40.

The profit you will make if you get the property with a bid of $13,000 is $3000 = $16,000 - 13,000. So your expected profit with a bid of $13,000 is

EP ($13,000) = .6 ($3000) + .4 (0) = $1800.

If you bid $15,000 the probability of getting the bid is 1, but the profit if you do get the bid is only $1000 = $16,000 - 15,000. So your expected profit with a bid of $15,000 is

EP ($15,000) = 1 ($1000) + 0 (0) = $1,000.

8.

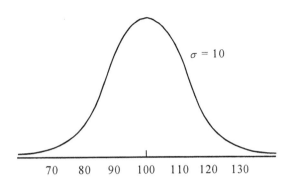

9.   a.

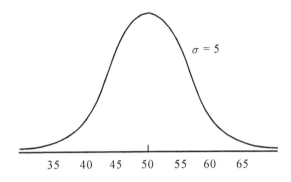

b.   .683 since 45 and 55 are within plus or minus 1 standard deviation from the mean of 50 (Use the table or see characteristic 7a of the normal distribution).

c.   .954 since 40 and 60 are within plus or minus 2 standard deviations from the mean of 50 (Use the table or see characteristic 7b of the normal distribution).

10.

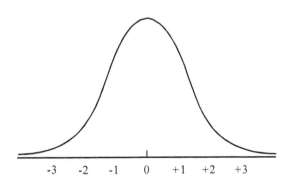

a. $P(z \leq 1.5) = .9332$

b. $P(z \leq 1.0) = .8413$

c. $P(1 \leq z \leq 1.5) = P(z \leq 1.5) - P(z < 1) = .9932 - .8413 = .0919$

d. $P(0 < z < 2.5) = P(z < 2.5) - P(z \leq 0) = .9938 - .5000 = .4938$

11. a. $P(z \leq -1) = .1587$

b. $P(z \geq -1) = 1 - P(z < -1) = 1 - .1587 = .8413$

c. $P(z \geq -1.5) = 1 - P(z < -1.5) = 1 - .0668 = .9332$

d. $P(-2.5 \leq z) = 1 - P(z < -2.5) = 1 - .0062 = .9938$

e. $P(-3 < z \leq 0) = P(z \leq 0) - P(z \leq -3) = .5000 - .0013 = .4987$

12. a. $P(0 \leq z \leq .83) = .7967 - .5000 = .2967$

b. $P(-1.57 \leq z \leq 0) = .5000 - .0582 = .4418$

c. $P(z > .44) = 1 - .6700 = .3300$
d. $P(z \geq -.23) = 1 - .4090 = .5910$

e. $P(z < 1.20) = .8849$

f. $P(z \leq -.71) = .2389$

13. a. $P(-1.98 \leq z \leq .49) = P(z \leq .49) - P(z < -1.98) = .6879 - .0239 = .6640$

b. $P(.52 \leq z \leq 1.22) = P(z \leq 1.22) - P(z < .52) = .8888 - .6985 = .1903$

c. $P(-1.75 \leq z \leq -1.04) = P(z \leq -1.04) - P(z < -1.75) = .1492 - .0401 = .1091$

14. a. The z value corresponding to a cumulative probability of .9750 is $z = 1.96$.

b. The z value here also corresponds to a cumulative probability of .9750: $z = 1.96$.

c. The z value corresponding to a cumulative probability of .7291 is $z = .61$.

d. Area to the left of z is $1 - .1314 = .8686$. So $z = 1.12$.

e. The z value corresponding to a cumulative probability of .6700 is $z = .44$.

f. The area to the left of z is .6700. So $z = .44$.

15. a. The z value corresponding to a cumulative probability of .2119 is $z = -.80$.

b. Compute $.9030/2 = .4515$; z corresponds to a cumulative probability of $.5000 + .4515 = .9515$. So $z = 1.66$.

c. Compute $.2052/2 = .1026$; z corresponds to a cumulative probability of $.5000 + .1026 = .6026$. So $z = .26$.

d. The z value corresponding to a cumulative probability of .9948 is $z = 2.56$.

e. The area to the left of z is $1 - .6915 = .3085$. So $z = -.50$.

16. a. The area to the left of z is $1 - .0100 = .9900$. The z value in the table with a cumulative probability closest to .9900 is $z = 2.33$.

b. The area to the left of z is .9750. So $z = 1.96$.

c. The area to the left of z is .9500. Since .9500 is exactly halfway between .9495 ($z = 1.64$) and .9505($z = 1.65$), we select $z = 1.645$. However, $z = 1.64$ or $z = 1.65$ are also acceptable answers.

d. The area to the left of z is .9000. So $z = 1.28$ is the closest z value.

17. $\mu = 385$ and $\sigma = 110$

a. $z = \dfrac{x - \mu}{\sigma} = \dfrac{550 - 385}{110} = 1.50$

$P(x \geq 550) = P(z \geq 1.50) = 1 - P(z \leq 1.50) = 1 - .9332 = .0668$

The probability that a domestic airfare will cost \$550 or more is .0668.

b. $z = \dfrac{x - \mu}{\sigma} = \dfrac{250 - 385}{110} = -1.23$

$P(x \leq 250) = P(z \leq -1.23) = .1093$

The probability that a domestic airfare will cost \$250 or less is .1093.

c. For $x = 500$, $z = \dfrac{x - \mu}{\sigma} = \dfrac{500 - 385}{110} = 1.05$

For $x = 300$, $z = \dfrac{x - \mu}{\sigma} = \dfrac{300 - 385}{110} = -.77$

$P(300 \leq x \leq 400) = P(z \leq 1.05) - P(z \leq -.77) = .8531 - .2206 = .6325$

The probability that a domestic airfare will cost between \$300 and \$500 is .6325.

d. The upper 3%, or area $= 1 - .03 = .97$ occurs for $z = 1.88$

$x = \mu + z\sigma = 385 + 1.88(110) = \$592$

For an airfare to be in the upper 3% it must be \$592 or more.

18. $\mu = 14.4$ and $\sigma = 4.4$

a. At $x = 20$, $z = \dfrac{20 - 14.4}{4.4} = 1.27$

$P(z \leq 1.27) = .8980$

$P(x \geq 20) = 1 - .8980 = .1020$

b. At $x = 10$, $z = \dfrac{10 - 14.4}{4.4} = -1.00$

$P(z \leq -1.00) = .1587$

So, $P(x \leq 10) = .1587$

c. A z-value of 1.28 cuts off an area of approximately 10% in the upper tail.

$x = 14.4 + 4.4(1.28) = 20.03$

A return of 20.03% or higher will put a domestic stock fund in the top 10%

19. $\mu = 328$ and $\sigma = 92$

a. $z = \dfrac{x - \mu}{\sigma} = \dfrac{500 - 328}{92} = 1.87$

$P(x > 500) = P(z > 1.87) = 1 - P(z \leq 1.87) = 1 - .9693 = .0307$

The probability that the emergency room visit will cost more than $500 is .0307.

b. $z = \dfrac{x - \mu}{\sigma} = \dfrac{250 - 328}{92} = -.85$

$P(x < 250) = P(z < -.85) = .1977$

The probability that the emergency room visit will cost less than $250 is .1977.

c. For $x = 400$, $z = \dfrac{x - \mu}{\sigma} = \dfrac{400 - 328}{92} = .78$

For $x = 300$, $z = \dfrac{x - \mu}{\sigma} = \dfrac{300 - 328}{92} = -.30$

$P(300 < x < 400) = P(z \leq .78) - P(z \leq -.30) = .7823 - .3821 = .4002$

The probability that the emergency room visit will cost between $300 and $400 is .4002.

d. The lower 8%, or area = .08, occurs for $z = -1.41$

$x = \mu + z\sigma = 328 - 1.41(92) = \$198.28$

For a patient to have a charge in the lower 8%, the cost of the visit must have been $198.28 or less.

20. a. United States: $\mu = 3.73 \quad \sigma = .25$

At $x = 3.50$, $z = \dfrac{3.5 - 3.73}{.25} = -.92$

$P(z < -.92) = .1788$

So, $P(x < 3.50) = .1788$

b. Russia: $\mu = 3.40$ $\sigma = .20$

At $x = 3.50$, $z = \dfrac{3.50 - 3.40}{.20} = .50$

$P(z < .50) = .6915$

So, $P(x < 3.50) = .6915$

69.15% of the gas stations in Russia charge less than $3.50 per gallon.

c. Use mean and standard deviation for Russia.

At $x = 3.73$, $z = \dfrac{3.73 - 3.40}{.20} = 1.65$

$P(z > 1.65) = 1 - P(z \le 1.65) = 1 - .9505 = .0495$

$P(x > 3.73) = .0495$

The probability that a randomly selected gas station in Russia charges more than the mean price in the United States is .0495. Stated another way, only 4.95% of the gas stations in Russia charge more than the average price in the United States.

21. From the normal probability tables, a z-value of 2.05 cuts off an area of approximately .02 in the upper tail of the distribution.

$x = \mu + z\sigma = 100 + 2.05(15) = 130.75$

A score of 131 or better should qualify a person for membership in Mensa.

22. Use $\mu = 8.35$ and $\sigma = 2.5$

a. We want to find $P(5 \le x \le 10)$

At $x = 10$,
$$z = \frac{x - \mu}{\sigma} = \frac{10 - 8.35}{2.5} = .66$$

At $x = 5$,
$$z = \frac{x - \mu}{\sigma} = \frac{5 - 8.35}{2.5} = -1.34$$

$P(5 \le x \le 10) = P(-1.34 \le z \le .66) = P(z \le .66) - P(z \le -1.34)$
$= .7454 - .0901$
$= .6553$

The probability of a household viewing television between 5 and 10 hours a day is .6553.

b. Find the z-value that cuts off an area of .03 in the upper tail. Using a cumulative probability of $1 - .03 = .97$, $z = 1.88$ provides an area of .03 in the upper tail of the normal distribution.

$$x = \mu + z\sigma = 8.35 + 1.88(2.5) = 13.05 \text{ hours}$$

A household must view slightly over 13 hours of television a day to be in the top 3% of television viewing households.

c. At $x = 3$, $z = \dfrac{x - \mu}{\sigma} = \dfrac{3 - 8.35}{2.5} = -2.14$

$P(x > 3) = 1 - P(z \leq -2.14) = 1 - .0162 = .9838$

The probability a household views more than 3 hours of television a day is .9838.

23. a. $z = \dfrac{60 - 80}{10} = -2$ $\qquad P(z \leq -2) = .0228$. So $P(x < 60) = .0228$

b. At $x = 60$

$$z = \frac{60 - 80}{10} = -2 \qquad \text{Area to left is .0228}$$

At $x = 75$

$$z = \frac{75 - 80}{10} = -.5 \qquad \text{Area to left is .3085}$$

$P(60 \leq x \leq 75) = .3085 - .0228 = .2857$

c. $z = \dfrac{90 - 80}{10} = 1$ $\qquad P(z \leq 1) = P(x \leq 90) = .1587$

Therefore 15.87% of students will not complete on time.

$$(60)(.1587) = 9.52$$

We would expect 9 or 10 students to be unable to complete the exam in time.

24. $\mu = 749$ and $\sigma = 225$

a. $z = \dfrac{x - \mu}{\sigma} = \dfrac{400 - 749}{225} = -1.55$

$P(x < 400) = P(z < -1.55) = .0606$

The probability that expenses will be less than $400 is .0606.

b. $z = \dfrac{x - \mu}{\sigma} = \dfrac{800 - 749}{225} = .23$

$P(x \geq 800) = P(z \geq .23) = 1 - P(z \leq .23) = 1 - .5910 = .4090$

The probability that expenses will be $800 or more is .4090.

c. For $x = 1000$, $z = \dfrac{x-\mu}{\sigma} = \dfrac{1000-749}{225} = 1.12$

For $x = 500$, $z = \dfrac{x-\mu}{\sigma} = \dfrac{500-749}{225} = -1.11$

$P(500 \leq x \leq 1000) = P(z \leq 1.12) - P(z \leq -1.11) = .8686 - .1335 = .7351$

The probability that expenses will be between \$500 and \$1000 is .7351.

d. The upper 5%, or area $= 1 - .05 = .95$ occurs for $z = 1.645$

$x = \mu + z\sigma = 749 + 1.645(225) = \$1119$

The 5% most expensive travel plans will be \$1119 or more.

25. $\mu = 204$ and $\sigma = 55$

a. $z = \dfrac{x-\mu}{\sigma} = \dfrac{225-204}{55} = .38$

$P(x \geq 225) = P(z \geq .38) = 1 - P(z \leq .38) = 1 - .6480 = .3520$

The probability that the hotel room will cost \$225 or more is .3520.

b. $z = \dfrac{x-\mu}{\sigma} = \dfrac{140-204}{55} = -1.16$

$P(x < 140) = P(z < -1.16) = .1230$

The probability that the hotel room will cost less than \$140 is .1230.

c. For $x = 300$, $z = \dfrac{x-\mu}{\sigma} = \dfrac{300-204}{55} = 1.75$

For $x = 200$, $z = \dfrac{x-\mu}{\sigma} = \dfrac{200-204}{55} = -.07$

$P(200 \leq x \leq 300) = P(z \leq 1.75) - P(z \leq -.07) = .9599 - .4721 = .4878$

The probability that the hotel room will cost between \$200 and \$300 is .4878.

d. The upper 20%, or area $= 1 - .20 = .80$ occurs for $z = .84$

$x = \mu + z\sigma = 204 + .84(55) = \$250$

The 20% most expensive hotel rooms will cost \$250 or more per night.

26. a. $\mu = np = 100(.20) = 20$

$\sigma^2 = np(1-p) = 100(.20)(.80) = 16$

$\sigma = \sqrt{16} = 4$

b.   Yes because $np = 20$ and $n(1 - p) = 80$

c. $P(23.5 \leq x \leq 24.5)$

$$z = \frac{24.5 - 20}{4} = +1.13 \qquad P(z \leq 1.13) = .8708$$

$$z = \frac{23.5 - 20}{4} = +.88 \qquad P(z \leq .88) = .8106$$

$$P(23.5 \leq x \leq 24.5) = .8708 - .8106 = .0602$$

d. $P(17.5 \leq x \leq 22.5)$

$$z = \frac{22.5 - 20}{4} = +.63 \qquad P(z \leq .63) = .7357$$

$$z = \frac{17.5 - 20}{4} = -.63 \qquad P(z \leq -.63) = .2643$$

$$P(17.5 \leq x \leq 22.5) = .7357 - .2643 = .4714$$

e. $P(x \leq 15.5)$

$$z = \frac{15.5 - 20}{4} = -1.13$$

$$P(x \leq 15.5) = P(z \leq -1.13) = .1292$$

27. a. $\mu = np = 200(.60) = 120$

$$\sigma^2 = np(1 - p) = 200(.60)(.40) = 48$$

$$\sigma = \sqrt{48} = 6.93$$

b.   Yes since $np = 120$ and $n(1 - p) = 80$

c. $P(99.5 \leq x \leq 110.5)$

$$z = \frac{110.5 - 120}{6.93} = -1.37 \qquad P(z \leq -1.37) = .0853$$

$$z = \frac{99.5 - 120}{6.93} = -2.96 \qquad P(z \leq -2.96) = .0015$$

$$P(99.5 \leq x \leq 110.5) = .0853 - .0015 = .0838$$

d. $P(x \geq 129.5)$

$$z = \frac{129.5 - 120}{6.93} = +1.37 \qquad P(z \geq 1.37) = 1 - .9147 = .0853$$

$P(x \geq 129.5) = .0853$

e. Simplifies computation. By direct computation of binomial probabilities we would have to compute

$$P(x \geq 130) = f(130) + f(131) + f(132) + f(133) + \ldots$$

28. a. $\mu = np = (250)(.20) = 50$

b. $\sigma^2 = np(1-p) = 250(.20)(1-.20) = 40$

$\sigma = \sqrt{40} = 6.3246$

Allowing for the continuity correction factor, $P(x < 40) = P(x \leq 39.5)$

At $x = 39.5$, $z = \dfrac{x - \mu}{\sigma} = \dfrac{39.5 - 50}{6.3246} = -1.66$

$P(x \leq 39.5) = .0485$

c. Allowing for the continuity correction factor, $P(55 \leq x \leq 60) = P(54.5 \leq x \leq 60.5)$

At $x = 54.5$, $z = \dfrac{x - \mu}{\sigma} = \dfrac{54.5 - 50}{6.3246} = .71$

At $x = 60.5$, $z = \dfrac{x - \mu}{\sigma} = \dfrac{60.5 - 50}{6.3246} = 1.66$

$P(54.5 \leq x \leq 60.5) = .9515 - .7611 = .1904$

d. Allowing for the continuity correction factor, $P(x \geq 70) = P(x \geq 69.5)$

At $x = 69.5$, $z = \dfrac{x - \mu}{\sigma} = \dfrac{69.5 - 50}{6.3246} = 3.08$

$P(x \geq 69.5) = 1 - .9990 = .0010$

29. a. $f(x) = \binom{n}{x} p^x (1-p)^{n-x} = \dfrac{n!}{x!(n-x)!} p^x (1-p)^{n-x}$

$n = 8, p = .82$

$P(x \geq 6) = f(6) + f(7) + f(8)$

$f(6) = \dfrac{8!}{6!(8-6)!} .82^6 (1-.82)^{8-6} = 28(.82)^6 (1-.82)^2 = .2758$

$f(7) = \dfrac{8!}{7!(8-7)!} .82^7 (1-.82)^{8-7} = 8(.82)^7 (1-.82)^1 = .3590$

$f(8) = \dfrac{8!}{8!(8-8)!} .82^8 (1-.82)^{8-8} = 1(.82)^8 (1-.82)^0 = .2044$

$$P(x \geq 6) = f(6) + f(7) + f(8) = .2758 + .3590 + .2044 = .8392$$

b. $\mu = np = (80)(.82) = 65.6$

$\sigma^2 = np(1-p) = 80(.82)(1-.82) = 11.808$

$\sigma = \sqrt{11.8080} = 3.4363$

Allowing for the continuity correction factor, $P(x \geq 60) = P(x \geq 59.5)$

At $x = 59.5$, $z = \dfrac{x - \mu}{\sigma} = \dfrac{59.5 - 65.6}{3.4363} = -1.78$

$$P(x \geq 59.5) = 1 - .0375 = .9625$$

c.   The advantage of using the normal approximation of the binomial distribution is that it eases and simplifies the calculations required to obtain the desired probability. For part (b) with $n = 80$, we would have had to compute $f(60) + f(61) + f(62) + \ldots + f(80)$ using the binomial probability function $f(x)$. This would have been tedious and time consuming.

d.   Students may be tempted to say that with the speed of computers, the developers of statistical software would be able to use the binomial probability function $f(x)$ as described in part (c) and compute the exact probability rather than the normal approximation. However, developers of statistical software are also interested in fast, efficient, and easy to program computational procedures provided such procedures provide reliable and accurate answers. With a large number of trials, the normal approximation of the binomial probability distribution is very good. Statistical software developers may chose to use the normal approximation of the binomial probability distribution in some statistical routines. For example, Minitab uses the normal approximation of binomial probabilities in the Nonparametric sign test whenever n is greater than 50.

30. a. $\mu = np = 800(.18) = 144$

b. $\mu = np = 600(.18) = 108$

$\sigma = \sqrt{np(1-p)} = \sqrt{(600)(.18)(.82)} = 9.4106$

For $x < 100$, use the continuity correction to find $P(x < 99.5)$

At $x = 99.5$,

$z = \dfrac{x - \mu}{\sigma} = \dfrac{99.5 - 108}{9.4106} = -.90$ $P(z < -.90) = .1841$

$P(x < 99.5) = .1841$

The probability that less than 100 individuals will be under 18 years of age is .1841.

c. $\sigma = \sqrt{np(1-p)} = \sqrt{(800)(.29)(.71)} = 12.8343$

For $x = 200$ or more, use the continuity correction to find $P(x \geq 199.5)$

6 - 14

At $x = 199.5$,

$$z = \frac{x - \mu}{\sigma} = \frac{199.5 - 232}{12.8343} = -2.53 \qquad P(z \geq -2.53) = 1 - .0057 = .9943$$

$P(x \geq 199.5) = .9943$

The probability that 200 or more individuals will be over 59 is .9943.

31. a. $\mu = np = 120(.79) = 94.8$

$$\sigma = \sqrt{np(1-p)} = \sqrt{(120)(.79)(.21)} = 4.46$$

The probability that at least 85 employers provide a two-day Thanksgiving holiday = $P(x \geq 84.5)$.

At $x = 84..5$

$$z = \frac{x - \mu}{\sigma} = \frac{84.5 - 94.8}{4.46} = -2.31$$

Therefore, $P(x \geq 84.5) = 1 - P(z \leq -2.31) = 1 - .0104 = .9896$

b. Find the normal probability: $P(89.5 \leq x \leq 100.5)$

At $x = 100.5$

$$z = \frac{x - \mu}{\sigma} = \frac{100.5 - 94.8}{4.46} = 1.28$$

$P(x \leq 100.5) = P(z \leq 1.28) = .8997$

At $x = 89.5$,

$$z = \frac{x - \mu}{\sigma} = \frac{89.5 - 94.8}{4.46} = -1.19$$

$P(x \leq 89.5) = P(z \leq -1.19) = .1170$

Therefore, $P(89.5 \leq x \leq 100.5) = .8997 - .1170 = .7827$

c. $\mu = np = 120(.19) = 22.8$

$$\sigma = \sqrt{np(1-p)} = \sqrt{(120)(.19)(.81)} = 4.30$$

The probability less than 20 employers provide a one-day Thanksgiving holiday = $P(x \leq 19.5)$.

At $x = 19..5$

$$z = \frac{x - \mu}{\sigma} = \frac{19.5 - 22.8}{4.30} = -.77$$

Therefore, $P(x \le 19.5) = P(z \le -.77) = .2206$

32. a. $P(x \le 6) = 1 - e^{-6/8} = 1 - .4724 = .5276$

   b. $P(x \le 4) = 1 - e^{-4/8} = 1 - .6065 = .3935$

   c. $P(x \ge 6) = 1 - P(x \le 6) = 1 - .5276 = .4724$

   d. $P(4 \le x \le 6) = P(x \le 6) - P(x \le 4) = .5276 - .3935 = .1341$

33. a. $P(x \le x_0) = 1 - e^{-x_0/3}$

   b. $P(x \le 2) = 1 - e^{-2/3} = 1 - .5134 = .4866$

   c. $P(x \ge 3) = 1 - P(x \le 3) = 1 - (1 - e^{-3/3}) = e^{-1} = .3679$

   d. $P(x \le 5) = 1 - e^{-5/3} = 1 - .1889 = .8111$

   e. $P(2 \le x \le 5) = P(x \le 5) - P(x \le 2) = .8111 - .4866 = .3245$

34. a. With $\mu = 20$, $f(x) = \frac{1}{20} e^{-x/20}$

   b. $P(x \le 15) = 1 - e^{-x/\mu} = 1 - e^{-15/20} = .5276$

   c. $P(x > 20) = 1 - P(x \le 20)$

   $$= 1 - (1 - e^{-20/20}) = e^{-1} = .3679$$

   d. With $\mu = 7$, $f(x) = \frac{1}{7} e^{-x/7}$

   $P(x \le 5) = 1 - e^{-x/\mu} = 1 - e^{-5/7} = .5105$

35. a.

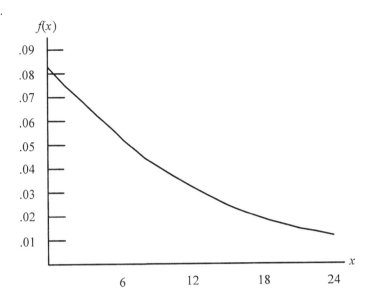

b. $P(x \le 12) = 1 - e^{-12/12} = 1 - .3679 = .6321$

c. $P(x \le 6) = 1 - e^{-6/12} = 1 - .6065 = .3935$

d. $P(x \ge 30) = 1 - P(x < 30)$

$$= 1 - (1 - e^{-30/12})$$

$$= .0821$$

36. a. $f(x) = \frac{1}{\mu} e^{-x/\mu} = \frac{1}{2} e^{-x/2}$ for $x \ge 0$

$P(x \le x_0) = 1 - e^{-x_0/\mu}$

$P(x \le 1) = 1 - e^{-1/2} = 1 - e^{-.5} = 1 - .6065 = .3935$

b. $P(x \le 2) = 1 - e^{-2/2} = 1 - e^{-1.0} = 1 - .3679 = .6321$

$P(1 \le x \le 2) = P(x \le 2) - P(x \le 1) = .6321 - .3935 = .2386$

c. For this customer, the cable service repair would have to take longer than 4 hours.

$P(x > 4) = 1 - P(x \le 4) = 1 - (1 - e^{-4/2}) = e^{-2.0} = .1353$

37. a. $f(x) = \frac{1}{\mu} e^{-x/\mu} = \frac{1}{25} e^{-x/25}$ for $x \ge 0$

$P(x \le x_0) = 1 - e^{-x_0/\mu}$

$P(x \le 20) = 1 - e^{-20/25} = 1 - e^{-.80} = 1 - .4493 = .5507$

b. $P(x > 30) = 1 - P(x \le 30) = 1 - (1 - e^{-30/25}) = e^{-1.2} = .3012$

c. For the customer to make the 15-minute return trip home by 6:00 p.m., the order must be ready by 5:45 p.m. Since the order was placed at 5:20 p.m., the order must to be ready within 25 minutes.

$P(x \le 25) = 1 - e^{-25/25} = 1 - e^{-1} = 1 - .3679 = .6321$

This may seem surprising high since the mean time is 25 minutes. But, for the exponential distribution, the probability x being greater than the mean is significantly less than the probability of x being less than the mean. This is because the exponential distribution is skewed to the right.

38. a. Because the number of calls per hour follows a Poisson distribution, the time between calls follows an exponential distribution. So,

for a mean of 1.6 calls per hour, the mean time between calls is

$$\mu = \frac{60 \text{ minutes/hour}}{1.6 \text{ calls/hour}} = 37.5 \text{ minutes per call}$$

b. The exponential probability density function is $f(x) = \left(\dfrac{1}{37.5}\right) e^{-x/37.5}$ for $x \ge 0$

where x is the minutes between 911 calls.

c. Using time in minutes,

$P(x < 60) = 1 - e^{-60/37.5} = 1 - .2019 = .7981$

d. $P(x \ge 30) = 1 - P(x \le 30) = 1 - (1 - e^{-30/37.5}) = 1 - .5507 = .4493$

e. $P(5 \le x \le 20) = (1 - e^{-20/37.5}) - (1 - e^{5/37.5}) = .4134 - .1248 = .2886$

39. a. Let x = sales price ($1000s)

$$f(x) = \begin{cases} \dfrac{1}{25} & \text{for } 200 \le x \le 225 \\ 0 & \text{elsewhere} \end{cases}$$

b. $P(x \ge 215) = (1/25)(225 - 215) = .40$

c. $P(x < 210) = (1/25)(210 - 200) = .40$

d. $E(x) = (200 + 225)/2 = 212{,}500$

If the executive leaves the house on the market for another month, the expected sales price will be $2,500 higher than if the house is sold back to the company for $210,000. However, if the house is left on the market for another month, there is a .40 probability that the executive will get less than the company offer of $210,000. It is a close call. But the expected value of $212,500 suggests the executive should leave the house on the market another month.

40. a. Find the z value that cuts off an area of .10 in the lower tail.

From the standard normal table $z \approx -1.28$. Solve for x,

$$z = -1.28 = \frac{x - 19,000}{2100}$$

$$x = 19,000 - 1.28(2100) = 16,312$$

10% of athletic scholarships are valued at $16,312 or less.

b. $z = \dfrac{x - \mu}{\sigma} = \dfrac{22,000 - 19,000}{2100} = 1.43$

$P(x \geq 22,000) = 1 - P(z \leq 1.43) = 1 - .9236 = .0764$

7.64% of athletic scholarships are valued at $22,000 or more.

c. Find the z value that cuts off an area of .03 in the upper tail: $z = 1.88$. Solve for x,

$$z = 1.88 = \frac{x - 19,000}{2100}$$

$$x = 19,000 + 1.88(2100) = 22,948$$

3% of athletic scholarships are valued at $22,948 or more.

41. a. $P(defect) = 1 - P(9.85 \leq x \leq 10.15)$

$= 1 - P(-1 \leq z \leq 1) = 1 - .6826 = .3174$

Expected number of defects $= 1000(.3174) = 317.4$

b. $P(defect) = 1 - P(9.85 \leq x \leq 10.15)$

$= 1 - P(-3 \leq z \leq 3) = 1 - .9974 = .0026$

Expected number of defects $= 1000(.0026) = 2.6$

c. Reducing the process standard deviation causes a substantial reduction in the number of defects.

42. $\mu = 658$

a. $z = -1.88$ cuts off .03 in the lower tail

So,

$$z = -1.88 = \frac{610 - 658}{\sigma}$$

$$\sigma = \frac{610 - 658}{-1.88} = 25.5319$$

b. At 700, $z = \dfrac{x - \mu}{\sigma} = \dfrac{700 - 658}{25.5319} = 1.65$

At 600, $z = \dfrac{x - \mu}{\sigma} = \dfrac{600 - 659}{25.5319} = -2.31$

$P(600 < x < 700) - P(-2.31 < z < 1.65) = .9505 - .0104 = .9401$

c. $z = 1.88$ cuts off approximately .03 in the upper tail

$x = 658 + 1.88(25.5319) = 706.$

On the busiest 3% of days 706 or more people show up at the pawnshop.

43. $\mu = 4.5$ and $\sigma = .82$

a. $z = \dfrac{x - \mu}{\sigma} = \dfrac{5 - 4.5}{.82} = .61$

$P(x < 5) = P(z < -.61) = .7291$

b. $z = \dfrac{x - \mu}{\sigma} = \dfrac{3 - 4.5}{.82} = -1.83$

$P(x \geq 3) = P(z \geq -1.83) = 1 - P(z \leq -1.83) = 1 - .0336 = .9664$

c.   For $x = 4$, $z = \dfrac{x - \mu}{\sigma} = \dfrac{4 - 4.5}{.82} = -.61$

For $x = 3$, $z = \dfrac{x - \mu}{\sigma} = \dfrac{3 - 4.5}{.82} = -1.83$

$P(3 \leq x \leq 4) = P(z \leq -.61) - P(z \leq -1.83) = .2709 - .0336 = .2373$

d. 85% of the weekly cargo volumes can be handled without requiring the port to extend operating hours; 15% of the time the tons of cargo is so large it requires the port to extend operating hours.

The upper 15%, or area $= 1 - .15 = .85$ occurs for $z = 1.04$

$x = \mu + z\sigma = 4.5 + 1.04(.82) = 5.35$ tons

A weekly volume of 5.35 tons or more will require the port to extend operating hours.

44. a.   At $x = 200$

$$z = \frac{200 - 150}{25} = 2$$

$P(x > 200) = P(z > 2) = 1 - P(z \leq 2) = 1 - .9772 = .0228$

b. Expected Profit = Expected Revenue - Expected Cost

$$= 200 - 150 = \$50$$

45. a. Mean monthly revenue = ($368)(330)/12 = $10,120

b. $\mu = 10,120$ and $\sigma = 2200$

$$z = \frac{x - \mu}{\sigma} = \frac{12,000 - 10,120}{2200} = .85$$

$$P(x > 12,000) = P(z > .85) = 1 - P(z \le .85) = 1 - .8023 = .1977$$

c. $$z = \frac{x - \mu}{\sigma} = \frac{7,500 - 10,120}{2200} = -1.19$$

$$P(x < 7,500) = P(z < -1.19) = .1170$$

d. Mean monthly revenue = ($420)(330)/12 = $11,550

$\mu = 11,550$ and $\sigma = 2500$

$$z = \frac{x - \mu}{\sigma} = \frac{12,000 - 11,550}{2500} = .18$$

$$P(x > 12,000) = P(z > .18) = 1 - P(z \le .18) = 1 - .5714 = .4286$$

$$z = \frac{x - \mu}{\sigma} = \frac{7,500 - 11,550}{2500} = -1.62$$

$$P(x < 7,500) = P(z < -1.62) = .0526$$

Current annual revenue = ($368)(330) = $121,400

New annual revenue = ($420)(330) = $138,600

The increase in annual revenue $138,600 - $121,400 = $17,160 (14.1%) and the higher probability of monthly revenues over $12,000 make the upgraded minibar service worthwhile.

46. a. At 400,

$$z = \frac{400 - 450}{100} = -.500$$

Area to left is .3085

At 500,

$$z = \frac{500 - 450}{100} = +.500$$

Area to left is .6915

$$P(400 \le x \le 500) = .6915 - .3085 = .3830$$

38.3% will score between 400 and 500.

b. At 630,

$$z = \frac{630 - 450}{100} = 1.80$$

96.41% do worse and 3.59% do better .

c. At 480,

$$z = \frac{480 - 450}{100} = .30$$

Area to left is .6179

38.21% are acceptable.

47. a. At 100,000

$$z = \frac{100,000 - 88,592}{19,900} = .57$$

$P(x > 100,000) = P(z > .57) = 1 - P(z \le .57) = 1 - .7157 = .2843$

The probability of a Houston brand manager having a base salary in excess of \$100,000 is .2843.

b. At 100,000

$$z = \frac{100,000 - 97,417}{21,800} = .12$$

$P(x > 100,000) = P(z > .12) = 1 - P(z \le .12) = 1 - .5478 = .4522$

The probability of a Los Angeles brand manager having a base salary in excess of \$100,000 is .4522

c. At $x = 75,000$

$$z = \frac{75,000 - 97,417}{21,800} = -1.03$$

$P(x < 75,000) = P(z < -1.03) = .1515$

The probability of a Los Angeles brand manager receiving a base salary below \$75,000 is small: .1515

d. The answer to this is the Houston brand manager base salary that cuts off an area of .01 in the upper tail of the distribution for Houston brand managers.

Use $z = 2.33$

$x = 88,592 + 2.33(19,900) = 134,959$

A Los Angeles brand manager who makes \$134,959 or more will earn more than 99% of the Houston brand managers.

48. $\sigma = .6$

At 2%

$$z \approx -2.05 \quad x = 18$$

$$z = \frac{x - \mu}{\sigma} \qquad \therefore -2.05 = \frac{18 - \mu}{.6}$$

$$\mu = 18 + 2.05\,(.6) = 19.23 \text{ oz.}$$

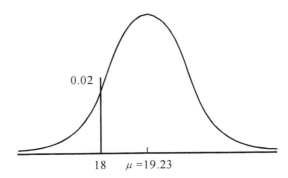

The mean filling weight must be 19.23 oz.

49.   Use normal approximation to binomial.

a. $\mu = np = 50\,(.75) = 37.5$

$$\sigma = \sqrt{np(1-p)} = \sqrt{50(.75)(.25)} = 3.06$$

At $x = 42.5$

$$z = \frac{x - \mu}{\sigma} = \frac{42.5 - 37.5}{3.06} = 1.63$$

$$P(z \leq 1.63) = .9484$$

Probability of an A grade $= 1 - .9484 = .0516$ or 5.16% will obtain an A grade.

b.   At $x = 34.5$

$$z = \frac{34.5 - 37.5}{3.06} = -.98$$

At $x = 39.5$

$$z = \frac{39.5 - 37.5}{3.06} = .65$$

$$P(-.98 \leq z \leq .65) = .7422 - .1635 = .5787$$

or 57.87% will obtain a C grade.

c. At $x = 29.5$

$$z = \frac{29.5 - 37.5}{3.06} = -2.61$$

$P(z \geq -2.61) = 1 - .0045 = .9955$

or 99.55% of the students who have done their homework and attended lectures will pass the examination.

d. $\mu = np = 50\,(.25) = 12.5$ (We use $p = .25$ for a guess.)

$$\sigma = \sqrt{np(1-p)} = \sqrt{50(.25)(.75)} = 3.06$$

At $x = 29.5$

$$z = \frac{29.5 - 12.5}{3.06} = 5.55$$

$P(z \geq 5.55) \approx 0$

Thus, essentially no one who simply guesses will pass the examination.

50. a. $\mu = np = (240)(0.49) = 117.6$

Expected number of wins is 117.6

Expected number of losses $= 240(0.51) = 122.4$

Expected payoff $= 117.6(50) - 122.4(50) = (-4.8)(50) = -240$.

The player should expect to lose $240.

b. To lose $1000, the player must lose 20 more hands than he wins. With 240 hands in 4 hours, the player must win 110 or less in order to lose $1000. Use normal approximation to binomial.
$$\mu = np = (240)(0.49) = 117.6$$

$$\sigma = \sqrt{240(.49)(.51)} = 7.7444$$

Find $P(x \leq 110.5)$

At $x = 110.5$

$$z = \frac{110.5 - 117.6}{7.7444} = -.92$$

$P(x \leq 110.5) = .1788$

The probability he will lose $1000 or more is .1788.

c. In order to win, the player must win 121 or more hands.

Find $P(x \geq 120.5)$

At $x = 120.5$

$$z = \frac{120.5 - 117.6}{7.7444} = .37$$

$P(x \geq 120.5) = 1 - .6443 = .3557$

The probability that the player will win is .3557. The odds are clearly in the house's favor.

d. To lose $1500, the player must lose 30 hands more than he wins. This means he wins 105 or fewer hands.

Find $P(x \leq 105.5)$

At $x = 105.5$

$$z = \frac{105.5 - 117.6}{7.7444} = -1.56$$

$P(x \leq 105.5) = .0594$

The probability the player will go broke is .0594.

51. a. Given $P(x \leq 5) = 1 - e^{-x/\mu} = 1 - e^{-5/\mu} = .53$

Compute $P(x \leq 5)$ for $\mu = 5.8, 6.2$ and 7.0

$P(x \leq 5) = 1 - e^{-5/5.8} = .5777$

$P(x \leq 5) = 1 - e^{-5/6.2} = .5536$

$P(x \leq 5) = 1 - e^{-5/6.6} = .5312$

$P(x \leq 5) = 1 - e^{-5/7} = .5105$
$\mu = 6.6$ provides the closest probability to $P(x \leq 5) = .53$

b. $P(x > 10) = 1 - P(x \leq 10) = 1 - (1 - e^{-10/6.6}) = 1 - .7802 = .2198$

c. $P(x \leq 4) = 1 - e^{-4/6.6} = .4545$

$P(x \leq 8) = 1 - e^{-8/6.6} = .7024$

The probability that a worker uses the office computer between four and eight hours is $.7024 - .4545 = .2479$

52. a. Mean time between arrivals = 1/7 minutes

b. $f(x) = 7e^{-7x}$

c. $P(x > 1) = 1 - P(x < 1) = 1 - [1 - e^{-7(1)}] = e^{-7} = .0009$

d. 12 seconds is .2 minutes

$P(x > .2) = 1 - P(x < .2) = 1 - [1 - e^{-7(.2)}] = e^{-1.4} = .2466$

53. a. $f(x) = \frac{1}{\mu} e^{-x/\mu} = \frac{1}{38.3} e^{-x/38.3}$ for $x \geq 0$

b. $P(x \leq x_0) = 1 - e^{-x_0/\mu}$

$P(x \leq 40) = 1 - e^{-40/38.3} = 1 - .3519 = .6481$

$P(x \leq 20) = 1 - e^{-20/38.3} = 1 - .5932 = .4068$

$P(20 \leq x \leq 40) = P(x \leq 40) - P(x \leq 20) = .6481 - .4068 = .2413$

c. $P(x > 60) = 1 - P(x \leq 60) = 1 - (1 - e^{-60/38.3}) = e^{-60/38.3} = .2088$

54. a. $\frac{1}{\mu} = .50$ therefore $\mu = 2$ minutes is the mean time between telephone calls

b. 30 seconds = .5 minutes

$P(x \leq .5) = 1 - e^{-.5/2} = 1 - .7788 = .2212$

c. $P(x \leq 1) = 1 - e^{-1/2} = 1 - .6065 = .3935$

d. $P(x \geq 5) = 1 - P(x < 5) = 1 - (1 - e^{-5/2}) = .0821$

Chapter 7
Sampling and Sampling Distributions

Learning Objectives

1. Understand the importance of sampling and how results from samples can be used to provide estimates of population characteristics such as the population mean, the population standard deviation and / or the population proportion.

2. Understand the difference between sampling from a finite population and sampling from an infinite population.

3. Know what simple random sampling is and how simple random samples are selected.

4. Understand the concept of a sampling distribution.

5. Understand the central limit theorem and the important role it plays in sampling.

6. Know the characteristics of the sampling distribution of the sample mean ($\bar{x}$) and the sampling distribution of the sample proportion ($\bar{p}$).

7. Learn about a variety of sampling methods including stratified random sampling, cluster sampling, systematic sampling, convenience sampling and judgment sampling.

8. Know the definition of the following terms:

parameter	sampling distribution
sampled population	finite population correction factor
sample statistic	standard error
simple random sampling	central limit theorem
sampling without replacement	unbiased
sampling with replacement	
point estimator	
point estimate	
target population	

Solutions:

1. a. AB, AC, AD, AE, BC, BD, BE, CD, CE, DE

    b. With 10 samples, each has a 1/10 probability.

    c. E and C because 8 and 0 do not apply; 5 identifies E; 7 does not apply; 5 is skipped since E is already in the sample; 3 identifies C; 2 is not needed since the sample of size 2 is complete.

2. Using the last 3-digits of each 5-digit grouping provides the random numbers:

    601, 022, 448, 147, 229, 553, 147, 289, 209

    Numbers greater than 350 do not apply and the 147 can only be used once. Thus, the simple random sample of four includes 22, 147, 229, and 289.

3. 459, 147, 385, 113, 340, 401, 215, 2, 33, 348

4. a. 6, 6, 3, 3 ,9 We need 5 random digits because the second 6 and the second 3 are repeats.

    Davis Love III, Jim Fuyrk, Charles Howell III

    b. $\dfrac{N!}{n!(N-n)!} = \dfrac{10!}{3!(10-3)!} = \dfrac{3,628,800}{(6)(5040)} = 120$

5. 283, 610, 39, 254, 568, 353, 602, 421, 638, 164

6. 2782, 493, 825, 1807, 289

7. 108, 290, 201, 292, 322, 9, 244, 249, 226, 125, (continuing at the top of column 9) 147, and 113.

8. Random numbers used: 13, 8, 27, 23, 25, 18

    The second occurrence of the random number 13 is ignored.

    Companies selected: ExxonMobil, Chevron, Travelers, Microsoft, Pfizer, and Intel

9. 102, 115, 122, 290, 351, 157, 55, 165, 25, 324

10. a. Finite population. A frame could be constructed obtaining a list of licensed drivers from the New York State driver's license bureau.

    b. Infinite population. Sampling from a process. The process is the production line producing boxes of cereal.

    c. Infinite population. Sampling from a process. The process is one of generating arrivals to the Golden Gate Bridge.

    d. Finite population. A frame could be constructed by obtaining a listing of students enrolled in the course from the professor.

    e. Infinite population. Sampling from a process. The process is one of generating orders for the mail-order firm.

11. a. $\bar{x} = \Sigma x_i / n = \dfrac{54}{6} = 9$

    b. $s = \sqrt{\dfrac{\Sigma(x_i - \bar{x})^2}{n-1}}$

    $\Sigma(x_i - \bar{x})^2 = (-4)^2 + (-1)^2 + 1^2 (-2)^2 + 1^2 + 5^2 = 48$

    $s = \sqrt{\dfrac{48}{6-1}} = 3.1$

12. a. $\bar{p} = 75/150 = .50$

    b. $\bar{p} = 55/150 = .3667$

13. a. $\bar{x} = \Sigma x_i / n = \dfrac{465}{5} = 93$

    b.

	x_i	$(x_i - \bar{x})$	$(x_i - \bar{x})^2$
	94	+1	1
	100	+7	49
	85	-8	64
	94	+1	1
	92	-1	1
Totals	465	0	116

    $s = \sqrt{\dfrac{\Sigma(x_i - \bar{x})^2}{n-1}} = \sqrt{\dfrac{116}{4}} = 5.39$

14. a. Two of the 40 stocks in the sample received a 5 Star rating.

    $\bar{p} = \dfrac{2}{40} = .05$

    b. Seventeen of the 40 stocks in the sample are rated Above Average with respect to risk.

    $\bar{p} = \dfrac{17}{40} = .425$

    c. There are eight stocks in the sample that are rated 1 Star or 2 Star.

    $\bar{p} = \dfrac{8}{40} = .20$

15. a. $\bar{x} = \dfrac{\Sigma x_i}{n} = \dfrac{816}{12} = 68$

    b. $s = \sqrt{\dfrac{\Sigma(x_i - \bar{x})^2}{n-1}} = \sqrt{\dfrac{3522}{12-1}} = 17.8936$

16. a. The sampled population is U. S. adults that are 50 years of age or older.

    b. We would use the sample proportion for the estimate of the population proportion.

    $$\bar{p} = \frac{350}{426} = .8216$$

    c. The sample proportion for this issue is .74 and the sample size is 426.

       The number of respondents citing education as "very important" is (.74)426 = 315.

    d. We would use the sample proportion for the estimate of the population proportion.

    $$\bar{p} = \frac{354}{426} = .8310$$

    e. The inferences in parts (b) and (d) are being made about the population of U.S. adults who are age 50 or older. So, the population of U.S. adults who are age 50 or older is the target population. The target population is the same as the sampled population. If the sampled population was restricted to members of AARP who were 50 years of age or older, the sampled population would not be the same as the target population. The inferences made in parts (b) and (d) would only be valid if the population of AARP members age 50 or older was representative of the U.S. population of adults age 50 and over.

17. a. $\bar{p} = 454/478 = .9498$

    b. $\bar{p} = 741/833 = .8896$

    c. $\bar{p} = 1058/1644 = .6436$

    d. Younger adults are more likely to use the Internet.

    e. $\bar{p} = (454 + 741 + 1058)/(478 + 833 + 1644) = .7624$

18. a. $E(\bar{x}) = \mu = 200$

    b. $\sigma_{\bar{x}} = \sigma / \sqrt{n} = 50 / \sqrt{100} = 5$

    c. Normal with $E(\bar{x}) = 200$ and $\sigma_{\bar{x}} = 5$

    d. It shows the probability distribution of all possible sample means that can be observed with random samples of size 100. This distribution can be used to compute the probability that $\bar{x}$ is within a specified $\pm$ from μ.

19. a. The sampling distribution is normal with

       $E(\bar{x}) = \mu = 200$

       $\sigma_{\bar{x}} = \sigma / \sqrt{n} = 50 / \sqrt{100} = 5$

       For ± 5, $195 \le \bar{x} \le 205$

Using Standard Normal Probability Table:

At $\bar{x} = 205$, $z = \dfrac{\bar{x} - \mu}{\sigma_{\bar{x}}} = \dfrac{5}{5} = 1$ $P(z \leq 1) = .8413$

At $\bar{x} = 195$, $z = \dfrac{\bar{x} - \mu}{\sigma_{\bar{x}}} = \dfrac{-5}{5} = -1$ $P(z < -1) = .1587$

$P(195 \leq \bar{x} \leq 205) = .8413 - .1587 = .6826$

b. For ± 10, $190 \leq \bar{x} \leq 210$

Using Standard Normal Probability Table:

At $\bar{x} = 210$, $z = \dfrac{\bar{x} - \mu}{\sigma_{\bar{x}}} = \dfrac{10}{5} = 2$ $P(z \leq 2) = .9772$

At $\bar{x} = 190$, $z = \dfrac{\bar{x} - \mu}{\sigma_{\bar{x}}} = \dfrac{-10}{5} = -2$ $P(z < -2) = .0228$

$P(190 \leq \bar{x} \leq 210) = .9772 - .0228 = .9544$

20. $\sigma_{\bar{x}} = \sigma / \sqrt{n}$

$\sigma_{\bar{x}} = 25 / \sqrt{50} = 3.54$

$\sigma_{\bar{x}} = 25 / \sqrt{100} = 2.50$

$\sigma_{\bar{x}} = 25 / \sqrt{150} = 2.04$

$\sigma_{\bar{x}} = 25 / \sqrt{200} = 1.77$

The standard error of the mean decreases as the sample size increases.

21. a. $\sigma_{\bar{x}} = \sigma / \sqrt{n} = 10 / \sqrt{50} = 1.41$

b. $n / N = 50 / 50{,}000 = .001$

Use $\sigma_{\bar{x}} = \sigma / \sqrt{n} = 10 / \sqrt{50} = 1.41$

c. $n / N = 50 / 5000 = .01$

Use $\sigma_{\bar{x}} = \sigma / \sqrt{n} = 10 / \sqrt{50} = 1.41$

d. $n/N = 50/500 = .10$

Use $\sigma_{\bar{x}} = \sqrt{\dfrac{N-n}{N-1}}\dfrac{\sigma}{\sqrt{n}} = \sqrt{\dfrac{500-50}{500-1}}\dfrac{10}{\sqrt{50}} = 1.34$

Note: Only case (d) where $n/N = .10$ requires the use of the finite population correction factor.

22. a. $E(\bar{x}) = 51,800$ and $\sigma_{\bar{x}} = \sigma/\sqrt{n} = 4000/\sqrt{60} = 516.40$

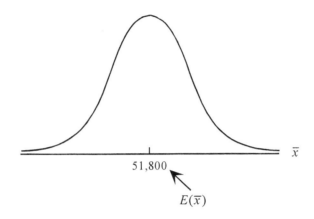

51,800

$E(\bar{x})$

The normal distribution for $\bar{x}$ is based on the Central Limit Theorem.

b. For $n = 120$, $E(\bar{x})$ remains $51,800 and the sampling distribution of $\bar{x}$ can still be approximated by a normal distribution. However, $\sigma_{\bar{x}}$ is reduced to $4000/\sqrt{120} = 365.15$.

c. As the sample size is increased, the standard error of the mean, $\sigma_{\bar{x}}$, is reduced. This appears logical from the point of view that larger samples should tend to provide sample means that are closer to the population mean. Thus, the variability in the sample mean, measured in terms of $\sigma_{\bar{x}}$, should decrease as the sample size is increased.

23. a. With a sample of size 60 $\sigma_{\bar{x}} = \dfrac{4000}{\sqrt{60}} = 516.40$

At $\bar{x} = 52,300$, $z = \dfrac{52,300 - 51,800}{516.40} = .97$

$P(\bar{x} \le 52,300) = P(z \le .97) = .8340$

At $\bar{x} = 51,300$, $z = \dfrac{51,300 - 51,800}{516.40} = -.97$

$P(\bar{x} < 51,300) = P(z < -.97) = .1660$

$P(51,300 \le \bar{x} \le 52,300) = .8340 - .1660 = .6680$

b. $\sigma_{\bar{x}} = \dfrac{4000}{\sqrt{120}} = 365.15$

At $\bar{x} = 52,300$, $z = \dfrac{52,300 - 51,800}{365.15} = 1.37$

$P(\bar{x} \le 52,300) = P(z \le 1.37) = .9147$

At $\bar{x} = 51,300$, $z = \dfrac{51,300 - 51,800}{365.15} = -1.37$

$P(\bar{x} < 51,300) = P(z < -1.37) = .0853$

$P(51,300 \le \bar{x} \le 52,300) = .9147 - .0853 = .8294$

24. a. Normal distribution, $E(\bar{x}) = 17.5$

$\sigma_{\bar{x}} = \sigma / \sqrt{n} = 4 / \sqrt{50} = .57$

b. Within 1 week means $16.5 \le \bar{x} \le 18.5$

At $\bar{x} = 18.5$, $z = \dfrac{18.5 - 17.5}{.57} = 1.75$ $P(z \le 1.75) = .9599$

At $\bar{x} = 16.5$, $z = -1.75$. $P(z < -1.75) = .0401$

So $P(16.5 \le \bar{x} \le 18.5) = .9599 - .0401 = .9198$

c. Within 1/2 week means $17.0 \le \bar{x} \le 18.0$

At $\bar{x} = 18.0$, $z = \dfrac{18.0 - 17.5}{.57} = .88$ $P(z \le .88) = .8106$

At $\bar{x} = 17.0$, $z = -.88$ $P(z < -.88) = .1894$

$P(17.0 \le \bar{x} \le 18.0) = .8106 - .1894 = .6212$

25. $\sigma_{\bar{x}} = \sigma / \sqrt{n} = 100 / \sqrt{90} = 10.54$ This value for the standard error can be used for parts (a) and (b) below.

a. $z = \dfrac{512 - 502}{10.54} = .95$ $P(z \le .95) = .8289$

$z = \dfrac{492 - 502}{10.54} = -.95$ $P(z < -.95) = .1711$

probability $= .8289 - .1711 = .6578$

b. $\quad z = \dfrac{525 - 515}{10.54} = .95 \qquad P(z \le .95) = .8289$

$\quad z = \dfrac{505 - 515}{10.54} = -.95 \qquad P(z < -.95) = .1711$

probability = .8289 - .1711 = .6578

The probability of being within 10 of the mean on the Mathematics portion of the test is exactly the same as the probability of being within 10 on the Critical Reading portion of the SAT. This is because the standard error is the same in both cases. The fact that the means differ does not affect the probability calculation.

c. $\quad \sigma_{\bar{x}} = \sigma / \sqrt{n} = 100 / \sqrt{100} = 10.0$ The standard error is smaller here because the sample size is larger.

$\quad z = \dfrac{504 - 494}{10.0} = 1.00 \qquad P(z \le 1.00) = .8413$

$\quad z = \dfrac{484 - 494}{10.0} = -1.00 \qquad P(z < -1.00) = .1587$

probability = .8413 - .1587 = .6826

The probability is larger here than it is in parts (a) and (b) because the larger sample size has made the standard error smaller.

26. a. $\quad z = \dfrac{\bar{x} - 16642}{\sigma / \sqrt{n}}$

Within ± 200 means $\bar{x}$ - 16,642 must be between -200 and +200.

The z value for $\bar{x}$ - 16,642 = -200 is the negative of the z value for $\bar{x}$ - 16,642 = 200. So we just show the computation of z for $\bar{x}$ - 16,642 = 200.

$n = 30 \qquad z = \dfrac{200}{2400 / \sqrt{30}} = .46 \qquad P(-.46 \le z \le .46) = .6772 - .3228 = .3544$

$n = 50 \qquad z = \dfrac{200}{2400 / \sqrt{50}} = .59 \qquad P(-.59 \le z \le .59) = .7224 - .2776 = .4448$

$n = 100 \qquad z = \dfrac{200}{2400 / \sqrt{100}} = .83 \qquad P(-.83 \le z \le .83) = .7967 - .2033 = .5934$

$n = 400 \qquad z = \dfrac{200}{2400 / \sqrt{400}} = 1.67 \qquad P(-.1.67 \le z \le .1.67) = .9525 - .0475 = .9050$

b. A larger sample increases the probability that the sample mean will be within a specified distance of the population mean. In this instance, the probability of being within ±200 of μ ranges from .3544 for a sample of size 30 to .9050 for a sample of size 400.

27. a. $\sigma_{\bar{x}} = \sigma / \sqrt{n} = 2.30 / \sqrt{50} = .3253$

At $\bar{x} = 22.18$, $z = \dfrac{\bar{x} - \mu}{\sigma / \sqrt{n}} = \dfrac{22.18 - 21.68}{.3253} = 1.54$ $P(z \le 1.54) = .9382$

At $\bar{x} = 21.18$, $z = -1.54$

$P(z < -1.54) = .0618$, thus

$P(21.18 \le \bar{x} \le 22.18) = .9382 - .0618 = .8764$

b. $\sigma_{\bar{x}} = \sigma / \sqrt{n} = 2.05 / \sqrt{50} = .2899$

At $\bar{x} = 19.30$, $z = \dfrac{\bar{x} - \mu}{\sigma / \sqrt{n}} = \dfrac{19.30 - 18.80}{.2899} = 1.72$ $P(z \le 1.72) = .9573$

At $\bar{x} = 18.30$, $z = -1.72$, $P(z < -1.72) = .0427$, thus

$P(18.30 \le \bar{x} \le 19.30) = .9573 - .0427 = .9146$

c.   In part (b) we have a higher probability of obtaining a sample mean within \$.50 of the population mean because the standard error for female graduates (.2899) is smaller than the standard error for male graduates (.3253).

d.   With $n = 120$, $\sigma_{\bar{x}} = \sigma / \sqrt{n} = 2.05 / \sqrt{120} = .1871$

At $\bar{x} = 18.50$, $z = \dfrac{18.50 - 18.80}{.1871} = -1.60$

$P(\bar{x} < 18.50) = P(z < -1.60) = .0548$

28. a.   This is a graph of a normal distribution with $E(\bar{x}) = 22$ and

$\sigma_{\bar{x}} = \sigma / \sqrt{n} = 4 / \sqrt{30} = .7303$

b.   Within 1 inch means $21 \le \bar{x} \le 23$

$z = \dfrac{23 - 22}{.7303} = 1.37$ $z = \dfrac{21 - 22}{.7303} = -1.37$

$P(21 \le \bar{x} \le 23) = P(-1.37 \le z \le 1.37) = .9147 - .0853 = .8294$

The probability the sample mean will be within 1 inch of the population mean of 22 is .8294.

c. $\sigma_{\bar{x}} = \sigma / \sqrt{n} = 4 / \sqrt{45} = .5963$

Within 1 inch means $41 \le \bar{x} \le 43$

$z = \dfrac{43 - 42}{.5963} = 1.68$ $z = \dfrac{41 - 42}{.5963} = -1.68$

$P(41 \leq \bar{x} \leq 43) = P(-1.68 \leq z \leq 1.68) = .9535 - .0465 = .9070$

The probability the sample mean will be within 1 inch of the population mean of 42 is .9070.

d. The probability of being within 1 inch is greater for New York in part (c) because the sample size is larger.

29. $\mu = 183 \quad \sigma = 50$

    a. $n = 30$ Within 8 means $175 \leq \bar{x} \leq 191$

$$z = \frac{\bar{x} - \mu}{\sigma / \sqrt{n}} = \frac{8}{50 / \sqrt{30}} = .88$$

$P(175 \leq \bar{x} \leq 191) = P(-.88 \leq z \leq .88) = .8106 - .1894 = .6212$

    b. $n = 50$ Within 8 means $175 \leq \bar{x} \leq 191$

$$z = \frac{\bar{x} - \mu}{\sigma / \sqrt{n}} = \frac{8}{50 / \sqrt{50}} = 1.13$$

$P(175 \leq \bar{x} \leq 191) = P(-1.13 \leq z \leq 1.13) = .8708 - .1292 = .7416$

    c. $n = 100$ Within 8 means $175 \leq \bar{x} \leq 191$

$$z = \frac{\bar{x} - \mu}{\sigma / \sqrt{n}} = \frac{8}{50 / \sqrt{100}} = 1.60$$

$P(175 \leq \bar{x} \leq 191) = P(-1.60 \leq z \leq 1.60) = .9452 - .0548 = .8904$

    d. None of the sample sizes in parts (a), (b), and (c) are large enough. The sample size will need to be greater than $n = 100$, which was used in part (c).

30. a. $n / N = 40 / 4000 = .01 < .05$; therefore, the finite population correction factor is not necessary.

    b. With the finite population correction factor

$$\sigma_{\bar{x}} = \sqrt{\frac{N - n}{N - 1}} \frac{\sigma}{\sqrt{n}} = \sqrt{\frac{4000 - 40}{4000 - 1}} \frac{8.2}{\sqrt{40}} = 1.29$$

Without the finite population correction factor

$$\sigma_{\bar{x}} = \sigma / \sqrt{n} = 1.30$$

Including the finite population correction factor provides only a slightly different value for $\sigma_{\bar{x}}$ than when the correction factor is not used.

c. $z = \dfrac{\bar{x} - \mu}{1.30} = \dfrac{2}{1.30} = 1.54 \quad P(z \le 1.54) = .9382$

$P(z < -1.54) = .0618$

Probability = .9382 - .0618 = .8764

31. a. $E(\bar{p}) = p = .40$

b. $\sigma_{\bar{p}} = \sqrt{\dfrac{p(1-p)}{n}} = \sqrt{\dfrac{.40(.60)}{100}} = .0490$

c. Normal distribution with $E(\bar{p}) = .40$ and $\sigma_{\bar{p}} = .0490$

d. It shows the probability distribution for the sample proportion $\bar{p}$.

32. a. $E(\bar{p}) = .40$

$\sigma_{\bar{p}} = \sqrt{\dfrac{p(1-p)}{n}} = \sqrt{\dfrac{.40(.60)}{200}} = .0346$

Within $\pm .03$ means $.37 \le \bar{p} \le .43$

$z = \dfrac{\bar{p} - p}{\sigma_{\bar{p}}} = \dfrac{.03}{.0346} = .87 \quad P(z \le .87) = .8078$

$P(z < -.87) = .1922$

$P(.37 \le \bar{p} \le .43) = .8078 - .1922 = .6156$

b. $z = \dfrac{\bar{p} - p}{\sigma_{\bar{p}}} = \dfrac{.05}{.0346} = 1.44 \quad P(z \le 1.44) = .9251$

$P(z < -1.44) = .0749$

$P(.35 \le \bar{p} \le .45) = .9251 - .0749 = .8502$

33. $\sigma_{\bar{p}} = \sqrt{\dfrac{p(1-p)}{n}}$

$\sigma_{\bar{p}} = \sqrt{\dfrac{(.55)(.45)}{100}} = .0497$

$\sigma_{\bar{p}} = \sqrt{\dfrac{(.55)(.45)}{200}} = .0352$

$\sigma_{\bar{p}} = \sqrt{\dfrac{(.55)(.45)}{500}} = .0222$

$$\sigma_{\bar{p}} = \sqrt{\frac{(.55)(.45)}{1000}} = .0157$$

The standard error of the proportion, $\sigma_{\bar{p}}$, decreases as n increases

34. a. $\sigma_{\bar{p}} = \sqrt{\frac{(.30)(.70)}{100}} = .0458$

Within $\pm .04$ means $.26 \leq \bar{p} \leq .34$

$$z = \frac{\bar{p} - p}{\sigma_{\bar{p}}} = \frac{.04}{.0458} = .87 \quad P(z \leq .87) = .8078$$

$P(z < -.87) = .1922$

$P(.26 \leq \bar{p} \leq .34) = .8078 - .1922 = .6156$

b. $\sigma_{\bar{p}} = \sqrt{\frac{(.30)(.70)}{200}} = .0324$

$$z = \frac{\bar{p} - p}{\sigma_{\bar{p}}} = \frac{.04}{.0324} = 1.23 \quad P(z \leq 1.23) = .8907$$

$P(z < -1.23) = .1093$

$P(.26 \leq \bar{p} \leq .34) = .8907 - .1093 = .7814$

c. $\sigma_{\bar{p}} = \sqrt{\frac{(.30)(.70)}{500}} = .0205$

$$z = \frac{\bar{p} - p}{\sigma_{\bar{p}}} = \frac{.04}{.0205} = 1.95 \quad P(z \leq 1.95) = .9744$$

$P(z < -1.95) = .0256$

$P(.26 \leq \bar{p} \leq .34) = .9744 - .0256 = .9488$

d. $\sigma_{\bar{p}} = \sqrt{\frac{(.30)(.70)}{1000}} = .0145$

$$z = \frac{\bar{p} - p}{\sigma_{\bar{p}}} = \frac{.04}{.0145} = 2.76 \quad P(z \leq 2.76) = .9971$$

$P(z < -2.76) = .0029$

$P(.26 \leq \bar{p} \leq .34) = .9971 - .0029 = .9942$

e. With a larger sample, there is a higher probability $\bar{p}$ will be within $\pm .04$ of the population proportion p.

35. a.

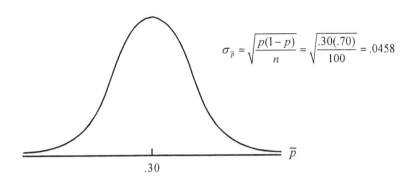

$$\sigma_{\bar{p}} = \sqrt{\frac{p(1-p)}{n}} = \sqrt{\frac{.30(.70)}{100}} = .0458$$

The normal distribution is appropriate because $np = 100(.30) = 30$ and $n(1 - p) = 100(.70) = 70$ are both greater than 5.

b. $P(.20 \le \bar{p} \le .40) = ?$

$$z = \frac{.40 - .30}{.0458} = 2.18 \quad P(z \le 2.18) = .9854$$

$P(z < -2.18) = .0146$

$P(.20 \le \bar{p} \le .40) = .9854 - .0146 = .9708$

c. $P(.25 \le \bar{p} \le .35) = ?$

$$z = \frac{.35 - .30}{.0458} = 1.09 \quad P(z \le 1.09) = .8621$$

$P(z < -1.09) = .1379$

$P(.25 \le \bar{p} \le .35) = .8621 - .1379 = .7242$

36. a. This is a graph of a normal distribution with a mean of $E(\bar{p}) = .55$ and

$$\sigma_{\bar{p}} = \sqrt{\frac{p(1-p)}{n}} = \sqrt{\frac{.55(1-.55)}{200}} = .0352$$

b. Within $\pm .05$ means $.50 \le \bar{p} \le .60$

$$z = \frac{\bar{p} - p}{\sigma_{\bar{p}}} = \frac{.60 - .55}{.0352} = 1.42 \qquad z = \frac{\bar{p} - p}{\sigma_{\bar{p}}} = \frac{.50 - .55}{.0352} = -1.42$$

$P(.50 \le \bar{p} \le .60) = P(-1.42 \le z \le 1.42) = .9222 - .0778 = .8444$

c. This is a graph of a normal distribution with a mean of $E(\bar{p}) = .45$ and

$$\sigma_{\bar{p}} = \sqrt{\frac{p(1-p)}{n}} = \sqrt{\frac{.45(1-.45)}{200}} = .0352$$

d. $\sigma_{\bar{p}} = \sqrt{\frac{p(1-p)}{n}} = \sqrt{\frac{.45(1-.45)}{200}} = .0352$

Within $\pm .05$ means $.40 \le \bar{p} \le .50$

$$z = \frac{\bar{p} - p}{\sigma_{\bar{p}}} = \frac{.50 - .45}{.0352} = 1.42 \qquad\qquad z = \frac{\bar{p} - p}{\sigma_{\bar{p}}} = \frac{.40 - .45}{.0352} = -1.42$$

$P(.40 \le \bar{p} \le .50) = P(-1.42 \le z \le 1.42) = .9222 - .0778 = .8444$

e. No, the probabilities are exactly the same. This is because $\sigma_{\bar{p}}$, the standard error, and the width of the interval are the same in both cases. Notice the formula for computing the standard error. It involves $p(1-p)$. So whenever $p = 1 - p$ the standard error will be the same. In part (b), $p = .45$ and $1 - p = .55$. In part (d), $p = .55$ and $1 - p = .45$.

f. For $n = 400$, $\sigma_{\bar{p}} = \sqrt{\frac{p(1-p)}{n}} = \sqrt{\frac{.55(1-.55)}{400}} = .0249$

Within $\pm .05$ means $.50 \le \bar{p} \le .60$

$$z = \frac{\bar{p} - p}{\sigma_{\bar{p}}} = \frac{.60 - .55}{.0249} = 2.01 \qquad\qquad z = \frac{\bar{p} - p}{\sigma_{\bar{p}}} = \frac{.50 - .55}{.0249} = -2.01$$

$P(.50 \le \bar{p} \le .60) = P(-2.01 \le z \le 2.01) = .9778 - .0222 = .9556$

The probability is larger than in part (b). This is because the larger sample size has reduced the standard error from .0352 to .0249.

37. a. Normal distribution

$E(\bar{p}) = .12$

$$\sigma_{\bar{p}} = \sqrt{\frac{p(1-p)}{n}} = \sqrt{\frac{(.12)(1-.12)}{540}} = .0140$$

b. $z = \frac{\bar{p} - p}{\sigma_{\bar{p}}} = \frac{.03}{.0140} = 2.14 \qquad P(z \le 1.94) = .9838$

$P(z < -2.14) = .0162$

$P(.09 \le \bar{p} \le .15) = .9838 - .0162 = .9676$

c. $z = \dfrac{\bar{p} - p}{\sigma_{\bar{p}}} = \dfrac{.015}{.0140} = 1.07$ $P(z \le 1.07) = .8577$

$P(z < -1.07) = .1423$

$P(.105 \le \bar{p} \le .135) = .8577 - .1423 = .7154$

38. a. It is a normal distribution with

$E(\bar{p}) = .42$

$\sigma_{\bar{p}} = \sqrt{\dfrac{p(1-p)}{n}} = \sqrt{\dfrac{(.42)(.58)}{300}} = .0285$

b. $z = \dfrac{\bar{p} - p}{\sigma_{\bar{p}}} = \dfrac{.03}{.0285} = 1.05$ $P(z \le 1.05) = .8531$

$P(z < -1.05) = .1469$

$P(.39 \le \bar{p} \le .44) = .8531 - .1469 = .7062$

c. $z = \dfrac{\bar{p} - p}{\sigma_{\bar{p}}} = \dfrac{.05}{.0285} = 1.75$ $P(z \le 1.75) = .9599$

$P(z < -1.75) = .0401$

$P(.39 \le \bar{p} \le .44) = .9599 - .0401 = .9198$

d. The probabilities would increase. This is because the increase in the sample size makes the standard error, $\sigma_{\bar{p}}$, smaller.

39. a. Normal distribution with $E(\bar{p}) = p = .75$ and

$\sigma_{\bar{p}} = \sqrt{\dfrac{p(1-p)}{n}} = \sqrt{\dfrac{.75(1-.75)}{450}} = .0204$

b. $z = \dfrac{\bar{p} - p}{\sigma_{\bar{p}}} = \dfrac{.04}{.0204} = 1.96$ $P(z \le 1.96) = .9750$

$P(z < -1.96) = .0250$

$P(.71 \le \bar{p} \le .79) = P(-1.96 \le z \le 1.96) = .9750 - .0275 = .9500$

c. Normal distribution with $E(\bar{p}) = p = .75$ and

$\sigma_{\bar{p}} = \sqrt{\dfrac{p(1-p)}{n}} = \sqrt{\dfrac{.75(1-.75)}{200}} = .0306$

d. $z = \dfrac{\bar{p} - p}{\sqrt{\dfrac{.75(1-.75)}{200}}} = \dfrac{.04}{.0306} = 1.31$ $P(z \leq 1.31) = .9049$

$P(z < -1.31) = .0951$

$P(.71 \leq \bar{p} \leq .79) = P(-1.31 \leq z \leq 1.31) = .9049 - .0951 = .8098$

e. The probability of the sample proportion being within .04 of the population mean was reduced from .9500 to .8098. So there is a gain in precision by increasing the sample size from 200 to 450. If the extra cost of using the larger sample size is not too great, we should probably do so.

40. a. $E(\bar{p}) = .76$

$\sigma_{\bar{p}} = \sqrt{\dfrac{p(1-p)}{n}} = \sqrt{\dfrac{.76(1-.76)}{400}} = .0214$

Normal distribution because $np = 400(.76) = 304$ and $n(1 - p) = 400(.24) = 96$

b. $z = \dfrac{.79 - .76}{.0214} = 1.40$ $P(z \leq 1.40) = .9192$

$P(z < -1.40) = .0808$

$P(.73 \leq \bar{p} \leq .79) = P(-1.40 \leq z \leq 1.40) = .9192 - .0808 = .8384$

c. $\sigma_{\bar{p}} = \sqrt{\dfrac{p(1-p)}{n}} = \sqrt{\dfrac{.76(1-.76)}{750}} = .0156$

$z = \dfrac{.79 - .76}{.0156} = 1.92$ $P(z \leq 1.92) = .9726$

$P(z < -1.92) = .0274$

$P(.73 \leq \bar{p} \leq .79) = P(-1.92 \leq z \leq 1.92) = .9726 - .0274 = .9452$

41. a. $E(\bar{p}) = .17$

$\sigma_{\bar{p}} = \sqrt{\dfrac{p(1-p)}{n}} = \sqrt{\dfrac{(.17)(1-.17)}{800}} = .0133$

Distribution is approximately normal because $np = 800(.17) = 136 > 5$ and $n(1 - p) = 800(.83) = 664 > 5$

b. $z = \dfrac{.19 - .17}{.0133} = 1.51$ $P(z \leq 1.51) = .9345$

$P(z < -1.51) = .0655$

$P(.15 \leq \bar{p} \leq .19) = P(-1.51 \leq z \leq 1.51) = .9345 - .0655 = .8690$

c. $\quad \sigma_{\bar{p}} = \sqrt{\dfrac{p(1-p)}{n}} = \sqrt{\dfrac{(.17)(1-.17)}{1600}} = .0094$

$z = \dfrac{.19 - .17}{.0094} = 2.13 \qquad P(z \le 2.13) = .9834$

$P(z < -2.13) = .0166$

$P(.15 \le \bar{p} \le .19) = P(-2.13 \le z \le 2.13) = .9834 - .0166 = .9668$

42. The random numbers corresponding to the first seven universities selected are

$\qquad$ 122, 99, 25, 55, 115, 102, 61

The third, fourth and fifth columns of Table 7.1 were needed to find 7 random numbers of 133 or less without duplicate numbers.

Author's note: The universities identified are: Clarkson U. (122), U. of Arizona (99), UCLA (25), U. of Maryland (55), U. of New Hampshire (115), Florida State U. (102), Clemson U. (61).

43. a. With $n = 100$, we can approximate the sampling distribution with a normal distribution having

$E(\bar{x}) = 8086$

$\sigma_{\bar{x}} = \dfrac{\sigma}{\sqrt{n}} = \dfrac{2500}{\sqrt{100}} = 250$

b. $\quad z = \dfrac{\bar{x} - \mu}{\sigma / \sqrt{n}} = \dfrac{200}{2500 / \sqrt{100}} = .80 \qquad P(z \le .80) = .7881$

$P(z < -.80) = .2119$

$P(7886 \le \bar{x} \le 8286) = P(-.80 \le z \le .80) = .7881 - .2119 = .5762$

The probability that the sample mean will be within \$200 of the population mean is .5762.

c. At 9000, $z = \dfrac{9000 - 8086}{2500 / \sqrt{100}} = 3.66$

$P(\bar{x} \ge 9000) = P(z \ge 3.66) \approx 0$

Yes, the research firm should be questioned. A sample mean this large is extremely unlikely (almost 0 probability) if a simple random sample is taken from a population with a mean of \$8086.

44. a. Normal distribution with

$E(\bar{x}) = 406$

$\sigma_{\bar{x}} = \dfrac{\sigma}{\sqrt{n}} = \dfrac{80}{\sqrt{64}} = 10$

b. $z = \dfrac{\bar{x} - \mu}{\sigma / \sqrt{n}} = \dfrac{15}{80 / \sqrt{64}} = 1.50$ $P(z \leq 1.50) = .9332$

$P(z < -1.50) = .0668$

$P(391 \leq \bar{x} \leq 421) = P(-1.50 \leq z \leq 1.50) = .9332 - .0668 = .8664$

c. At $\bar{x} = 380$, $z = \dfrac{\bar{x} - \mu}{\sigma / \sqrt{n}} = \dfrac{380 - 406}{80 / \sqrt{64}} = -2.60$

$P(\bar{x} \leq 380) = P(z \leq -2.60) = .0047$

Yes, this is an unusually low performing group of 64 stores. The probability of a sample mean annual sales per square foot of $380 or less is only .0047.

45. With $n = 60$ the central limit theorem allows us to conclude the sampling distribution is approximately normal.

a. With a mean base rate for the fare of $89 and a mean of $39 for additional charges, the population mean total cost per flight is $\mu = \$128$.

b. This means $118 \leq \bar{x} \leq 138$

At $\bar{x} = 138$, $z = \dfrac{138 - 128}{40 / \sqrt{60}} = 1.94$ $P(z \leq 1.94) = .9738$

$P(z < -1.94) = .0262$

$P(118 \leq \bar{x} \leq 138) = P(-1.94 \leq z \leq 1.94) = .9738 - .0262 = .9476$

c. This means $123 \leq \bar{x} \leq 133$

At $\bar{x} = 133$, $z = \dfrac{133 - 128}{40 / \sqrt{60}} = .97$ $P(z \leq .97) = .8340$

$P(z < -.97) = .1660$

$P(123 \leq \bar{x} \leq 133) = P(-.97 \leq z \leq .97) = .8340 - .1660 = .6680$

46. $\mu = 27,175$ $\sigma = 7400$

a. $\sigma_{\bar{x}} = 7400 / \sqrt{60} = 955$

b. $z = \dfrac{\bar{x} - \mu}{\sigma_{\bar{x}}} = \dfrac{0}{955} = 0$

$P(\bar{x} > 27,175) = P(z > 0) = .50$

Note: This could have been answered easily without any calculations ; 27,175 is the expected value of the sampling distribution of $\bar{x}$.

c. $z = \dfrac{\bar{x} - \mu}{\sigma_{\bar{x}}} = \dfrac{1000}{955} = 1.05$ $P(z \leq 1.05) = .8531$

$P(z < -1.05) = .1469$

$P(26,175 \leq \bar{x} \leq 28,175) = P(-1.05 \leq z \leq 1.05) = .8531 - .1469 = .7062$

d. $\sigma_{\bar{x}} = 7400 / \sqrt{100} = 740$

$z = \dfrac{\bar{x} - \mu}{\sigma_{\bar{x}}} = \dfrac{1000}{740} = 1.35$ $P(z \leq 1.35) = .9115$

$P(z < -1.35) = .0885$

$P(26,175 \leq \bar{x} \leq 28,175) = P(-1.35 \leq z \leq 1.35) = .9115 - .0885 = .8230$

47. a. $\sigma_{\bar{x}} = \sqrt{\dfrac{N-n}{N-1}} \dfrac{\sigma}{\sqrt{n}}$

$N = 2000$

$\sigma_{\bar{x}} = \sqrt{\dfrac{2000-50}{2000-1}} \dfrac{144}{\sqrt{50}} = 20.11$

$N = 5000$

$\sigma_{\bar{x}} = \sqrt{\dfrac{5000-50}{5000-1}} \dfrac{144}{\sqrt{50}} = 20.26$

$N = 10,000$

$\sigma_{\bar{x}} = \sqrt{\dfrac{10,000-50}{10,000-1}} \dfrac{144}{\sqrt{50}} = 20.31$

Note: With $n / N \leq .05$ for all three cases, common statistical practice would be to ignore the finite population correction factor and use $\sigma_{\bar{x}} = \dfrac{144}{\sqrt{50}} = 20.36$ for each case.

b. $N = 2000$

$z = \dfrac{25}{20.11} = 1.24$ $P(z \leq 1.24) = .8925$

$P(z < -1.24) = .1075$

Probability $= P(-1.24 \leq z \leq 1.24) = .8925 - .1075 = .7850$

$N = 5000$

$$z = \frac{25}{20.26} = 1.23 \quad P(z \leq 1.23) = .8907$$

$P(z < -1.23) = .1093$

Probability $= P(-1.23 \leq z \leq 1.23) = .8907 - .1093 = .7814$

$N = 10,000$

$$z = \frac{25}{20.31} = 1.23 \quad P(z \leq 1.23) = .8907$$

$P(z < -1.23) = .1093$

Probability $= P(-1.23 \leq z \leq 1.23) = .8907 - .1093 = .7814$

All probabilities are approximately .78 indicating that a sample of size 50 will work well for all 3 firms.

48. a. $\quad \sigma_{\bar{x}} = \dfrac{\sigma}{\sqrt{n}} = \dfrac{500}{\sqrt{n}} = 20$

$\sqrt{n} = 500/20 = 25$ and $n = (25)^2 = 625$

b. For ± 25,

$$z = \frac{25}{20} = 1.25 \qquad P(z \leq 1.25) = .8944$$

$P(z < -1.25) = .1056$

Probability $= P(-1.25 \leq z \leq 1.25) = .8944 - .1056 = .7888$

49. Sampling distribution of $\bar{x}$

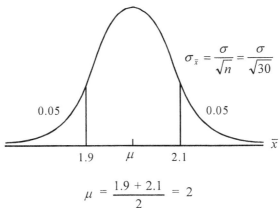

$$\mu = \frac{1.9 + 2.1}{2} = 2$$

The area below $\bar{x} = 2.1$ must be $1 - .05 = .95$. An area of .95 in the standard normal table shows $z = 1.645$.

Thus,

$$z = \frac{2.1 - 2.0}{\sigma/\sqrt{30}} = 1.645$$

Solve for σ.

$$\sigma = \frac{(.1)\sqrt{30}}{1.645} = .33$$

50. $p = .15$

a. This is the graph of a normal distribution with $E(\bar{p}) = p = .15$ and

$$\sigma_{\bar{p}} = \sqrt{\frac{p(1-p)}{n}} = \sqrt{\frac{.15(1-.15)}{240}} = .0230$$

b. Within $\pm .04$ means $.11 \leq \bar{p} \leq .19$

$$z = \frac{\bar{p} - p}{\sigma_{\bar{p}}} = \frac{.19 - .15}{.0230} = 1.74 \qquad z = \frac{.11 - .15}{.0230} = -1.74$$

$$P(.11 \leq \bar{p} \leq .19) = P(-1.74 \leq z \leq 1.74) = .9591 - .0409 = .9182$$

c. Within $\pm .02$ means $.13 \leq \bar{p} \leq .17$

$$z = \frac{\bar{p} - p}{\sigma_{\bar{p}}} = \frac{.17 - .15}{.0230} = .87 \qquad z = \frac{.13 - .15}{.0230} = -.87$$

$$P(.13 \leq \bar{p} \leq .17) = P(-.87 \leq z \leq .87) = .8078 - .1922 = .6156$$

51. $$\sigma_{\bar{p}} = \sqrt{\frac{p(1-p)}{n}} = \sqrt{\frac{(.40)(.60)}{400}} = .0245$$

$$P(\bar{p} \geq .375) = ?$$

$$z = \frac{.375 - .40}{.0245} = -1.02 \quad P(z < -1.02) = .1539$$

$$P(\bar{p} \geq .375) = 1 - .1539 = .8461$$

52. a. $$\sigma_{\bar{p}} = \sqrt{\frac{p(1-p)}{n}} = \sqrt{\frac{(.40)(1-.40)}{380}} = .0251$$

Within $\pm .04$ means $.36 \leq \bar{p} \leq .44$

$$z = \frac{.44 - .40}{.0251} = 1.59 \qquad z = \frac{.36 - .40}{.0251} = -1.59$$

$$P(.36 \le \bar{p} \le .44) = P(-1.59 \le z \le 1.59) = .9441 - .0559 = .8882$$

b.   We want $P(\bar{p} \ge .45)$

$$z = \frac{\bar{p} - p}{\sigma_{\bar{p}}} = \frac{.45 - .40}{.0251} = 1.99$$

$$P(\bar{p} \ge .45) = P(z \ge 1.99) = 1 - .9767 = .0233$$

53.   a.   Normal distribution with $E(\bar{p}) = .15$ and

$$\sigma_{\bar{p}} = \sqrt{\frac{p(1-p)}{n}} = \sqrt{\frac{(.15)(.85)}{150}} = .0292$$

b. $P(.12 \le \bar{p} \le .18) = ?$

$$z = \frac{.18 - .15}{.0292} = 1.03 \qquad P(z \le 1.03) = .8485$$

$$P(z < -1.03) = .1515$$

$$P(.12 \le \bar{p} \le .18) = P(-1.03 \le z \le 1.03) = .8485 - .1515 = .6970$$

54.   a. $\sigma_{\bar{p}} = \sqrt{\dfrac{p(1-p)}{n}} = \sqrt{\dfrac{.25(.75)}{n}} = .0625$

Solve for n

$$n = \frac{.25(.75)}{(.0625)^2} = 48$$

b.   Normal distribution with $E(\bar{p}) = .25$ and $\sigma_{\bar{p}} = .0625$

(Note: $(48)(.25) = 12 > 5$, and $(48)(.75) = 36 > 5$)

c. $P(\bar{p} \ge .30) = ?$

$$z = \frac{.30 - .25}{.0625} = .80 \qquad P(z \le .80) = .7881$$

$$P(\bar{p} \ge .30) = 1 - .7881 = .2119$$

Chapter 8
Interval Estimation

Learning Objectives

1. Know how to construct and interpret an interval estimate of a population mean and / or a population proportion.

2. Understand and be able to compute the margin of error.

3. Learn about the t distribution and its use in constructing an interval estimate when σ is unknown for a population mean.

4. Be able to determine the size of a simple random sample necessary to estimate a population mean and/or a population proportion with a specified margin of error.

5. Know the definition of the following terms:

    confidence interval   margin of error
    confidence coefficient   degrees of freedom
    confidence level

Solutions:

1. a. $\sigma_{\bar{x}} = \sigma / \sqrt{n} = 5/\sqrt{40} = .79$

    b.   At 95%, $z\sigma / \sqrt{n} = 1.96(5/\sqrt{40}) = 1.55$

2. a. $32 \pm 1.645 \ (6/\sqrt{50})$

         32 ± 1.4 or 30.6 to 33.4

    b. $32 \pm 1.96 \ (6/\sqrt{50})$

         32 ± 1.66 or 30.34 to 33.66

    c. $32 \pm 2.576 \ (6/\sqrt{50})$

         32 ± 2.19 or 29.81 to 34.19

3. a. $80 \pm 1.96 \ (15/\sqrt{60})$

         80 ± 3.8 or 76.2 to 83.8

    b. $80 \pm 1.96 \ (15/\sqrt{120})$

         80 ± 2.68 or 77.32 to 82.68

    c.   Larger sample provides a smaller margin of error.

4.   Sample mean $\bar{x} = \dfrac{160 + 152}{2} = 156$

         Margin of Error $= 160 - 156 = 4$

         $1.96(\sigma / \sqrt{n}) = 4$

         $\sqrt{n} = 1.96\sigma / 4 = 1.96(15)/4 = 7.35$

         $n = (7.35)^2 = 54$

5. a.   With 99% confidence $z_{\alpha/2} = z_{.005} = 2.576$

         Margin of Error $= 2.576\sigma / \sqrt{n} = 2.576(6/\sqrt{64}) = 1.93$

    b.   Confidence Interval: 21.52 ± 1.93 or 19.59 to 23.45

6. A 95% confidence interval is of the form

$$\bar{x} \pm z_{.025}(\sigma / \sqrt{n})$$

Using Excel or Minitab, and the webfile TravelTax, the sample mean is $\bar{x} = 40.31$ and the

sample size is $n = 400$. The sample-standard deviation $\sigma = 8.5$ is known. The confidence interval is

$$40.31 \pm 1.96(8.5 / \sqrt{200})$$

40.31 ± 1.18 or 39.13 to 41.49

7. Margin of error $= z_{.025}(\sigma / \sqrt{n})$

$z_{.025} = 1.96 \qquad \sigma = \$600 \qquad n = 50$

Margin of error $= 1.96(600 / \sqrt{50}) = 166.31$

A larger sample size would be needed to reduce the margin of error to \$150 or less. Section 8.3 can be used to show that the sample size would need to be increased to $n = 62$.

$$1.96(600 / \sqrt{n}) = 150$$

Solving for n shows $n = 62$

8. a. Since n is small, an assumption that the population is at least approximately normal is required so that the sampling distribution of $\bar{x}$ can be approximated by a normal distribution.

b. Margin of error: $z_{.025}(\sigma / \sqrt{n}) = 1.96(5.5 / \sqrt{10}) = 3.41$

c. Margin of error: $z_{.005}(\sigma / \sqrt{n}) = 2.576(5.5 / \sqrt{10}) = 4.48$

9. $\bar{x} \pm z_{.025}(\sigma / \sqrt{n})$

$33.5 \pm 1.96(9 / \sqrt{40})$

33.5 ± 2.8 or 30.7 to 36.3 hours

10. a. $\bar{x} \pm z_{\alpha/2} \dfrac{\sigma}{\sqrt{n}}$

$3486 \pm 1.645(650 / \sqrt{120})$

3486 ± 98 or \$3388 to \$3584

b. $3486 \pm 1.96(650 / \sqrt{120})$

3486 ± 116 or \$3370 to \$3602

8 - 3

c. $3486 \pm 2.576 \, (650 / \sqrt{120})$

3486 ± 153 or $3333 to $3639

d. The confidence interval gets wider as we increase our confidence level. We need a wider interval to be more confident that the interval will contain the population mean.

11. a. .025

b. $1 - .10 = .90$

c. .05

d. .01

e. $1 - 2(.025) = .95$

f. $1 - 2(.05) = .90$

12. a. 2.179

b. -1.676

c. 2.457

d. Use .05 column, -1.708 and 1.708

e. Use .025 column, -2.014 and 2.014

13. a. $\bar{x} = \dfrac{\Sigma x_i}{n} = \dfrac{80}{8} = 10$

b.

x_i	$(x_i - \bar{x})$	$(x_i - \bar{x})^2$
10	0	0
8	-2	4
12	2	4
15	5	25
13	3	9
11	1	1
6	-4	16
5	-5	25
		84

$$s = \sqrt{\frac{\Sigma(x_i - \bar{x})^2}{n-1}} = \sqrt{\frac{84}{7}} = 3.464$$

c. $t_{.025}(s/\sqrt{n}) = 2.365(3.464/\sqrt{8}) = 2.9$

d. $\bar{x} \pm t_{.025}(s/\sqrt{n})$

10 ± 2.9 or 7.1 to 12.9

14. $\bar{x} \pm t_{\alpha/2}(s/\sqrt{n})$ $df = 53$

   a. $22.5 \pm 1.674\,(4.4/\sqrt{54})$

      22.5 ± 1 or 21.5 to 23.5

   b. $22.5 \pm 2.006\,(4.4/\sqrt{54})$

      22.5 ± 1.2 or 21.3 to 23.7

   c. $22.5 \pm 2.672\,(4.4/\sqrt{54})$

      22.5 ± 1.6 or 20.9 to 24.1

   d. As the confidence level increases, there is a larger margin of error and a wider confidence interval.

15. $\bar{x} \pm t_{\alpha/2}(s/\sqrt{n})$

   90% confidence $df = 64$ $t_{.05} = 1.669$

   $19.5 \pm 1.669\,(5.2/\sqrt{65})$

   19.5 ± 1.08 or 18.42 to 20.58

   95% confidence $df = 64$ $t_{.025} = 1.998$

   $19.5 \pm 1.998\,(5.2/\sqrt{65})$

   19.5 ± 1.29 or 18.21 to 20.79

16. a. Using Minitab or Excel, $\bar{x} = 9.7063$ and $s = 7.9805$
      The sample mean years to maturity is 9.7063 years with a standard deviation of 7.9805.

   b. $\bar{x} \pm t_{.025}(s/\sqrt{n})$ $df = 39$ $t_{.025} = 2.023$

      $9.7063 \pm 2.023\,(7.9805/\sqrt{40})$

      9.7063 ± 2.5527 or 7.1536 to 12.2590

      The 95% confidence interval for the population mean years to maturity is 7.1536 to 12.2590 years.

   c. Using Minitab or Excel, $\bar{x} = 3.8854$ and $s = 1.6194$

      The sample mean yield on corporate bonds is 3.8854% with a standard deviation of 1.6194.

   d. $\bar{x} \pm t_{.025}(s/\sqrt{n})$ $df = 39$ $t_{.025} = 2.023$

      $3.8854 \pm 2.023\,(1.6194/\sqrt{40})$

      $3.8854 \pm .5180$ or 3.3674 to 4.4034

The 95% confidence interval for the population mean yield is 3.3674 to 4.4034 percent.

17. Using Minitab or Excel, $\bar{x} = 6.34$ and $s = 2.163$

$$\bar{x} \pm t_{.025}(s/\sqrt{n}) \qquad df = 49 \qquad t_{.025} = 2.010$$

$$6.34 \pm 2.010\,(2.163/\sqrt{50})$$

$$6.34 \pm .61 \text{ or } 5.73 \text{ to } 6.95$$

18. For the JobSearch data set,

$$\bar{x} = 22 \text{ and } s = 11.8862$$

a. $\bar{x} = 22$ weeks

b. margin of error $= t_{.025}s/\sqrt{n} = 2.023(11.8862)/\sqrt{40} = 3.8020$

c. The 95% confidence interval is $\bar{x} \pm$ margin of error

22 ± 3.8020 or 18.20 to 25.80

d. Skewness = 1.0062, data are skewed to the right. Use a larger sample next time.

19. a. $t_{.025}(s/\sqrt{n}) \qquad df = 44$

$t_{.025} = 2.015 \qquad s = 65$

$2.015\,(65/\sqrt{45}) = 19.52$ or approximately $20

b. $\bar{x} \pm t_{.025}(s/\sqrt{n})$

273 ± 20 or 253 to 293

c. At 95% confidence, the population mean is between $253 and $293. This is definitely above the $229 level of 2 years ago. Hotel room rates are increasing.

The point estimate of the increase is $273 - $229 = $44 or 19%.

20. $\bar{x} = \Sigma x_i / n = 22$ minutes

$$s = \sqrt{\frac{\Sigma(x_i - \bar{x})^2}{n-1}} = 1.12 \text{ minutes}$$

$$x \pm t_{.025}(s/\sqrt{n}) \quad df = 19$$

$$22.00 \pm 2.093\,(1.12/\sqrt{20})$$

$$22.00 \pm .52 \text{ or } 21.48 \text{ to } 22.52 \text{ minutes}$$

21.　　$\bar{x} = \dfrac{\Sigma x_i}{n} = \dfrac{2600}{20} = 130$ liters of alcoholic beverages

$s = \sqrt{\dfrac{\Sigma (x_i - \bar{x})^2}{n-1}} = \sqrt{\dfrac{81244}{20-1}} = 65.39$

$t_{.025} = 2.093$ 　　　　　　　$df = 19$

95% confidence interval: $\bar{x} \pm t_{.025}(s/\sqrt{n})$

$130 \pm 2.093\,(65.39/\sqrt{20})$

130 ± 30.60　　or 99.40 to 160.60　liters per year

22. a. 　$\bar{x} = \dfrac{\Sigma x_i}{n} = \dfrac{272,625}{25} = 10,905$

The point estimate of the population mean ticket sales revenue per theater is $10,905.

$s = \sqrt{\dfrac{\Sigma (x_i - \bar{x})^2}{n-1}} = \sqrt{\dfrac{376,760,400}{25-1}} = 3962.11$

95% confidence interval: $\bar{x} \pm t_{.025}(s/\sqrt{n})$ with $df = 24$　$t_{.025} = 2.064$

$$10,905 \pm 2.064\,\dfrac{3962.11}{\sqrt{25}}$$
$$10,905 \pm 1636$$

The 95% confidence interval for the population mean is $9,269 to $12,541. We are 95% confident that the population mean three-day tickets sales revenue per theater is between $9,269 and $12,541.

b. 　Mean number of customers per theater = 10,905/7.16 = 1523

c. 　Total number of customers = 3118(1523) = 4,748,714

Total box office ticket sales for the three-day weekend = 3118(10,905) $\approx$ $34 million

23.　　$n = \dfrac{z_{.025}^2 \sigma^2}{E^2} = \dfrac{(1.96)^2 (40)^2}{10^2} = 61.47$　　Use $n = 62$

24. a. 　Planning value of σ = Range/4 = 36/4 = 9

b. 　$n = \dfrac{z_{.025}^2 \sigma^2}{E^2} = \dfrac{(1.96)^2 (9)^2}{3^2} = 34.57$　　Use $n = 35$

c. 　$n = \dfrac{(1.96)^2 (9)^2}{2^2} = 77.79$　　Use $n = 78$

25. $$n = \frac{(1.96)^2 (6.84)^2}{(1.5)^2} = 79.88 \quad \text{Use } n = 80$$

$$n = \frac{(1.645)^2 (6.84)^2}{2^2} = 31.65 \quad \text{Use } n = 32$$

26. a. $$n = \frac{z_{.025}^2 \sigma^2}{E^2} = \frac{(1.96)^2 (.25)^2}{(.10)^2} = 24.01 \quad \text{Use } 25.$$

   If the normality assumption for the population appears questionable, this should be adjusted upward to at least 30.

   b. $$n = \frac{(1.96)^2 (.25)^2}{(.07)^2} = 49 \quad \text{Use } 49 \text{ to guarantee a margin of error no greater than .07. However, the US}$$

   EIA may choose to increase the sample size to a round number of 50

   c. $$n = \frac{(1.96)^2 (.25)^2}{(.05)^2} = 96.04 \quad \text{Use } 97$$

   For reporting purposes, the US EIA might decide to round up to a sample size of 100.

27. Planning value $\sigma = \dfrac{45,000 - 30,000}{4} = 3750$

   a. $$n = \frac{z_{.025}^2 \sigma^2}{E^2} = \frac{(1.96)^2 (3750)^2}{(500)^2} = 216.09 \quad \text{Use } n = 217$$

   b. $$n = \frac{(1.96)^2 (3750)^2}{(200)^2} = 1350.56 \quad \text{Use } n = 1351$$

   c. $$n = \frac{(1.96)^2 (3750)^2}{(100)^2} = 5402.25 \quad \text{Use } n = 5403$$

   d. Sampling 5403 college graduates to obtain the \$100 margin of error would be viewed as too expensive and too much effort by most researchers.

28. a. $$n = \frac{z_{\alpha/2}^2 \sigma^2}{E^2} = \frac{(1.645)^2 (1100)^2}{(100)^2} = 327.43 \quad \text{Use } n = 328$$

   b. $$n = \frac{(1.96)^2 (1100)^2}{(100)^2} = 464.83 \quad \text{Use } n = 465$$

   c. $$n = \frac{(2.576)^2 (1100)^2}{(100)^2} = 802.93 \quad \text{Use } n = 803$$

d. The sample size gets larger as the confidence is increased. We would not recommend 99% confidence. The sample size must be increased by 137 = 465 - 328 to go from 90% to 95%. This may be reasonable. However, increasing the sample size by 338 = 803 - 465 to go from 95% to 99% would probably be viewed as too expensive and time consuming for the 4% gain in confidence.

29. a. 75 seconds is 1.25 minutes, so

$$n = \frac{(1.96)^2 (4)^2}{(1.25)^2} = 39.3380 \quad \text{Use } n = 40$$

   b. $n = \dfrac{(1.96)^2 (4)^2}{1^2} = 61.4656 \quad \text{Use } n = 62$

30. Planning value from previous study: $\sigma = 2000$

$$n = \frac{z_{.025}^2 \sigma^2}{E^2} = \frac{(1.96)^2 (2000)^2}{(100)^2} = 1536.64$$

Use $n = 1537$ to guarantee the margin of error will not exceed 100.

31. a. $\bar{p} = 100/400 = .25$

   b. $\sqrt{\dfrac{\bar{p}(1-\bar{p})}{n}} = \sqrt{\dfrac{.25(.75)}{400}} = .0217$

   c. $\bar{p} \pm z_{.025} \sqrt{\dfrac{\bar{p}(1-\bar{p})}{n}}$

   .25 $\pm$ 1.96 (.0217)

   .25 $\pm$ .0424 or .2076 to .2924

32. a. .70 $\pm$ 1.645 $\sqrt{\dfrac{.70(.30)}{800}}$

   .70 $\pm$ .0267 or .6733 to .7267

   b. .70 $\pm$ 1.96 $\sqrt{\dfrac{.70(.30)}{800}}$

   .70 $\pm$ .0318 or .6682 to .7318

33. $n = \dfrac{z_{.025}^2 p^*(1-p^*)}{E^2} = \dfrac{(1.96)^2 (.35)(.65)}{(.05)^2} = 349.59 \quad \text{Use } n = 350$

34. Use planning value $p^* = .50$

$$n = \frac{(1.96)^2 (.50)(.50)}{(.03)^2} = 1067.11 \quad \text{Use } n = 1068$$

35. a. $\bar{p} = 1760/2000 = .88$

    b. Margin of Error

    $$z_{.05}\sqrt{\frac{\bar{p}(1-\bar{p})}{n}} = 1.645\sqrt{\frac{.88(1-.88)}{2000}} = .0120$$

    c. Confidence interval:

    $.88 \pm .0120$

    or .868 to .892

    d. Margin of Error

    $$z_{.025}\sqrt{\frac{\bar{p}(1-\bar{p})}{n}} = 1.96\sqrt{\frac{.88(1-.88)}{2000}} = .0142$$

    95% Confidence Interval

    $.88 \pm .0142$ or .8658 to .8942

36. a. $\bar{p} = 46/200 = .23$

    b. $\sqrt{\frac{\bar{p}(1-\bar{p})}{n}} = \sqrt{\frac{.23(1-.23)}{200}} = .0298$

    $\bar{p} \pm z_{.025}\sqrt{\frac{\bar{p}(1-\bar{p})}{n}}$

    $.23 \pm 1.96(.0298)$

    $.23 \pm .0584$ or .1716 to .2884

37. a. $\bar{p} = 240/1000 = .24$

    b. Margin of error: $z_{.025}\sqrt{\frac{\bar{p}(1-\bar{p})}{n}} = 1.96\sqrt{\frac{.24(1-.24)}{1000}} = .0265$

    c. $\bar{p} \pm .0265$

    Confidence Interval: $.24 \pm .0265$ or .2135 to .2665

    d. $\bar{p} = 530/1000 = .53$

    $$z_{.025}\sqrt{\frac{\bar{p}(1-\bar{p})}{n}} = 1.96\sqrt{\frac{.53(1-.53)}{1000}} = .0309$$

    Confidence Interval; $.53 \pm .0309$ or .4991 to .5609

e. Part (c) margin of error = .0265   Part (d) margin of error = .0309

The confidence interval in part (c) has the smaller margin of error. This is because $\bar{p}$ is smaller.

38. a. $\bar{p} = 29 / 162 = .1790$

b. $\bar{p} = 104 / 162 = .6420$

Margin of error $= 1.96\sqrt{\dfrac{\bar{p}(1-\bar{p})}{n}} = 1.96\sqrt{\dfrac{(.642)(.358)}{162}} = .0738$

Confidence interval: $.6420 \pm .0738$ or .5682 to .7158

c. $n = \dfrac{1.96^2(.642)(.358)}{(.05)^2} = 353.18$ Use $n = 354$

39. a. $n = \dfrac{z_{.025}^2\, p^*(1-p^*)}{E^2} = \dfrac{(1.96)^2(.156)(1-.156)}{(.03)^2} = 562$

b. $n = \dfrac{z_{.005}^2\, p^*(1-p^*)}{E^2} = \dfrac{(2.576)^2(.156)(1-.156)}{(.03)^2} = 970.77$ Use 971

40. Margin of error: $z_{.025}\sqrt{\dfrac{\bar{p}(1-\bar{p})}{n}} = 1.96\sqrt{\dfrac{.52(1-.52)}{800}} = .0346$

95% Confidence interval: $\bar{p} \pm .0346$

$.52 \pm .0346$ or .4854 to .5546

41. a. Margin of error $= z_{.025}\sqrt{\dfrac{\bar{p}(1-\bar{p})}{n}} = 1.96\sqrt{\dfrac{.87(1-.87)}{1200}} = .0190$

Interval estimate: $.87 \pm .0190$ or .851 to .889

b. Margin of error $= z_{.025}\sqrt{\dfrac{\bar{p}(1-\bar{p})}{n}} = 1.96\sqrt{\dfrac{.75(1-.75)}{1200}} = .0245$

Interval estimate: $.75 \pm .0245$ or .7255 to .7745

c. The margin of error is larger in part (b). This is because the sample proportion is closer to .50 in part (b) than in part (a). This also leads to a larger interval estimate in part (b).

42. a. $\sqrt{\dfrac{p^*(1-p^*)}{n}} = \sqrt{\dfrac{.50(1-.50)}{491}} = .0226$

$z_{.025}\sqrt{\dfrac{p^*(1-p^*)}{n}} = 1.96(.0226) = .0442$

b. $n = \dfrac{z_{.025}^2 p^*(1-p^*)}{E^2}$

September $n = \dfrac{1.96^2(.50)(1-.50)}{.04^2} = 600.25$ Use 601

October $n = \dfrac{1.96^2(.50)(1-.50)}{.03^2} = 1067.11$ Use 1068

November $n = \dfrac{1.96^2(.50)(1-.50)}{.02^2} = 2401$

Pre-Election $n = \dfrac{1.96^2(.50)(1-.50)}{.01^2} = 9604$

43. a. Margin of Error $= z_{\alpha/2}\sqrt{\dfrac{\overline{p}(1-\overline{p})}{n}} = 1.96\sqrt{\dfrac{(.53)(.47)}{1500}} = .0253$

   95% Confidence Interval: .53 ± .0253 or .5047 to .5553

   b. Margin of Error $= 1.96\sqrt{\dfrac{(.31)(.69)}{1500}} = .0234$

   95% Confidence Interval: .31 ± .0234 or .2866 to .3334

   c. Margin of Error $= 1.96\sqrt{\dfrac{(.05)(.95)}{1500}} = .0110$

   95% Confidence Interval: .05 ± .0110 or .039 to .061

   d. The margin of error decreases as $\overline{p}$ gets smaller. If the margin of error for all of the interval estimates must be less than a given value (say .03), an estimate of the largest proportion should be used as a planning value. Using $p^* = .50$ as a planning value guarantees that the margin of error for all the interval estimates will be small enough.

44. a. Margin of error: $z_{.025}\dfrac{\sigma}{\sqrt{n}} = 1.96\dfrac{15}{\sqrt{54}} = 4.00$

   b. Confidence interval: $\overline{x} \pm$ margin of error

   33.77 ± 4.00 or \$29.77 to \$37.77

45. a. $\overline{x} \pm t_{.025}(s/\sqrt{n})$ $df = 63$ $t_{.025} = 1.998$

   $252.45 \pm 1.998(74.50/\sqrt{64})$

   252.45 ± 18.61 or \$233.84 to \$271.06

b. Yes. the lower limit for the population mean at Niagara Falls is $233.84 which is greater than $215.60.

46. a. Margin of error = $t_{.025}(s/\sqrt{n})$

$df = 79$ $t_{.025} = 1.990$ $s = 550$

$1.990(550/\sqrt{80}) = 122$

b. $\bar{x} \pm$ margin of error

1873 ± 122 or $1751 to $1995

c. As of March, 2008, 92 million Americans were of age 50 and over

Estimate of total expenditures = 92(1873) = 172,316

In dollars, we estimate that $172,316 million dollars are spent annually by Americans of age 50 and over on restaurants and carryout food.

d. We would expect the median to be less than the mean of $1873. The few individuals that spend much more than the average cause the mean to be larger than the median. This is typical for data of this type.

47. a. From the sample of 300 Russians, the proportion who smoke is $\bar{p} = 120/300 = .40$. This is our point estimate of the proportion for the population.

The margin of error is

$$\text{Margin of error} = z_{.025}\sqrt{\frac{\bar{p}(1-\bar{p})}{n}} = 1.96\sqrt{\frac{.40(1-.40)}{300}} = .0554$$

95% Confidence Interval: $.40 \pm .0554$ or .3446 to .4554

b. From the sample of 300 Russians, use Excel or Minitab to find that the sample mean annual consumption (number of cigarettes) is $\bar{x} = 2786$. Thus, our point estimate of the population mean annual per capita consumption of cigarettes is 2786.

Using Excel or Minitab, we find that the sample standard deviation is $s = 3929$. Therefore,

$$\text{Margin of error} = t_{.025}\frac{s}{\sqrt{n}} = 1.96\frac{3929}{\sqrt{300}} = 445$$

95% Confidence Interval: 2786 ± 445 or 2341 to 3231

c. From the sample we see that 120 Russians smoke. The annual consumption per person for those who smoke is given by $\bar{x} = 835800/120 = 6965$. With 365 days in a year, an estimate of the number of cigarettes smoked per day by those Russians who smoke is 6965/365 = 19. A cigarette pack holds 20 cigarettes. So, the typical Russian smoker smokes almost a pack a day.

48. a. Using Excel or Minitab shows that the sample mean and sample standard deviation are

$$\bar{x} = 773 \text{ and } s = 738.3835$$

$$\text{Margin of error} = t_{.05}\left(\frac{s}{\sqrt{n}}\right) = 1.645\left(\frac{738.3835}{\sqrt{400}}\right) = 60.73$$

90% Confidence Interval: 773 ± 60.73 or \$712.27 to \$833.73

b. Using Excel or Minitab shows that the sample mean and sample standard deviation are

$$\bar{x} = 187 \text{ and } s = 178.6207$$

$$\text{Margin of error} = t_{.05}\left(\frac{s}{\sqrt{n}}\right) = 1.645\left(\frac{178.6207}{\sqrt{400}}\right) = 14.69$$

90% Confidence Interval: 187 ± 14.69 or \$172.31 to \$201.69

c. There were 136 employees who had no prescription medication cost for the year.

$$\bar{p} = 136 / 400 = .34$$

d. The margin of error in part (a) is 60.73; the margin of error in part (c) is 14.69. The margin of error in part (a) is larger because the sample standard deviation in part (a) is larger. The sample size and confidence level are the same in both parts.

49. a. Using Excel or Minitab: $\bar{x} = 66.93$

The amount of playing time is approximately 11 minutes. So the time standing around is over 6 times as much. You may find this difference surprising; the authors did.

b. Using Excel or Minitab: $s = 4.4943$ minutes

c. $\bar{x} \pm t_{.025} s / \sqrt{n}$ $df = 59$ $t_{.025} = 2.001$

$$66.93 \pm 2.001 \,(4.4943/\sqrt{60}\,)$$

$$66.93 \pm 1.16 \quad \text{or } 65.77 \text{ to } 68.09$$

50. $n = \dfrac{(2.33)^2 (2.6)^2}{1^2} = 36.7$ Use $n = 37$

51. $n = \dfrac{(1.96)^2 (8)^2}{2^2} = 61.47$ Use $n = 62$

$n = \dfrac{(2.576)^2 (8)^2}{2^2} = 106.17$ Use $n = 107$

52. $n = \dfrac{(1.96)^2 (675)^2}{100^2} = 175.03$ Use $n = 176$

53. a. $\bar{p} \pm 1.96 \sqrt{\dfrac{\bar{p}(1-\bar{p})}{n}}$

    $.47 \pm 1.96 \sqrt{\dfrac{(.47)(.53)}{450}}$

    $.47 \pm .0461$ or $.4239$ to $.5161$

    b. $.47 \pm 2.576 \sqrt{\dfrac{(.47)(.53)}{450}}$

    $.47 \pm .0606$ or $.4094$ to $.5306$

    c. The margin of error becomes larger.

54. a. $\bar{p} = 200/369 = .5420$

    b. $1.96 \sqrt{\dfrac{\bar{p}(1-\bar{p})}{n}} = 1.96 \sqrt{\dfrac{(.5420)(.4580)}{369}} = .0508$

    c. $.5420 \pm .0508$ or $.4912$ to $.5928$

55. a. $\bar{p} = .93$

    Margin of error $= z_{.025} \sqrt{\dfrac{\bar{p}(1-\bar{p})}{n}} = 1.96 \sqrt{\dfrac{(.93)(.07)}{500}} = .0224$

    95% Confidence Interval: $.93 \pm .0224$ or $.9076$ to $.9524$

    b. $\bar{p} = .21$

    Margin of error $= z_{.005} \sqrt{\dfrac{\bar{p}(1-\bar{p})}{n}} = 2.576 \sqrt{\dfrac{(.21)(.79)}{500}} = .0469$

    95% Confidence Interval: $.21 \pm .0469$ or $.1631$ to $.2569$

    c. The margin of error is larger in part (b) for two reasons. With $\bar{p} = .21$, the estimate of the standard error is larger than with $\bar{p} = .930$. And $z_{.005} = 2.576$ for 99% confidence is larger than $z_{.025} = 1.96$ for 95% confidence.

56. a. With 165 out of 750 respondents rating the economy as good or excellent,

    $\bar{p} = 165/750 = .22$

    b. Margin of error $= 1.96 \sqrt{\dfrac{\bar{p}(1-\bar{p})}{n}} = 1.96 \sqrt{\dfrac{.22(1-.22)}{750}} = .0296$

    95% Confidence interval: $.22 \pm .0296$ or $.1904$ to $.2496$

    c. With 315 out of 750 respondents rating the economy as poor,

    $\bar{p} = 315/750 = .42$

$$\text{Margin of error} = 1.96 \sqrt{\frac{\bar{p}(1-\bar{p})}{n}} = 1.96 \sqrt{\frac{.42(1-.42)}{750}} = .0353$$

95% Confidence interval: $.42 \pm .0353$ or .3847 to .4553

    d.   The confidence interval in part (c) is wider. This is because the sample proportion is closer to .5 in part (c).

57. a. $n = \dfrac{(1.96)^2(.3)(.7)}{(.02)^2} = 2016.84 \qquad$ Use $n = 2017$

    b. $\bar{p} = 520/2017 = .2578$

    c. $\bar{p} \pm 1.96 \sqrt{\dfrac{\bar{p}(1-\bar{p})}{n}}$

         $.2578 \pm 1.96 \sqrt{\dfrac{(.2578)(.7422)}{2017}}$

         $.2578 \pm .0191$ or .2387 to .2769

58. a. $n = \dfrac{(2.33)^2(.70)(.30)}{(.03)^2} = 1266.74 \qquad$ Use $n = 1267$

    b. $n = \dfrac{(2.33)^2(.50)(.50)}{(.03)^2} = 1508.03 \qquad$ Use $n = 1509$

59. a.   Government industry 95% margin of error: $1.96 \sqrt{\dfrac{.37(1-.37)}{200}} = .0669$

         95% Confidence interval: $.37 \pm .0669 \qquad$ or .3031 to .4369

       Health care industry 95% margin of error: $1.96 \sqrt{\dfrac{.33(1-.33)}{200}} = .0652$

         95% Confidence interval: $.33 \pm .0652 \qquad$ or .2648 to .3952

       Education industry 95% margin of error: $1.96 \sqrt{\dfrac{.28(1-.28)}{200}} = .0622$

         95% Confidence interval: $.28 \pm .0622 \qquad$ or .2178 to .3422

    b.   The government industry has the largest margin of error. So the sample size must be large enough to reduce the margin of error for the government industry to .05 or less. Using the proportions found in the study reported in *USA Today* as a planning value $p^* = .37$.

         $n = \dfrac{(1.96)^2(.37)(.63)}{(.05)^2} = 358.1908 \qquad$ Use $n = 359$

This is an increase of 159 workers surveyed in each industry. The added cost of the larger sample size would have to be taken into account before deciding whether the smaller margin of error is worth the added cost of obtaining the data.

60. a. $\bar{p} = 618/1993 = .3101$

b. $\bar{p} \pm 1.96 \sqrt{\dfrac{\bar{p}(1-\bar{p})}{1993}}$

$.3101 \pm 1.96 \sqrt{\dfrac{(.3101)(.6899)}{1993}}$

$.3101 \pm .0203$ or $.2898$ to $.3304$

c. $n = \dfrac{z^2 p^*(1-p^*)}{E^2}$

$z = \dfrac{(1.96)^2 (.3101)(.6899)}{(.01)^2} = 8218.64$ Use $n = 8219$

No; the sample appears unnecessarily large. The .02 margin of error reported in part (b) should provide adequate precision.

Chapter 9
Hypothesis Tests

Learning Objectives

1. Learn how to formulate and test hypotheses about a population mean and/or a population proportion.

2. Understand the types of errors possible when conducting a hypothesis test.

3. Understand the level of significance and be able to determine the probability of making a Type I error.

4. Know how to compute and interpret p-values.

5. Be able to use critical values to draw hypothesis testing conclusions.

6. Know the definition of the following terms:

null hypothesis   two-tailed test
alternative hypothesis p-value
Type I error   level of significance
Type II error   critical value
one-tailed test

Solutions:

1. a. H_0: $\mu \leq 600$ Manager's claim.
      H_a: $\mu > 600$

   b. We are not able to conclude that the manager's claim is wrong.

   c. The manager's claim can be rejected. We can conclude that $\mu > 600$.

2. a. H_0: $\mu \leq 14$
      H_a: $\mu > 14$ Research hypothesis

   b. There is no statistical evidence that the new bonus plan increases sales volume.

   c. The research hypothesis that $\mu > 14$ is supported. We can conclude that the new bonus plan increases the mean sales volume.

3. a. H_0: $\mu = 32$ Specified filling weight
      H_a: $\mu \neq 32$ Overfilling or underfilling exists

   b. There is no evidence that the production line is not operating properly. Allow the production process to continue.

   c. Conclude $\mu \neq 32$ and that overfilling or underfilling exists. Shut down and adjust the production line.

4. a. H_0: $\mu \geq 220$
      H_a: $\mu < 220$ Research hypothesis to see if mean cost is less than $220.

   b. We are unable to conclude that the new method reduces costs.

   c. Conclude $\mu < 220$. Consider implementing the new method based on the conclusion that it lowers the mean cost per hour.

5. a. Conclude that the population mean monthly cost of electricity in the Chicago neighborhood is greater than $104 and hence higher than in the comparable neighborhood in Cincinnati.

   b. The Type I error is rejecting H_0 when it is true. This error occurs if the researcher concludes that the population mean monthly cost of electricity is greater than $104 in the Chicago neighborhood when the population mean cost is actually less than or equal to $104.

   c. The Type II error is accepting H_0 when it is false. This error occurs if the researcher concludes that the population mean monthly cost for the Chicago neighborhood is less than or equal to $104 when it is not.

6. a. H_0: $\mu \leq 1$ The label claim or assumption.
      H_a: $\mu > 1$

   b. Claiming $\mu > 1$ when it is not. This is the error of rejecting the product's claim when the claim is true.

   c. Concluding $\mu \leq 1$ when it is not. In this case, we miss the fact that the product is not meeting its label specification.

7. a. H_0: $\mu \leq 8000$
   H_a: $\mu > 8000$ Research hypothesis to see if the plan increases average sales.

   b. Claiming $\mu > 8000$ when the plan does not increase sales. A mistake could be implementing the plan when it does not help.

   c. Concluding $\mu \leq 8000$ when the plan really would increase sales. This could lead to not implementing a plan that would increase sales.

8. a. H_0: $\mu \geq 220$
   H_a: $\mu < 220$

   b. Claiming $\mu < 220$ when the new method does not lower costs. A mistake could be implementing the method when it does not help.

   c. Concluding $\mu \geq 220$ when the method really would lower costs. This could lead to not implementing a method that would lower costs.

9. a. $z = \dfrac{\overline{x} - \mu_0}{\sigma / \sqrt{n}} = \dfrac{19.4 - 20}{2 / \sqrt{50}} = -2.12$

   b. Lower tail p-value is the area to the left of the test statistic

   Using normal table with $z = -2.12$: p-value $= .0170$

   c. p-value $\leq .05$, reject H_0

   d. Reject H_0 if $z \leq -1.645$

   $-2.12 \leq -1.645$, reject H_0

10. a. $z = \dfrac{\overline{x} - \mu_0}{\sigma / \sqrt{n}} = \dfrac{26.4 - 25}{6 / \sqrt{40}} = 1.48$

    b. Upper tail p-value is the area to the right of the test statistic

    Using normal table with $z = 1.48$: p-value $= 1.0000 - .9306 = .0694$

    c. p-value $> .01$, do not reject H_0

    d. Reject H_0 if $z \geq 2.33$

    $1.48 < 2.33$, do not reject H_0

11. a. $z = \dfrac{\overline{x} - \mu_0}{\sigma / \sqrt{n}} = \dfrac{14.15 - 15}{3 / \sqrt{50}} = -2.00$

    b. Because $z < 0$, p-value is two times the lower tail area

    Using normal table with $z = -2.00$: p-value $= 2(.0228) = .0456$

    c. p-value $\leq .05$, reject H_0

    d.   Reject H_0 if $z \leq -1.96$ or $z \geq 1.96$

        $-2.00 \leq -1.96$, reject H_0

12.   a. $z = \dfrac{\bar{x} - \mu_0}{\sigma / \sqrt{n}} = \dfrac{78.5 - 80}{12 / \sqrt{100}} = -1.25$

        Lower tail p-value is the area to the left of the test statistic

        Using normal table with $z = -1.25$: p-value $= .1056$

        p-value $> .01$, do not reject H_0

    b. $z = \dfrac{\bar{x} - \mu_0}{\sigma / \sqrt{n}} = \dfrac{77 - 80}{12 / \sqrt{100}} = -2.50$

        Lower tail p-value is the area to the left of the test statistic

        Using normal table with $z = -2.50$: p-value $= .0062$

        p-value $\leq .01$, reject H_0

    c. $z = \dfrac{\bar{x} - \mu_0}{\sigma / \sqrt{n}} = \dfrac{75.5 - 80}{12 / \sqrt{100}} = -3.75$

        Lower tail p-value is the area to the left of the test statistic

        Using normal table with $z = -3.75$: p-value ≈ 0

        p-value $\leq .01$, reject H_0

    d. $z = \dfrac{\bar{x} - \mu_0}{\sigma / \sqrt{n}} = \dfrac{81 - 80}{12 / \sqrt{100}} = .83$

        Lower tail p-value is the area to the left of the test statistic

        Using normal table with $z = .83$: p-value $= .7967$

        p-value $> .01$, do not reject H_0

13.   Reject H_0 if $z \geq 1.645$

    a. $z = \dfrac{\bar{x} - \mu_0}{\sigma / \sqrt{n}} = \dfrac{52.5 - 50}{8 / \sqrt{60}} = 2.42$

        $2.42 \geq 1.645$, reject H_0

    b. $z = \dfrac{\bar{x} - \mu_0}{\sigma / \sqrt{n}} = \dfrac{51 - 50}{8 / \sqrt{60}} = .97$

        $.97 < 1.645$, do not reject H_0

c. $z = \dfrac{\bar{x} - \mu_0}{\sigma/\sqrt{n}} = \dfrac{51.8 - 50}{8/\sqrt{60}} = 1.74$

1.74 ≥ 1.645, reject H_0

14. a. $z = \dfrac{\bar{x} - \mu_0}{\sigma/\sqrt{n}} = \dfrac{23 - 22}{10/\sqrt{75}} = .87$

Because $z > 0$, p-value is two times the upper tail area

Using normal table with $z = .87$: p-value $= 2(1 - .8078) = .3844$

p-value $> .01$, do not reject H_0

b. $z = \dfrac{\bar{x} - \mu_0}{\sigma/\sqrt{n}} = \dfrac{25.1 - 22}{10/\sqrt{75}} = 2.68$

Because $z > 0$, p-value is two times the upper tail area

Using normal table with $z = 2.68$: p-value $= 2(1 - .9963) = .0074$

p-value $\leq .01$, reject H_0

c. $z = \dfrac{\bar{x} - \mu_0}{\sigma/\sqrt{n}} = \dfrac{20 - 22}{10/\sqrt{75}} = -1.73$

Because $z < 0$, p-value is two times the lower tail area

Using normal table with $z = -1.73$: p-value $= 2(.0418) = .0836$

p-value $> .01$, do not reject H_0

15. a. H_0: $\mu \geq 1056$
H_a: $\mu < 1056$

b. $z = \dfrac{\bar{x} - \mu_0}{\sigma/\sqrt{n}} = \dfrac{910 - 1056}{1600/\sqrt{400}} = -1.83$

Lower tail p-value is the area to the left of the test statistic

Using normal table with $z = -1.83$: p-value $=.0336$

c. p-value $\leq .05$, reject H_0. Conclude the mean refund of "last minute" filers is less than $1056.

d. Reject H_0 if $z \leq -1.645$

-1.83 $\leq$ -1.645, reject H_0

16. a. H_0: $\mu \leq 3173$
    H_a: $\mu > 3173$

    b. $z = \dfrac{\bar{x} - \mu_0}{\sigma / \sqrt{n}} = \dfrac{3325 - 3173}{1000 / \sqrt{180}} = 2.04$

    p-value = 1.0000 - .9793 = .0207

    c. p-value $\leq .05$. Reject H_0. The current population mean credit card balance for undergraduate students has increased compared to the previous all-time high of $3173 reported in April 2009.

17. a. H_0: $\mu = 24.57$
    H_a: $\mu \neq 24.57$

    b. $z = \dfrac{\bar{x} - \mu_0}{\sigma / \sqrt{n}} = \dfrac{23.89 - 24.57}{2.4 / \sqrt{30}} = -1.55$

    Because $z < 0$, p-value is two times the lower tail area

    Using normal table with $z = -1.55$: p-value = 2(.0606) = .1212

    c. p-value $> .05$, do not reject H_0. We cannot conclude that the population mean hourly wage for

    manufacturing workers differs significantly from the population mean of $24.57 for the goods-

    producing industries.

    d. Reject H_0 if $z \leq -1.96$ or $z \geq 1.96$

    $z = -1.55$; cannot reject H_0. The conclusion is the same as in part (c).

18. a. H_0: $\mu = 192$
    H_a: $\mu \neq 192$

    b. $z = \dfrac{\bar{x} - \mu_0}{\sigma / \sqrt{n}} = \dfrac{182 - 192}{55 / \sqrt{150}} = -2.23$

    Because $z < 0$, p-value is two times the lower tail area

    Using normal table with $z = -2.23$: p-value = 2(.0129) = .0258

    c. p-value = .0258 $\leq \alpha = .05$

    Reject H_0 and conclude that the mean number of restaurant meals eaten by young millennials has changed in 2012.

19. H_0: $\mu \geq 12$
    H_a: $\mu < 12$

    $z = \dfrac{\bar{x} - \mu_0}{\sigma / \sqrt{n}} = \dfrac{10 - 12}{8 / \sqrt{50}} = -1.77$

p-value is the area in the lower tail

Using normal table with $z = -1.77$: p-value = .0384

p-value $\leq$ .05, reject H_0. Conclude that the actual mean waiting time is significantly less than the claim of 12 minutes made by the taxpayer advocate.

20. a. H_0: $\mu \geq 838$
    H_a: $\mu < 838$

    b. $z = \dfrac{\bar{x} - \mu_0}{\sigma / \sqrt{n}} = \dfrac{745 - 838}{300 / \sqrt{60}} = -2.40$

    c. Lower tail p-value is area to left of the test statistic.

      Using normal table with $z = -2.40$: p-value = .0082.

    d. p-value $\leq$ .01; reject H_0. Conclude that the annual expenditure per person on prescription drugs is less in the Midwest than in the Northeast.

21. a. H_0: $\mu \leq 15$
    H_a: $\mu > 15$

    b. $z = \dfrac{\bar{x} - \mu}{\sigma / \sqrt{n}} = \dfrac{17 - 15}{4 / \sqrt{35}} = 2.96$

    c. Upper tail p-value is the area to the right of the test statistic

      Using normal table with $z = 2.96$: p-value = 1.0000 - .9985 = .0015

    d. p-value $\leq$ .01; reject H_0; the premium rate should be charged.

22. a. H_0: $\mu = 8$
    H_a: $\mu \neq 8$

    b. $z = \dfrac{\bar{x} - \mu}{\sigma / \sqrt{n}} = \dfrac{8.4 - 8.0}{3.2 / \sqrt{120}} = 1.37$

      Because $z > 0$, p-value is two times the upper tail area

      Using normal table with $z = 1.37$: p-value = 2(1 - .9147) = .1706

    c. p-value > .05; do not reject H_0. Cannot conclude that the population mean waiting time differs from 8 minutes.

    d. $\bar{x} \pm z_{.025} (\sigma / \sqrt{n})$

      $8.4 \pm 1.96 (3.2 / \sqrt{120})$

      $8.4 \pm .57$ (7.83 to 8.97)

      Yes; $\mu = 8$ is in the interval. Do not reject H_0.

23. a. $t = \dfrac{\overline{x} - \mu_0}{s / \sqrt{n}} = \dfrac{14 - 12}{4.32 / \sqrt{25}} = 2.31$

    b. Degrees of freedom $= n - 1 = 24$

    Upper tail p-value is the area to the right of the test statistic

    Using t table: p-value is between .01 and .025

    Exact p-value corresponding to $t = 2.31$ is .0149

    c. p-value $\leq .05$, reject H_0.

    d. With $df = 24$, $t_{.05} = 1.711$

    Reject H_0 if $t \geq 1.711$

    $2.31 > 1.711$, reject H_0.

24. a. $t = \dfrac{\overline{x} - \mu_0}{s / \sqrt{n}} = \dfrac{17 - 18}{4.5 / \sqrt{48}} = -1.54$

    b. Degrees of freedom $= n - 1 = 47$

    Because $t < 0$, p-value is two times the lower tail area

    Using t table: area in lower tail is between .05 and .10; therefore, p-value is between .10 and .20.

    Exact p-value corresponding to $t = -1.54$ is .1303

    c. p-value $> .05$, do not reject H_0.

    d. With $df = 47$, $t_{.025} = 2.012$

    Reject H_0 if $t \leq -2.012$ or $t \geq 2.012$

    $t = -1.54$; do not reject H_0

25. a. $t = \dfrac{\overline{x} - \mu_0}{s / \sqrt{n}} = \dfrac{44 - 45}{5.2 / \sqrt{36}} = -1.15$

    Degrees of freedom $= n - 1 = 35$

    Lower tail p-value is the area to the left of the test statistic

    Using t table: p-value is between .10 and .20

    Exact p-value corresponding to $t = -1.15$ is .1290

    p-value $> .01$, do not reject H_0

b. $t = \dfrac{\bar{x} - \mu_0}{s / \sqrt{n}} = \dfrac{43 - 45}{4.6 / \sqrt{36}} = -2.61$

Lower tail p-value is the area to the left of the test statistic

Using t table: p-value is between .005 and .01

Exact p-value corresponding to $t = -2.61$ is .0066

p-value $\leq$ .01, reject H_0

c. $t = \dfrac{\bar{x} - \mu_0}{s / \sqrt{n}} = \dfrac{46 - 45}{5 / \sqrt{36}} = 1.20$

Lower tail p-value is the area to the left of the test statistic

Using t table: p-value is between .80 and .90

Exact p-value corresponding to $t = 1.20$ is .8809

p-value $>$ .01, do not reject H_0

26. a. $t = \dfrac{\bar{x} - \mu_0}{s / \sqrt{n}} = \dfrac{103 - 100}{11.5 / \sqrt{65}} = 2.10$

Degrees of freedom $= n - 1 = 64$

Because $t > 0$, p-value is two times the upper tail area

Using t table; area in upper tail is between .01 and .025; therefore, p-value is between .02 and .05.

Exact p-value corresponding to $t = 2.10$ is .0397

p-value $\leq$ .05, reject H_0

b. $t = \dfrac{\bar{x} - \mu_0}{s / \sqrt{n}} = \dfrac{96.5 - 100}{11 / \sqrt{65}} = -2.57$

Because $t < 0$, p-value is two times the lower tail area

Using t table: area in lower tail is between .005 and .01; therefore, p-value is between .01 and .02.

Exact p-value corresponding to $t = -2.57$ is .0125

p-value $\leq$ .05, reject H_0

c. $t = \dfrac{\bar{x} - \mu_0}{s / \sqrt{n}} = \dfrac{102 - 100}{10.5 / \sqrt{65}} = 1.54$

Because $t > 0$, p-value is two times the upper tail area

Using t table: area in upper tail is between .05 and .10; therefore, p-value is between .10 and .20.

Exact p-value corresponding to $t = 1.54$ is .1285

p-value > .05, do not reject H_0

27. a. H_0: $\mu \geq 13.04$
    H_a: $\mu < 13.04$

    b. $t = \dfrac{\overline{x} - \mu_0}{s / \sqrt{n}} = \dfrac{12.75 - 13.04}{2 / \sqrt{100}} = -1.45$

       Degrees of freedom $= n - 1 = 99$

       p-value is the lower tail area at the test statistic

       Using t table: p-value is between .05 and .10

       Exact p-value corresponding to $t = -1.45$ is .0751

    c. p-value > .05; do not reject H_0. We cannot conclude that the cost of a restaurant meal is significantly cheaper than a comparable meal fixed at home.

    d. $df = 99$ $t_{.05} = -1.66$

       Reject H_0 if $t \leq -1.66$

       $-1.45 > -1.66$; do not reject H_0

28. a. H_0: $\mu \geq 9$
    H_a: $\mu < 9$

    b. $t = \dfrac{\overline{x} - \mu_0}{s / \sqrt{n}} = \dfrac{7.27 - 9}{6.38 / \sqrt{85}} = -2.50$

       Degrees of freedom $= n - 1 = 84$

       Lower tail p-value is $P(t \leq -2.50)$

       Using t table: p-value is between .005 and .01

       Exact p-value corresponding to $t = -2.50$ is .0072

    c. p-value $\leq$ .01; reject H_0. The mean tenure of a CEO is significantly lower than 9 years. The claim of the shareholders group is not valid.

29. a. H_0: $\mu = 90,000$
    H_a: $\mu \neq 90,000$

    b. $t = \dfrac{\overline{x} - \mu_0}{s / \sqrt{n}} = \dfrac{85,272 - 90,000.00}{11,039.23 / \sqrt{25}} = -2.14$

       Degrees of freedom $= n - 1 = 24$

       Because $t < 0$, p-value is two times the lower tail area

Using t table: area in lower tail is between .01 and .025; therefore, p-value is between .02 and .05.

Exact p-value corresponding to $t = -2.14$ is .0427

    c. p-value $\le$ .05; reject H_0. The mean annual administrator salary in Ohio differs significantly from the national mean annual salary.

    d. $df = 24$ $t_{.025} = 2.064$

Reject H_0 if $t < -2.064$ or $t > 2.064$

$-2.14 < -2.064$; reject H_0. The conclusion is the same as in part (c).

30. a. H_0: $\mu = 6.4$
          H_a: $\mu \ne 6.4$

    b.   Using Excel or Minitab, we find $\bar{x} = 7.0$ and $s = 2.4276$

$$t = \frac{\bar{x} - \mu_0}{s / \sqrt{n}} = \frac{7.0 - 6.4}{2.4276 / \sqrt{40}} = 1.56$$

$df = n - 1 = 39$

Because $t > 0$, p-value is two times the upper tail area at $t = 1.56$

Using t table: area in upper tail is between .05 and .10; therefore, p-value is between .10 and .20.

Exact p-value corresponding to $t = 1.56$ is .1268

    c.   Most researchers would choose $\alpha = .10$ or less. If you chose $\alpha = .10$ or less, you cannot reject H_0. You are unable to conclude that the population mean number of hours married men with children in your area spend in child care differs from the mean reported by *Time*.

31. H_0: $\mu \le 423$
       H_a: $\mu > 423$

$$t = \frac{\bar{x} - \mu_0}{s / \sqrt{n}} = \frac{460.4 - 423.0}{101.9 / \sqrt{36}} = 2.20$$

Degrees of freedom $= n - 1 = 35$
Upper tail p-value is the area to the right of the test statistic

Using t table: p-value is between .01 and .025.

Exact p-value corresponding to $t = 2.02$ is .0173

Because p-value $= .0173 < \alpha$, reject H_0; Atlanta customers have a higher annual rate of consumption of Coca Cola beverages.

32. a. H_0: $\mu = 10,192$
          H_a: $\mu \ne 10,192$

    b. $t = \dfrac{\bar{x} - \mu_0}{s / \sqrt{n}} = \dfrac{9750 - 10,192}{1400 / \sqrt{50}} = -2.23$

Degrees of freedom $= n - 1 = 49$

Because $t < 0$, p-value is two times the lower tail area

Using t table: area in lower tail is between .01 and .025; therefore, p-value is between .02 and .05.

Exact p-value corresponding to $t = -2.23$ is .0304

c. p-value $\leq .05$; reject H_0. The population mean price at this dealership differs from the national mean price \$10,192.

33. a. H_0: $\mu \leq 21.6$
H_a: $\mu > 21.6$

b. $24.1 - 21.6 = 2.5$ gallons

c. $t = \dfrac{\bar{x} - \mu_0}{s / \sqrt{n}} = \dfrac{24.1 - 21.6}{4.8 / \sqrt{16}} = 2.08$

Degrees of freedom $= n - 1 = 15$

Upper tail p-value is the area to the right of the test statistic

Using t table: p-value is between .025 and .05

Exact p-value corresponding to $t = 2.08$ is .0275

d. p-value $\leq .05$; reject H_0. The population mean consumption of milk in Webster City is greater than the National mean.

34. a. H_0: $\mu = 2$
H_a: $\mu \neq 2$

b. $\bar{x} = \dfrac{\Sigma x_i}{n} = \dfrac{22}{10} = 2.2$

c. $s = \sqrt{\dfrac{\Sigma (x_i - \bar{x})^2}{n - 1}} = .516$

d. $t = \dfrac{\bar{x} - \mu_0}{s / \sqrt{n}} = \dfrac{2.2 - 2}{.516 / \sqrt{10}} = 1.22$

Degrees of freedom $= n - 1 = 9$

Because $t > 0$, p-value is two times the upper tail area

Using t table: area in upper tail is between .10 and .20; therefore, p-value is between .20 and .40.

Exact p-value corresponding to $t = 1.22$ is .2535

e. p-value $> .05$; do not reject H_0. No reason to change from the 2 hours for cost estimating purposes.

35. a. $z = \dfrac{\bar{p} - p_0}{\sqrt{\dfrac{p_0(1-p_0)}{n}}} = \dfrac{.175 - .20}{\sqrt{\dfrac{.20(1-.20)}{400}}} = -1.25$

b. Because $z < 0$, p-value is two times the lower tail area

Using normal table with $z = -1.25$: p-value $= 2(.1056) = .2112$

c. p-value $> .05$; do not reject H_0

d. $z_{.025} = 1.96$

Reject H_0 if $z \leq -1.96$ or $z \geq 1.96$

$z = -1.25$; do not reject H_0

36. a. $z = \dfrac{\bar{p} - p_0}{\sqrt{\dfrac{p_0(1-p_0)}{n}}} = \dfrac{.68 - .75}{\sqrt{\dfrac{.75(1-.75)}{300}}} = -2.80$

Lower tail p-value is the area to the left of the test statistic

Using normal table with $z = -2.80$: p-value $= .0026$

p-value $\leq .05$; Reject H_0

b. $z = \dfrac{.72 - .75}{\sqrt{\dfrac{.75(1-.75)}{300}}} = -1.20$

Lower tail p-value is the area to the left of the test statistic

Using normal table with $z = -1.20$: p-value $= .1151$

p-value $> .05$; Do not reject H_0

c. $z = \dfrac{.70 - .75}{\sqrt{\dfrac{.75(1-.75)}{300}}} = -2.00$

Lower tail p-value is the area to the left of the test statistic

Using normal table with $z = -2.00$: p-value $= .0228$

p-value $\leq .05$; Reject H_0

d. $z = \dfrac{.77 - .75}{\sqrt{\dfrac{.75(1-.75)}{300}}} = .80$

Lower tail p-value is the area to the left of the test statistic

Using normal table with $z = .80$: p-value $= .7881$

p-value $> .05$; Do not reject H_0

37. a. $H_0: p \le .125$
         $H_a: p > .125$

     b. $\bar{p} = \dfrac{52}{400} = .13$

         $z = \dfrac{\bar{p} - p_0}{\sqrt{\dfrac{p_0(1 - p_0)}{n}}} = \dfrac{.13 - .125}{\sqrt{\dfrac{.125(1 - .125)}{400}}} = .30$

         Upper tail p-value is the area to the right of the test statistic

         Using normal table with $z = .30$: p-value $= 1.0000 - .6179 = .3821$

     c. p-value $> .05$; do not reject H_0. We cannot conclude that there has been an increase in union membership.

38. a. $H_0: p = .64$
         $H_a: p \ne .64$

     b. $\bar{p} = \dfrac{52}{100} = .52$

         $z = \dfrac{\bar{p} - p_0}{\sqrt{\dfrac{p_0(1 - p_0)}{n}}} = \dfrac{.52 - .64}{\sqrt{\dfrac{.64(1 - .64)}{100}}} = -2.50$

         Because $z < 0$, p-value is two times the lower tail area

         Using normal table with $z = -2.50$: p-value $= 2(.0062) = .0124$

     c. p-value $\le .05$; reject H_0. Proportion differs from the reported .64.

     d. Yes. Since $\bar{p} = .52$, it indicates that fewer than 64% of the shoppers believe the supermarket brand is as good as the name brand.

39. a. $H_0: p = .75$
         $H_a: p \ne .75$

     b. 30 – 49 Age Group $\bar{p} = \dfrac{85}{100} = .85$

         $z = \dfrac{\bar{p} - p_0}{\sqrt{\dfrac{p_0(1 - p_0)}{n}}} = \dfrac{.85 - .75}{\sqrt{\dfrac{.75(1 - .75)}{100}}} = 2.31$

Because $z > 0$, p-value is two times the upper tail area

Using normal table with $z = 2.31$: p-value $= 2(.0104) = .0208$

Reject H_0. Conclude that the proportion of users in the $30 - 49$ age group is higher than the overall proportion of .75.

c. $50 - 64$ Age Group $\bar{p} = \dfrac{144}{200} = .72$

$$z = \frac{.72 - .75}{\sqrt{\dfrac{.75(1-.75)}{200}}} = -.98$$

Because $z < 0$, p-value is two times the lower tail area

Using the normal table with $z = -.98$: p-value $= 2(.1635) = .3270$

Do not reject H_0. The proportion for the $50 - 64$ age group does not differ significantly from the overall proportion.

d. The proportion of internet users increases from .72 to .85 as we go from the $50 - 64$ age group to the younger $30 - 49$ age group. So we might expect the proportion to increase further for the even younger $18 - 29$ age group. Indeed, the Pew project found the proportion of users in the $18 - 29$ age group to be .92.

40. a. Sample proportion: $\bar{p} = .35$

Number planning to provide holiday gifts: $n\bar{p} = 60(.35) = 21$

b. H_0: $p \geq .46$
   H_a: $p < .46$

$$z = \frac{\bar{p} - p_0}{\sqrt{\dfrac{p_0(1-p_0)}{n}}} = \frac{.35 - .46}{\sqrt{\dfrac{.46(1-.46)}{60}}} = -1.71$$

p-value is area in lower tail

Using normal table with $z = -1.71$: p-value $= .0436$

c. Using a .05 level of significance, we can conclude that the proportion of business owners providing gifts has decreased from 2008 to 2009. The smallest level of significance for which we could draw this conclusion is .0436; this corresponds to the p-value $= .0436$. This is why the p-value is often called the observed level of significance.

41. a. H_0: $p \geq .53$
    H_a: $p < .53$

b. $$z = \frac{\bar{p} - p_0}{\sqrt{\dfrac{p_0(1-p_0)}{n}}} = \frac{.46 - .53}{\sqrt{\dfrac{.53(1-.53)}{300}}} = -2.43$$

9 - 15

p-value is the lower-tail area at the test statistic

Using normal table with $z = -2.43$: p-value $= .0075$

c.   p-value $\leq \alpha = .01$; reject H_0. We conclude that there has been a statistically significant decline in the proportion of American families owning stocks or stock funds over the ten-year period.

42. a. $\bar{p} = 12/80 = .15$

b. $\sqrt{\dfrac{\bar{p}(1-\bar{p})}{n}} = \sqrt{\dfrac{.15(.85)}{80}} = .0399$

$\bar{p} \pm z_{.025} \sqrt{\dfrac{\bar{p}(1-\bar{p})}{n}}$

$.15 \pm 1.96\,(.0399)$

$.15 \pm .0782$ or $.0718$ to $.2282$

c. $H_0\colon\ p = .06$
$H_a\colon\ p \neq .06$

$\bar{p} = .15$

$z = \dfrac{\bar{p} - p_0}{\sqrt{\dfrac{p_0(1-p_0)}{n}}} = \dfrac{.15 - .06}{\sqrt{\dfrac{.06(.94)}{80}}} = 3.38$

p-value ≈ 0

We conclude that the return rate for the Houston store is different than the U.S. national return rate.

43. a. $H_0\colon\ p \leq .10$
$H_a\colon\ p > .10$

b.   There are 13 "Yes" responses in the Eagle data set.

$\bar{p} = \dfrac{13}{100} = .13$

c. $z = \dfrac{\bar{p} - p_0}{\sqrt{\dfrac{p_0(1-p_0)}{n}}} = \dfrac{.13 - .10}{\sqrt{\dfrac{.10(1-.10)}{100}}} = 1.00$

Upper tail p-value is the area to the right of the test statistic

Using normal table with $z = 1.00$: p-value $= 1 - .8413 = .1587$

p-value $> .05$; do not reject H_0.

On the basis of the test results, Eagle should not go national. But, since $\bar{p} > .13$, it may be worth expanding the sample size for a larger test.

44.   a. H_0: $p \le .50$
             H_a: $p > .50$

      b.   Using Excel or Minitab we find that 92 of the 150 physicians in the sample have been sued.

             So, $\bar{p} = \dfrac{92}{150} = .6133$

$$z = \frac{\bar{p} - p_0}{\sqrt{\dfrac{p_0(1 - p_0)}{n}}} = \frac{.6133 - .50}{\sqrt{\dfrac{(.50)(.50)}{150}}} = 2.78$$

             p-value is the area in the upper tail at $z = 2.78$

             Using normal table with $z = 2.78$: p-value $= 1 - .9973 = .0027$

      c.   Since p-value $= .0027 \le .01$, we reject H_0 and conclude that the proportion of physicians over the age of 55 who have been sued at least once is greater than .50.

45.   a. H_0: $p = .39$
             H_a: $p \ne .39$

             $\bar{p} = .385$

$$z = \frac{\bar{p} - p_0}{\sqrt{\dfrac{p_0(1 - p_0)}{n}}} = \frac{.385 - .39}{\sqrt{\dfrac{.39(1 - .39)}{300}}} = -.18$$

             Because $z < 0$, p-value is 2 times the lower tail area at $z = -.18$

             Using normal table with $z = -.18$: p-value $= 2(.4286) = .8572$

             $p - value > .05$; do not reject H_0. We cannot conclude that bullish sentiment differs significantly from its long-term average of .39.

      b. $H_0 : p \le .30$
             $H_0 : p > .30$

             $\bar{p} = .399$

$$z = \frac{\bar{p} - p_0}{\sqrt{\dfrac{p_0(1 - p_0)}{n}}} = \frac{.399 - .30}{\sqrt{\dfrac{.30(1 - .30)}{300}}} = 3.74$$

             Because $z > 0$, p-value is the upper tail area at $z = 3.74$

             Using normal table with $z = 3.74$: p-value ≈ 0

$p - value \leq \alpha = .01$; reject H_0. We conclude that bearish sentiment is significantly greater than its long-term average of .30.

c. It would be dangerous to generalize these results. The target population for this study is members of the American Association of Individual Investors. We might be willing to extend these results to the target population of all *individual* investors. But, should not extend the results to a target population of *all* investors.

46. a. H_0: $\mu = 16$
    H_a: $\mu \neq 16$

    b. $z = \dfrac{\bar{x} - \mu_0}{\sigma / \sqrt{n}} = \dfrac{16.32 - 16}{.8 / \sqrt{30}} = 2.19$

    Because $z > 0$, p-value is two times the upper tail area

    Using normal table with $z = 2.19$: p-value $= 2(.0143) = .0286$

    p-value $\leq .05$; reject H_0. Readjust production line.

    c. $z = \dfrac{\bar{x} - \mu_0}{\sigma / \sqrt{n}} = \dfrac{15.82 - 16}{.8 / \sqrt{30}} = -1.23$

    Because $z < 0$, p-value is two times the lower tail area

    Using normal table with $z = -1.23$: p-value $= 2(.1093) = .2186$

    p-value $> .05$; do not reject H_0. Continue the production line.

    d. Reject H_0 if $z \leq -1.96$ or $z \geq 1.96$

    For $\bar{x} = 16.32$, $z = 2.19$; reject H_0

    For $\bar{x} = 15.82$, $z = -1.23$; do not reject H_0

    Yes, same conclusion.

47. a. H_0: $\mu = 900$
    H_a: $\mu \neq 900$

    b. $\bar{x} \pm z_{.025} \dfrac{\sigma}{\sqrt{n}}$

    $935 \pm 1.96 \dfrac{180}{\sqrt{200}}$

    935 ± 25 \qquad (910 to 960)

    c. Reject H_0 because $\mu = 900$ is not in the interval.

d. $z = \dfrac{\bar{x} - \mu_0}{\sigma / \sqrt{n}} = \dfrac{935 - 900}{180 / \sqrt{200}} = 2.75$

Because $z > 0$, p-value is two times the upper tail area

Using normal table with $z = 2.75$: p-value $= 2(.0030) = .0060$

48. a. H_0: $\mu \leq 4$
H_a: $\mu > 4$

b. $z = \dfrac{\bar{x} - \mu_0}{\sigma / \sqrt{n}} = \dfrac{4.5 - 4}{1.5 / \sqrt{60}} = 2.58$

p-value is the upper tail area at $z = 2.58$

Using normal table with $z = 2.58$: p-value $= 1.0000 - .9951 = .0049$

c. p-value $\leq .01$, reject H_0. Conclude that the mean daily background television that children from low-income families are exposed to is greater than four hours.

49. The hypothesis test that will allow us to conclude that the consensus estimate has increased is given below.

H_0: $\mu \leq 250{,}000$
H_a: $\mu > 250{,}000$

$t = \dfrac{\bar{x} - \mu_0}{s / \sqrt{n}} = \dfrac{266{,}000 - 250{,}000}{24{,}000 / \sqrt{20}} = 2.981$

Degrees of freedom $= n - 1 = 19$

Upper tail p-value is the area to the right of the test statistic

Using t table: p-value is less than .005

Exact p-value corresponding to $t = 2.981$ is .0038

p-value $\leq .01$; reject H_0. The consensus estimate has increased.

50. H_0: $\mu = 25$
H_a: $\mu \neq 25$

$t = \dfrac{\bar{x} - \mu_0}{s / \sqrt{n}} = \dfrac{24.0476 - 25.0}{5.8849 / \sqrt{42}} = -1.05$

Degrees of freedom $= n - 1 = 41$

Because $t < 0$, p-value is two times the lower tail area

Using t table: area in lower tail is between .10 and .20; therefore, p-value is between

.20 and .40.

Exact p-value corresponding to $t = -1.05$ is .2999

Because p-value $> \alpha = .05$, do not reject H_0. There is no evidence to conclude that the mean age at which women had their first child has changed.

51.   a. H_0: $\mu \leq 520$
           H_a: $\mu > 520$

      b.   Sample mean: 637.94

           Sample standard deviation: 148.4694

           $$t = \frac{\overline{x} - \mu_0}{s / \sqrt{n}} = \frac{637.94 - 520}{148.4694 / \sqrt{50}} = 5.62$$

           Degrees of freedom $= n - 1 = 49$

           p-value is the area in the upper tail

           Using t table: p-value is $< .005$

           Exact p-value corresponding to $t = 5.62 \approx 0$

      c.   We can conclude that the mean weekly pay for all women is higher than that for women with only a high school degree.

      d.   Using the critical value approach we would:

           Reject H_0 if $t \geq t_{.05} = 1.677$

           Since $t = 5.62 > 1.677$, we reject H_0.

52. H_0: $\mu \leq 125{,}000$
      H_a: $\mu > 125{,}000$

      $$t = \frac{\overline{x} - \mu_0}{s / \sqrt{n}} = \frac{130{,}000 - 125{,}000}{12{,}500 / \sqrt{32}} = 2.26$$

      Degrees of freedom $= 32 - 1 = 31$

      Upper tail p-value is the area to the right of the test statistic

      Using t table: p-value is between .01 and .025

      Exact p-value corresponding to $t = 2.26$ is .0155

      p-value $\leq .05$; reject H_0. Conclude that the mean cost is greater than \$125,000 per lot.

53. H_0: $\mu = 86$
      H_a: $\mu \neq 86$

      $\overline{x} = 80$

      $s = 20$

$$t = \frac{\bar{x} - \mu_0}{s/\sqrt{n}} = \frac{80 - 86}{20/\sqrt{40}} = -1.90$$

Degrees of freedom = 40 - 1 = 39

Because $t < 0$, p-value is two times the lower tail area

Using t table: area in lower tail is between .025 and .05; therefore, p-value is between .05 and .10.

Exact p-value corresponding to $t = -1.90$ is .0648

p-value > .05; do not reject H_0.

There is not a statistically significant difference between the population mean for the nearby county and the population mean of 86 days for Hamilton county.

54. a. H_0: $p \le .80$
       H_a: $p > .80$

$$\bar{p} = \frac{455}{542} = .84$$

$$z = \frac{\bar{p} - p_0}{\sqrt{\frac{p_0(1 - p_0)}{n}}} = \frac{.84 - .80}{\sqrt{\frac{.80(1 - .80)}{542}}} = 2.33$$

p-value is the area in the upper tail

Using normal table with $z = 2.33$: p-value = 1.0000 - .9901 = .0099

p-value $\le$ .05; reject H_0. We conclude that over 80% of airline travelers feel that use of the full body scanners will improve airline security.

b. H_0: $p \le .75$
   H_a: $p > .75$

$$\bar{p} = \frac{423}{542} = .78$$

$$z = \frac{\bar{p} - p_0}{\sqrt{\frac{p_0(1 - p_0)}{n}}} = \frac{.78 - .75}{\sqrt{\frac{.75(1 - .75)}{542}}} = 1.61$$

p-value is the area in the upper tail

Using normal table with $z = 1.61$: p-value = 1.0000 - .9463 = .0537

p-value > .01; we cannot reject H_0. Thus, we cannot conclude that over 75% of airline travelers approve of using full body scanners. Mandatory use of full body scanners is not recommended.

Author's note: The TSA is also considering making the use of full body scanners optional. Travelers would be given a choice of a full body scan or a pat down search.

55. a. H_0: $p = .6667$
    H_a: $p \neq .6667$

    b. $\bar{p} = \dfrac{355}{546} = .6502$

    c. $z = \dfrac{\bar{p} - p_0}{\sqrt{\dfrac{p_0(1 - p_0)}{n}}} = \dfrac{.6502 - .6667}{\sqrt{\dfrac{.6667(1 - .6667)}{546}}} = -.82$

    Because $z < 0$, p-value is two times the lower tail area

    Using normal table with $z = -.82$: p-value $= 2(.2061) = .4122$

    p-value $> .05$; do not reject H_0; Cannot conclude that the population proportion differs from 2/3.

56. a. H_0: $p \leq .80$
    H_a: $p > .80$

    b. $\bar{p} = \dfrac{252}{300} = .84$ (84%)

    c. $z = \dfrac{\bar{p} - p_0}{\sqrt{\dfrac{p_0(1 - p_0)}{n}}} = \dfrac{.84 - .80}{\sqrt{\dfrac{.80(1 - .80)}{300}}} = 1.73$

    Upper tail p-value is the area to the right of the test statistic

    Using normal table with $z = 1.73$: p-value $= 1.0000 - .9582 = .0418$

    d. p-value $\leq .05$; reject H_0. Conclude that more than 80% of the customers are satisfied with the service provided by the home agents. Regional Airways should consider implementing the home agent system.

57. a. H_0: $p \leq .079$
    H_a: $p > .079$

    b. $z = \dfrac{\bar{p} - p_0}{\sqrt{\dfrac{p_0(1 - p_0)}{n}}} = \dfrac{.108 - .079}{\sqrt{\dfrac{(.079)(1 - .079)}{400}}} = 2.15$

    Upper tail p-value is the area to the right of the test statistic

    Using normal table with $z = 2.15$: p-value $= 1 - .9842 = .0158$

    Since p-value $= .0158 \leq \alpha = .05$, reject H_0. We can conclude that the unemployment rate for 18 to 34 year olds is significantly higher than the national unemployment rate of 7.9% for all adults.

c. You can tell the campaign manager that the observed level of significance is .0158 and that this means the results would have been significant even with α as small as .0158. Most reasonable people would reject the null hypotheses and conclude that the proportion of adults aged 18 to 34 who were unemployed was higher than the national unemployment rate for all adults.

58. H_0: $p \geq .90$
H_a: $p < .90$

$$\bar{p} = \frac{49}{58} = .8448$$

$$z = \frac{\bar{p} - p_0}{\sqrt{\dfrac{p_0(1 - p_0)}{n}}} = \frac{.8448 - .90}{\sqrt{\dfrac{.90(1 - .90)}{58}}} = -1.40$$

Lower tail p-value is the area to the left of the test statistic

Using normal table with $z = -1.40$: p-value = .0808

p-value > .05; do not reject H_0. Claim of at least 90% cannot be rejected.

59. a. The point estimate of the proportion of people aged 65-69 working is

$$\bar{p} = \frac{180}{600} = .30$$

b. H_0: $p \leq .27$
H_a: $p > .27$

c. $$z = \frac{\bar{p} - p_0}{\sqrt{\dfrac{p_0(1 - p_0)}{n}}} = \frac{.30 - .27}{\sqrt{\dfrac{.27(1 - .27)}{600}}} = 1.66$$

p-value is the upper tail area at $z = 1.66$

Using normal table with $z = 1.66$: p-value = 1 - .9515 = .0485

p-value $\leq .05$; reject H_0.

We conclude that the proportion of people aged 65-69 has increased since 2007.

Chapter 10
Comparisons Involving Means, Experimental Design, and Analysis of Variance

Learning Objectives

1. Be able to develop interval estimates and conduct hypothesis tests about the difference between two population means when σ_1 and σ_2 are known.

2. Know the properties of the sampling distribution of $\bar{x}_1 - \bar{x}_2$.

3. Be able to use the t distribution to conduct statistical inferences about the difference between two population means when σ_1 and σ_2 are unknown.

4. Learn how to analyze the difference between two population means when the samples are independent and when the samples are matched.

5. Understand the principles of experimental design.

6. Be able to analyze a completely randomized design.

7. Understand how the analysis of variance procedure can be used to determine if the means of more than two populations are equal.

8. Know the assumptions necessary to use the analysis of variance procedure.

9. Understand the use of the F distribution in performing the analysis of variance procedure.

10. Know how to set up an ANOVA table and interpret the entries in the table.

11. Be able to use output from computer software packages to solve analysis of variance problems.

Solutions:

1. a. $\bar{x}_1 - \bar{x}_2 = 13.6 - 11.6 = 2$

    b. $z_{\alpha/2} = z_{.05} = 1.645$

    $$\bar{x}_1 - \bar{x}_2 \pm 1.645 \sqrt{\frac{\sigma_1^2}{n_1} + \frac{\sigma_2^2}{n_2}}$$

    $$2 \pm 1.645 \sqrt{\frac{(2.2)^2}{50} + \frac{(3)^2}{35}}$$

    $2 \pm .98$ \qquad (1.02 to 2.98)

    c. $z_{\alpha/2} = z_{.025} = 1.96$

    $$2 \pm 1.96 \sqrt{\frac{(2.2)^2}{50} + \frac{(3)^2}{35}}$$

    2 ± 1.17 \qquad (.83 to 3.17)

2. a. $z = \dfrac{(\bar{x}_1 - \bar{x}_2) - D_0}{\sqrt{\dfrac{\sigma_1^2}{n_1} + \dfrac{\sigma_2^2}{n_2}}} = \dfrac{(25.2 - 22.8) - 0}{\sqrt{\dfrac{(5.2)^2}{40} + \dfrac{6^2}{50}}} = 2.03$

    b. p-value $= 1.0000 - .9788 = .0212$

    c. p-value $\le .05$, reject H_0.

3. a. $z = \dfrac{(\bar{x}_1 - \bar{x}_2) - D_0}{\sqrt{\dfrac{\sigma_1^2}{n_1} + \dfrac{\sigma_2^2}{n_2}}} = \dfrac{(104 - 106) - 0}{\sqrt{\dfrac{(8.4)^2}{80} + \dfrac{(7.6)^2}{70}}} = -1.53$

    b. p-value $= 2(.0630) = .1260$

    c. p-value $> .05$, do not reject H_0.

4. a. $\mu_1 =$ population mean for top-loading washing machines

    $\mu_2 =$ population mean for front-loading washing machines

    So the point estimate of the difference between the population mean rating for top-loading washing machines and front-loading washing machines is

    $\bar{x}_1 - \bar{x}_2 = 82.55 - 77.46 = 5.09$

    b. At 95% confidence, the margin of error is $z_{.025} \sqrt{\dfrac{\sigma_1^2}{n_1} + \dfrac{\sigma_2^2}{n_2}} = 1.96 \sqrt{\dfrac{(6.18)^2}{42} + \dfrac{(5.97)^2}{49}} = 2.51$

   c.   The 95% confidence interval estimate of the difference between the population mean ratings for the two types of washing machines is 5.09 ± 2.51 or (2.58 to 7.60). We estimate that top-loading washing machines receive a mean rating 5.09 points higher than do front-loading washing machines with a margin of error of 2.51 points.

5.   a.   The point estimate of the difference between the population mean expenditure for males and the population mean expenditure for females is

$$\bar{x}_1 - \bar{x}_2 = 12.9 - 8.4 = 4.5$$

   b.   At 99% confidence, the margin of error is $z_{\alpha/2}\sqrt{\dfrac{\sigma_1^2}{n_1} + \dfrac{\sigma_2^2}{n_2}} = 2.576\sqrt{\dfrac{(4.4)^2}{35} + \dfrac{(3.1)^2}{50}} = 2.22$

   c.   The 99% confidence interval for the difference between the two population means is 4.5 ± 2.22 or (2.28 to 6.72). Men consume a mean of 4.5 pounds more mozzarella cheese per year than do women with a margin of error of 2.22 pounds.

6. μ_1 = mean hotel price in Atlanta

        μ_2 = mean hotel price in Houston

$H_0: \mu_1 - \mu_2 \geq 0$

$H_a: \mu_1 - \mu_2 < 0$

$$z = \frac{(\bar{x}_1 - \bar{x}_2) - D_0}{\sqrt{\dfrac{\sigma_1^2}{n_1} + \dfrac{\sigma_2^2}{n_2}}} = \frac{(91.71 - 101.13) - 0}{\sqrt{\dfrac{20^2}{35} + \dfrac{25^2}{40}}} = -1.81$$

p-value = .0351

p-value $\leq$ .05; reject H_0. The mean price of a hotel room in Atlanta is lower than the mean price of a hotel room in Houston.

7.   a. μ_1 = population mean satisfaction score for Target customers

        μ_2 = population mean satisfaction score for Walmart customers

$H_0: \mu_1 - \mu_2 = 0$

$H_a: \mu_1 - \mu_2 \neq 0$

   b. $\bar{x}_1 - \bar{x}_2 = 79 - 71 = 8$

$$z = \frac{(\bar{x}_1 - \bar{x}_2) - D_0}{\sqrt{\dfrac{\sigma_1^2}{n_1} + \dfrac{\sigma_2^2}{n_2}}} = \frac{(79 - 71) - 0}{\sqrt{\dfrac{12^2}{25} + \dfrac{12^2}{30}}} = 2.46$$

For this two-tailed test, p-value is two times the upper-tail area at $z = 2.46$.

p-value = $2(1.0000 - .9931) = .0138$

p-value $\leq .05$; reject H_0. The population mean satisfaction scores differ for the two retailers.

c. $$\bar{x}_1 - \bar{x}_2 \pm z_{.025}\sqrt{\frac{\sigma_1^2}{n_1} + \frac{\sigma_2^2}{n_2}}$$

$$(79 - 71) \pm 1.96\sqrt{\frac{12^2}{25} + \frac{12^2}{30}}$$

8 ± 6.37 (1.63 to 14.37)

Target shows a higher population mean customer satisfaction score than Walmart with the 95% confidence interval indicating that Target has a population mean customer satisfaction score that is 1.63 to 14.37 higher than Walmart.

8.   a.   This is an upper tail hypothesis test.

$H_0: \mu_1 - \mu_2 \leq 0$
$H_a: \mu_1 - \mu_2 > 0$

$$z = \frac{(\bar{x}_1 - \bar{x}_2)}{\sqrt{\frac{\sigma_1^2}{n_1} + \frac{\sigma_2^2}{n_2}}} = \frac{(76 - 73)}{\sqrt{\frac{6^2}{60} + \frac{6^2}{60}}} = 2.74$$

p-value = area in upper tail at $z = 2.74$

p-value = 1.0000 - .9969 = .0031

Since $.0031 \leq \alpha = .05$, we reject the null hypothesis. The difference is significant. We can conclude that customer service has improved for Rite Aid.

b.   This is another upper tail test but it only involves one population.

$H_0: \mu \leq 75.7$
$H_a: \mu > 75.7$

$$z = \frac{(\bar{x}_1 - 75.7)}{\sqrt{\frac{\sigma^2}{n_1}}} = \frac{(76 - 75.7)}{\sqrt{\frac{6^2}{60}}} = .39$$

p-value = area in upper tail at $z = .39$

p-value = 1.0000 - .6517 = .3483

Since $.3483 > \alpha = .05$, we cannot reject the null hypothesis. The difference is not statistically significant.

c.   This is an upper tail test similar to the test in part (a).

$H_0: \mu_1 - \mu_2 \leq 0$

$H_a: \mu_1 - \mu_2 > 0$

$$z = \frac{(\bar{x}_1 - \bar{x}_2)}{\sqrt{\dfrac{\sigma_1^2}{n_1} + \dfrac{\sigma_2^2}{n_2}}} = \frac{(77 - 75)}{\sqrt{\dfrac{6^2}{60} + \dfrac{6^2}{60}}} = 1.83$$

p-value = area in upper tail at $z = 1.83$

p-value = 1.0000 - .9664 = .0336

Since $.0336 \le \alpha = .05$, we reject the null hypothesis. The difference is significant. We can conclude that customer service has improved for Expedia.

d. We will reject the null hypothesis of "no increase" if the p-value $\le .05$. For an upper tail hypothesis test, the p-value is the area in the upper tail at the value of the test statistic. A value of $z = 1.645$ provides an upper tail area of .05. So, we must solve the following equation for $\bar{x}_1 - \bar{x}_2$.

$$z = \frac{(\bar{x}_1 - \bar{x}_2)}{\sqrt{\dfrac{6^2}{60} + \dfrac{6^2}{60}}} = 1.645$$

$$\bar{x}_1 - \bar{x}_2 = 1.645\sqrt{\dfrac{6^2}{60} + \dfrac{6^2}{60}} = 1.80$$

This tells us that as long as the 2008 score for a company exceeds the 2007 score by 1.80 or more the difference will be statistically significant.

e. The increase from 2007 to 2008 for J.C. Penney is not statistically significant because it is less than 1.80. We cannot conclude that customer service has improved for J.C. Penney.

9. a. $\bar{x}_1 - \bar{x}_2 = 22.5 - 20.1 = 2.4$

b. $$df = \frac{\left(\dfrac{s_1^2}{n_1} + \dfrac{s_2^2}{n_2}\right)^2}{\dfrac{1}{n_1-1}\left(\dfrac{s_1^2}{n_1}\right)^2 + \dfrac{1}{n_2-1}\left(\dfrac{s_2^2}{n_2}\right)^2} = \frac{\left(\dfrac{2.5^2}{20} + \dfrac{4.8^2}{30}\right)^2}{\dfrac{1}{19}\left(\dfrac{2.5^2}{20}\right)^2 + \dfrac{1}{29}\left(\dfrac{4.8^2}{30}\right)^2} = 45.8$$

Use $df = 45$.

c. $t_{.025} = 2.014$

$$t_{.025}\sqrt{\dfrac{s_1^2}{n_1} + \dfrac{s_2^2}{n_2}} = 2.014\sqrt{\dfrac{2.5^2}{20} + \dfrac{4.8^2}{30}} = 2.1$$

d. 2.4 ± 2.1 (.3 to 4.5)

10. a. $t = \dfrac{(\bar{x}_1 - \bar{x}_2) - 0}{\sqrt{\dfrac{s_1^2}{n_1} + \dfrac{s_2^2}{n_2}}} = \dfrac{(13.6 - 10.1) - 0}{\sqrt{\dfrac{5.2^2}{35} + \dfrac{8.5^2}{40}}} = 2.18$

b. $df = \dfrac{\left(\dfrac{s_1^2}{n_1} + \dfrac{s_2^2}{n_2}\right)^2}{\dfrac{1}{n_1 - 1}\left(\dfrac{s_1^2}{n_1}\right)^2 + \dfrac{1}{n_2 - 1}\left(\dfrac{s_2^2}{n_2}\right)^2} = \dfrac{\left(\dfrac{5.2^2}{35} + \dfrac{8.5^2}{40}\right)^2}{\dfrac{1}{34}\left(\dfrac{5.2^2}{35}\right)^2 + \dfrac{1}{39}\left(\dfrac{8.5^2}{40}\right)^2} = 65.7$

Use $df = 65$

c. Using t table, area in tail is between .01 and .025

∴ two-tail p-value is between .02 and .05.

Exact p-value corresponding to $t = 2.18$ is .0329

d. p-value $\leq$ .05, reject H_0.

11. a. $\bar{x}_1 = \dfrac{54}{6} = 9 \qquad \bar{x}_2 = \dfrac{42}{6} = 7$

b. $s_1 = \sqrt{\dfrac{\Sigma(x_i - \bar{x}_1)^2}{n_1 - 1}} = 2.28$

$s_2 = \sqrt{\dfrac{\Sigma(x_i - \bar{x}_2)^2}{n_2 - 1}} = 1.79$

c. $\bar{x}_1 - \bar{x}_2 = 9 - 7 = 2$

d. $df = \dfrac{\left(\dfrac{s_1^2}{n_1} + \dfrac{s_2^2}{n_2}\right)^2}{\dfrac{1}{n_1 - 1}\left(\dfrac{s_1^2}{n_1}\right)^2 + \dfrac{1}{n_2 - 1}\left(\dfrac{s_2^2}{n_2}\right)^2} = \dfrac{\left(\dfrac{2.28^2}{6} + \dfrac{1.79^2}{6}\right)^2}{\dfrac{1}{5}\left(\dfrac{2.28^2}{6}\right)^2 + \dfrac{1}{5}\left(\dfrac{1.79^2}{6}\right)^2} = 9.5$

Use $df = 9$, $t_{.05} = 1.833$

$\bar{x}_1 - \bar{x}_2 \pm 1.833\sqrt{\dfrac{2.28^2}{6} + \dfrac{1.79^2}{6}}$

$2 \pm 2.17 \qquad\qquad (-.17 \text{ to } 4.17)$

12. a. $\bar{x}_1 - \bar{x}_2 = 22.5 - 18.6 = 3.9$

b. $$df = \frac{\left(\dfrac{s_1^2}{n_1} + \dfrac{s_2^2}{n_2}\right)^2}{\dfrac{1}{n_1-1}\left(\dfrac{s_1^2}{n_1}\right)^2 + \dfrac{1}{n_2-1}\left(\dfrac{s_2^2}{n_2}\right)^2} = \frac{\left(\dfrac{8.4^2}{50} + \dfrac{7.4^2}{40}\right)^2}{\dfrac{1}{49}\left(\dfrac{8.4^2}{50}\right)^2 + \dfrac{1}{39}\left(\dfrac{7.4^2}{40}\right)^2} = 87.1$$

Use $df = 87$, $t_{.025} = 1.988$

$$3.9 \pm 1.988\sqrt{\frac{8.4^2}{50} + \frac{7.4^2}{40}}$$

3.9 ± 3.3 (.6 to 7.2)

13. a. $$\bar{x}_1 = \frac{\Sigma x_i}{n_1} = \frac{425}{10} = 42.5$$

$$s_1 = \sqrt{\frac{\Sigma(x_i - \bar{x}_1)^2}{n_1-1}} = \sqrt{\frac{438.56}{10-1}} = 6.98$$

$$\bar{x}_2 = \frac{\Sigma x_i}{n_2} = 267.6 = 22.3$$

$$s_2 = \sqrt{\frac{\Sigma(x_i - \bar{x}_2)^2}{n_2-1}} = \sqrt{\frac{225.96}{12-1}} = 4.53$$

b. $\bar{x}_1 - \bar{x}_2 = 42.5 - 22.3 = 20.2$ or $20,200

The mean annual cost to attend private colleges is $20,200 more than the mean annual cost to attend public colleges.

c. $$df = \frac{\left(\dfrac{s_1^2}{n_1} + \dfrac{s_2^2}{n_2}\right)^2}{\dfrac{1}{n_1-1}\left(\dfrac{s_1^2}{n_1}\right)^2 + \dfrac{1}{n_2-1}\left(\dfrac{s_2^2}{n_2}\right)^2} = \frac{\left(\dfrac{6.98^2}{10} + \dfrac{4.53^2}{12}\right)^2}{\dfrac{1}{9}\left(\dfrac{6.98^2}{10}\right)^2 + \dfrac{1}{11}\left(\dfrac{4.53^2}{12}\right)^2} = 14.9$$

Use $df = 14$, $t_{.025} = 2.145$

$$(\bar{x}_1 - \bar{x}_2) \pm t_{.025}\sqrt{\frac{s_1^2}{n_1} + \frac{s_2^2}{n_2}}$$

$$20.2 \pm 2.145\sqrt{\frac{6.98^2}{10} + \frac{4.53^2}{12}}$$

20.3 ± 5.5 (14.8 to 25.8)

95% confidence interval, private colleges have a population mean annual cost $14,800 to $25,800 more expensive than public colleges.

14. a. μ_1 = population mean number of meals eaten at fast food chains per month by consumers in Oklahoma City

μ_2 = population mean number of meals eaten at fast food chains per month by consumers in Milwaukee

H_0: $\mu_1 - \mu_2 \geq 0$

H_a: $\mu_1 - \mu_2 < 0$

b. The value of the test statistic is

$$t = \frac{(\bar{x}_1 - \bar{x}_2) - 0}{\sqrt{\dfrac{s_1^2}{n_1} + \dfrac{s_2^2}{n_2}}} = \frac{(56.1 - 59.4) - 0^2}{\sqrt{\dfrac{6^2}{45} + \dfrac{7^2}{55}}} = -2.54$$

c. First we find the degrees of freedom:

$$df = \frac{\left(\dfrac{s_1^2}{n_1} + \dfrac{s_2^2}{n_2}\right)^2}{\dfrac{1}{n_1 - 1}\left(\dfrac{s_1^2}{n_1}\right)^2 + \dfrac{1}{n_2 - 1}\left(\dfrac{s_2^2}{n_2}\right)^2} = \frac{\left(\dfrac{6^2}{45} + \dfrac{7^2}{55}\right)^2}{\dfrac{1}{45 - 1}\left(\dfrac{6^2}{45}\right)^2 + \dfrac{1}{55 - 1}\left(\dfrac{7^2}{55}\right)^2} = 97.77$$

Rounding down, use a t distribution with 97degrees of freedom. From the t table $t = -2.54$ corresponds to a p-value between .005 and .01.

The p-value corresponding to $t = -2.54$ is .0063.

d. The p-value $\leq$ .05, so reject H_0 and conclude that the mean number of meals eaten at fast food chains per month is less in Oklahoma City than in Milwaukee.

15. a. μ_1 = population mean annual lease rate per square meter in Hong Kong

μ_2 = population mean annual lease rate per square meter in Paris

H_0: $\mu_1 - \mu_2 \leq 0$

H_a: $\mu_1 - \mu_2 > 0$

b. $\bar{x}_1 - \bar{x}_2 = \$1114 - \$989 = \$125$ per square meter

$$t = \frac{(\bar{x}_1 - \bar{x}_2) - 0}{\sqrt{\dfrac{s_1^2}{n_1} + \dfrac{s_2^2}{n_2}}} = \frac{(1114 - 989) - 0}{\sqrt{\dfrac{230^2}{30} + \dfrac{195^2}{40}}} = 2.40$$

$$df = \frac{\left(\dfrac{s_1^2}{n_1} + \dfrac{s_2^2}{n_2}\right)^2}{\dfrac{1}{n_1-1}\left(\dfrac{s_1^2}{n_1}\right)^2 + \dfrac{1}{n_2-1}\left(\dfrac{s_2^2}{n_2}\right)^2} = \frac{\left(\dfrac{230^2}{30} + \dfrac{195^2}{40}\right)^2}{\dfrac{1}{29}\left(\dfrac{230^2}{30}\right)^2 + \dfrac{1}{39}\left(\dfrac{195^2}{40}\right)^2} = 56.5$$

Use $df = 56$

Using t table, p-value is between .005 and .01.

Exact p-value corresponding to $t = 2.40$ is .0099

p-value $\le .01$, reject H_0. Conclusion: The annual lease rate in Hong Kong is significantly higher than in Paris.

16. a. μ_1 = population mean verbal score parents college grads

μ_2 = population mean verbal score parents high school grads

H_0: $\mu_1 - \mu_2 \le 0$
H_a: $\mu_1 - \mu_2 > 0$

b. $\bar{x}_1 = \dfrac{\Sigma x_i}{n} = \dfrac{8400}{16} = 525$

$\bar{x}_2 = \dfrac{\Sigma x_i}{n} = \dfrac{5844}{12} = 487$

$\bar{x}_1 - \bar{x}_2 = 525 - 487 = 38$ points higher if parents are college grads

c. $s_1 = \sqrt{\dfrac{\Sigma(x_i - \bar{x}_1)^2}{n_1 - 1}} = \sqrt{\dfrac{52962}{16-1}} = \sqrt{3530.8} = 59.42$

$s_2 = \sqrt{\dfrac{\Sigma(x_i - \bar{x}_2)^2}{n_2 - 1}} = \sqrt{\dfrac{29456}{12-1}} = \sqrt{2677.82} = 51.75$

$t = \dfrac{(\bar{x}_1 - \bar{x}_2) - D_0}{\sqrt{\dfrac{s_1^2}{n_1} + \dfrac{s_2^2}{n_2}}} = \dfrac{(525 - 487) - 0}{\sqrt{\dfrac{59.42^2}{16} + \dfrac{51.75^2}{12}}} = 1.80$

$$df = \frac{\left(\dfrac{s_1^2}{n_1} + \dfrac{s_2^2}{n_2}\right)^2}{\dfrac{1}{n_1-1}\left(\dfrac{s_1^2}{n_1}\right)^2 + \dfrac{1}{n_2-1}\left(\dfrac{s_2^2}{n_2}\right)^2} = \frac{\left(\dfrac{59.42^2}{16} + \dfrac{51.75^2}{12}\right)^2}{\dfrac{1}{15}\left(\dfrac{59.42^2}{16}\right)^2 + \dfrac{1}{11}\left(\dfrac{51.75^2}{12}\right)^2} = 25.3$$

Use $df = 25$

Using t table, p-value is between .025 and .05

Exact p-value corresponding to $t = 1.80$ is .0420

d. p-value $\le$ .05, reject H_0. Conclude higher population mean verbal scores for students whose parents are college grads.

17. a. H_0: $\mu_1 - \mu_2 \le 0$

      H_a: $\mu_1 - \mu_2 > 0$

b. $t = \dfrac{(\bar{x}_1 - \bar{x}_2) - D_0}{\sqrt{\dfrac{s_1^2}{n_1} + \dfrac{s_2^2}{n_2}}} = \dfrac{(6.82 - 6.25) - 0}{\sqrt{\dfrac{.64^2}{16} + \dfrac{.75^2}{10}}} = 1.99$

c. $df = \dfrac{\left(\dfrac{s_1^2}{n_1} + \dfrac{s_2^2}{n_2}\right)^2}{\dfrac{1}{n_1 - 1}\left(\dfrac{s_1^2}{n_1}\right)^2 + \dfrac{1}{n_2 - 1}\left(\dfrac{s_2^2}{n_2}\right)^2} = \dfrac{\left(\dfrac{.64^2}{16} + \dfrac{.75^2}{10}\right)^2}{\dfrac{1}{15}\left(\dfrac{.64^2}{16}\right)^2 + \dfrac{1}{9}\left(\dfrac{.75^2}{10}\right)^2} = 16.9$

Use $df = 16$

Using t table, p-value is between .025 and .05

Exact p-value corresponding to $t = 1.99$ is .0320

d. p-value $\le$ .05, reject H_0. The consultant with more experience has a higher population mean rating.

18. a. Let μ_1 = population mean minutes late for delayed AirTran flights

        μ_2 = population mean minutes late for delayed Southwest flights

    H_0: $\mu_1 - \mu_2 = 0$

    H_a: $\mu_1 - \mu_2 \ne 0$

b. $\bar{x}_1 = \dfrac{\sum\limits_{i=1}^{n} x_i}{n_1} = \dfrac{1265}{25} = 50.6\,\text{minutes}$

    $\bar{x}_2 = \dfrac{\sum\limits_{i=1}^{n} x_i}{n_2} = \dfrac{1056}{20} = 52.8\,\text{minutes}$

The difference between sample mean delay times is $50.6 - 52.8 = -2.2$ minutes, which indicates the sample mean delay time is 2.2 minutes less for AirTran Airways.

c. Sample standard deviations: $s_1 = 26.57$ and $s_2 = 20.11$

$$t = \frac{(\bar{x}_1 - \bar{x}_2) - D_0}{\sqrt{\dfrac{s_1^2}{n_1} + \dfrac{s_2^2}{n_2}}} = \frac{(50.6 - 52.8) - 0}{\sqrt{\dfrac{26.57^2}{25} + \dfrac{20.11^2}{20}}} = -.32$$

$$df = \frac{\left(\dfrac{s_1^2}{n_1} + \dfrac{s_2^2}{n_2}\right)^2}{\dfrac{1}{n_1-1}\left(\dfrac{s_1^2}{n_1}\right)^2 + \dfrac{1}{n_2-1}\left(\dfrac{s_2^2}{n_2}\right)^2} = \frac{\left(\dfrac{26.57^2}{25} + \dfrac{20.11^2}{20}\right)^2}{\dfrac{1}{24}\left(\dfrac{26.57^2}{25}\right)^2 + \dfrac{1}{19}\left(\dfrac{20.11^2}{20}\right)^2} = 42.9$$

Use $df = 42$

p-value for this two-tailed test is two times the lower-tail area for $t = -.32$.

Using t table, p-value is greater than $2(.20) = .40$

Exact p-value corresponding to $t = -.32$ with 42 df is .7506

p-value $> .05$, do not reject H_0. We cannot reject the assumption that the population mean delay times are the same at AirTran Airways and Southwest Airlines. There is no statistical evidence that one airline does better than the other in terms of their population mean delay time.

19. a. 1, 2, 0, 0, 2

   b. $\bar{d} = \Sigma d_i / n = 5/5 = 1$

   c. $s_d = \sqrt{\dfrac{\Sigma(d_i - \bar{d})^2}{n-1}} = \sqrt{\dfrac{4}{5-1}} = 1$

   d. $t = \dfrac{\bar{d} - \mu_d}{s_d / \sqrt{n}} = \dfrac{1-0}{1/\sqrt{5}} = 2.24$

   $df = n - 1 = 4$

   Using t table, p-value is between .025 and .05

   Exact p-value corresponding to $t = 2.24$ is .0443

   Reject H_0; conclude $\mu_d > 0$.

20. a. 3, -1, 3, 5, 3, 0, 1

   b. $\bar{d} = \Sigma d_i / n = 14/7 = 2$

   c. $s_d = \sqrt{\dfrac{\Sigma(d_i - \bar{d})^2}{n-1}} = \sqrt{\dfrac{26}{7-1}} = 2.08$

   d. $\bar{d} = 2$

e. With 6 degrees of freedom $t_{.025} = 2.447$

$$2 \pm 2.447 \left(2.082 / \sqrt{7} \right)$$

2 ± 1.93 (.07 to 3.93)

21.   Difference = rating after - rating before

H_0: $\mu_d \leq 0$
H_a: $\mu_d > 0$

$\bar{d} = .625$ and $s_d = 1.30$

$$t = \frac{\bar{d} - \mu_d}{s_d / \sqrt{n}} = \frac{.625 - 0}{1.30 / \sqrt{8}} = 1.36$$

$df = n - 1 = 7$

Using t table, p-value is between .10 and .20

Exact p-value corresponding to $t = 1.36$ is .1080

Do not reject H_0; we cannot conclude that seeing the commercial improves the mean potential to purchase.

22. a.   Let $d_i = 1^{st}$ quarter price per share – beginning of year price per share

$$\bar{d} = \frac{\sum d_i}{n} = \frac{85.25}{25} = 3.41$$

b. $$s_d = \sqrt{\frac{\sum (d_i - \bar{d})^2}{n-1}} = \sqrt{\frac{428.26}{25-1}} = 4.22$$

With $df = 24$, $t_{.025} = 2.064$

$$\bar{d} \pm t_{.025} \frac{s_d}{\sqrt{n}}$$

$$3.41 \pm 2.064 \left(\frac{4.22}{\sqrt{25}} \right)$$

Confidence interval: $3.41 \pm \$1.74$ ($1.67 to $5.15)

The 95% confidence interval shows that the population mean price per share of stock has increased between $1.67 and $5.15 over the three-month period.

Note that at the beginning of year

$$\bar{x} = \frac{\sum x_i}{n} = \frac{1153.16}{25} = \$46.13$$

With this as the sample mean price per share of stock at the beginning of 2012, the confidence interval ($1.67 to $5.15) indicates the percentage change in the population mean price per share of stock would have increased from

1.67/46.13 = .036, or 3.6%

to 5.15/46.13 = .112, or 11.2%

Thus, for the population of stocks, the mean price per share has increase between 3.6% and 11.2% over the three-month period. This was excellent news for the 1st quarter of 2012. Stock prices were having one of the largest quarterly increases in years. The outlook for a recovering economy was very good at the end of the 1st quarter of 2012.

23. a. μ_1 = population mean grocery expenditures

   μ_2 = population mean dining-out expenditures

   H_0: $\mu_d = 0$
   H_a: $\mu_d \neq 0$

   b. $t = \dfrac{\overline{d} - \mu_d}{s_d / \sqrt{n}} = \dfrac{850 - 0}{1123 / \sqrt{42}} = 4.91$

   $df = n - 1 = 41$

   p-value ≈ 0

   Conclude that there is a difference between the annual population mean expenditures for groceries and for dining-out.

   c. Groceries has the higher mean annual expenditure by an estimated $850.

   $\overline{d} \pm t_{.025} \dfrac{s_d}{\sqrt{n}}$

   $850 \pm 2.020 \dfrac{1123}{\sqrt{42}}$

   850 ± 350 \qquad (500 to 1200)

24. a. Difference = Current Year Airfare – Previous Year Airfare

   H_0: $\mu_d \leq 0$
   H_a: $\mu_d > 0$

   Differences 30, 63, -42, 10, 10, -27, 50, 60, 60, -30, 62, 30

   $\overline{d} = \dfrac{\Sigma d_i}{n} = \dfrac{276}{12} = 23$

$$s_d = \sqrt{\frac{\sum(d_i - \bar{d})^2}{n-1}} = \sqrt{\frac{16{,}558}{12-1}} = 38.80$$

$$t = \frac{\bar{d} - 0}{s_d/\sqrt{n}} = \frac{23-0}{38.80/\sqrt{12}} = 2.05$$

$df = n - 1 = 11$

Using t table, p-value is between .05 and .025

Exact p-value corresponding to $t = 2.05$ is .0325

Since p-value $< .05$, reject H_0. We can conclude that there has been a significance increase in business travel airfares over the one-year period.

b. Current year: $\bar{x} = \sum x_i / n = 5844/12 = \$487$

Previous year: $\bar{x} = \sum x_i / n = 5568/12 = \$464$

c. One-year increase = $\$487 - \$464 = \$23$

$\$23/\$464 = .05$, or a 5% increase in business travel airfares for the one-year period.

25. a. Difference = math score – writing score

H_0: $\mu_d = 0$
H_a: $\mu_d \neq 0$

Use difference data: 66, 52, 65, -38, 28, -24, 50, 40, -5, 31, 55, -20

$$\bar{d} = \frac{\sum d_i}{n} = \frac{300}{12} = 25$$

$$s_d = \sqrt{\frac{\sum(d_i - \bar{d})^2}{n-1}} = \sqrt{\frac{15{,}100}{12-1}} = 37.05$$

$$t = \frac{\bar{d} - \mu_d}{s_d/\sqrt{n}} = \frac{25-0}{37.05/\sqrt{12}} = -2.34$$

$df = n - 1 = 11$

Using t table, lower-tail area is between .025 and .01.

Thus, the two-tailed test p-value is between .05 and .02.

Exact p-value corresponding to $t = -2.34$ is .0392

p-value $\leq .05$, reject H_0. Conclude that there is a significant difference between the population mean scores for the SAT math test and the SAT writing test.

10 - 14

b. $\bar{d} = 25$

$$\bar{x}_M = \frac{\sum x_i}{n} = \frac{6168}{12} = 514 \text{ for the math test}$$

$$\bar{x}_W = \frac{\sum x_i}{n} = \frac{5868}{12} = 489 \text{ for the writing test}$$

The SAT math test has a higher mean score than the SAT writing test.

26. a. H_0: $\mu_d = 0$
H_a: $\mu_d \neq 0$

Differences: -2, -1, -5, 1, 1, 0, 4, -7, -6, 1, 0, 2, -3, -7, -2, 3, 1, 2, 1, -4

$$\bar{d} = \sum d_i / n = -21 / 20 = -1.05$$

$$s_d = \sqrt{\frac{\sum(d_i - \bar{d})^2}{n-1}} = 3.3162$$

$$t = \frac{\bar{d} - \mu_d}{s_d / \sqrt{n}} = \frac{-1.05 - 0}{3.3162 / \sqrt{20}} = -1.42$$

$df = n - 1 = 19$

Using t table, area in tail is between .05 and .10

Two-tail p-value must be between .10 and .20

Exact p-value corresponding to t = -1.42 is .1718

Cannot reject H_0. There is no significant difference between the mean scores for the first and fourth rounds.

b. $\bar{d}$ = -1.05; First round scores were lower than fourth round scores.

c. $\alpha = .05$ $\qquad$ $df = 19$ $\qquad$ $t = 1.729$

$$\text{Margin of error} = t_{.025} \frac{s_d}{\sqrt{n}} = 1.729 \frac{3.3162}{\sqrt{20}} = 1.28$$

Yes, just check to see if the 90% confidence interval includes a difference of zero. If it does, the difference is not statistically significant.

90% Confidence interval: -1.05 ± 1.28 (-2.33, .23)

The interval does include 0, so the difference is not statistically significant.

27. a. $\bar{\bar{x}} = (156 + 142 + 134)/3 = 144$

$$SSTR = \sum_{j=1}^{k} n_j \left(\bar{x}_j - \bar{\bar{x}}\right)^2 = 6(156 - 144)^2 + 6(142 - 144)^2 + 6(134 - 144)^2 = 1{,}488$$

   b. $MSTR = SSTR/(k-1) = 1488/2 = 744$

   c. $s_1^2 = 164.4 \quad s_2^2 = 131.2 \quad s_3^2 = 110.4$

$$SSE = \sum_{j=1}^{k} (n_j - 1)s_j^2 = 5(164.4) + 5(131.2) + 5(110.4) = 2030$$

   d. $MSE = SSE/(n_T - k) = 2030/(12 - 3) = 135.3$

   e.

Source of Variation	Sum of Squares	Degrees of Freedom	Mean Square	F	p-value
Treatments	1488	2	744	5.50	.0162
Error	2030	15	135.3		
Total	3518	17			

   f. $F = MSTR/MSE = 744/135.3 = 5.50$

   Using F table (2 degrees of freedom numerator and 15 denominator), p-value is between .01 and .025

   Using Excel or Minitab, the p-value corresponding to $F = 5.50$ is .0162.

   Because p-value $\leq \alpha = .05$, we reject the hypothesis that the means for the three treatments are equal.

28.

Source of Variation	Sum of Squares	Degrees of Freedom	Mean Square	F	p-value
Treatments	300	4	75	14.07	.0000
Error	160	30	5.33		
Total	460	34			

29. a. $H_0: u_1 = u_2 = u_3 = u_4 = u_5$

   H_a: Not all the population means are equal

   b. Using F table (4 degrees of freedom numerator and 30 denominator), p-value is less than .01

   Using Excel or Minitab, the p-value corresponding to $F = 14.07$ is .0000.

   Because p-value $\leq \alpha = .05$, we reject H_0

10 - 16

30.

Source of Variation	Sum of Squares	Degrees of Freedom	Mean Square	F	p-value
Treatments	150	2	75	4.80	.0233
Error	250	16	15.63		
Total	400	18			

Using F table (2 degrees of freedom numerator and 16 denominator), p-value is between .01 and .025

Using Excel or Minitab, the p-value corresponding to $F = 4.80$ is .0233.

Because p-value $\leq \alpha = .05$, we reject the null hypothesis that the means of the three treatments are equal.

31.

Source of Variation	Sum of Squares	Degrees of Freedom	Mean Square	F	p-value
Treatments	1200	2	600	43.99	.0000
Error	600	44	13.64		
Total	1800	46			

Using F table (2 degrees of freedom numerator and 44 denominator), p-value is less than .01

Using Excel or Minitab, the p-value corresponding to $F = 43.99$ is .0000.

Because p-value $\leq \alpha = .05$, we reject the hypothesis that the treatment means are equal.

32.

	A	B	C
Sample Mean	119	107	100
Sample Variance	146.89	96.43	173.78

$$\bar{\bar{x}} = \frac{8(119) + 10(107) + 10(100)}{28} = 107.93$$

$$\text{SSTR} = \sum_{j=1}^{k} n_j \left(\bar{x}_j - \bar{\bar{x}} \right)^2 = 8(119 - 107.93)^2 + 10(107 - 107.93)^2 + 10(100 - 107.93)^2 = 1617.9$$

$$\text{MSTR} = \text{SSTR} / (k - 1) = 1617.9 / 2 = 809.95$$

$$\text{SSE} = \sum_{j=1}^{k} (n_j - 1)s_j^2 = 7(146.86) + 9(96.44) + 9(173.78) = 3,460$$

$$\text{MSE} = \text{SSE} / (n_T - k) = 3,460 / (28 - 3) = 138.4$$

$$F = \text{MSTR} / \text{MSE} = 809.95 / 138.4 = 5.85$$

Using F table (2 degrees of freedom numerator and 25 denominator), p-value is less than .01

Using Excel or Minitab, the p-value corresponding to $F = 5.85$ is .0082.

Because $p\text{-value} \le \alpha = .05$, we reject the null hypothesis that the means of the three treatments are equal.

33. a.

Source of Variation	Sum of Squares	Degrees of Freedom	Mean Square	F	p-value
Treatments	4560	2	2280	9.87	.0006
Error	6240	27	231.11		
Total	10800	29			

b. Using F table (2 degrees of freedom numerator and 27 denominator), p-value is less than .01

Using Excel or Minitab, the p-value corresponding to $F = 9.87$ is .0006.

Because $p\text{-value} \le \alpha = .05$, we reject the null hypothesis that the means of the three assembly methods are equal.

34. $\bar{\bar{x}} = (79 + 74 + 66)/3 = 73$

$$\text{SSTR} = \sum_{j=1}^{k} n_j \left(\bar{x}_j - \bar{\bar{x}}\right)^2 = 6(79 - 73)^2 + 6(74 - 73)^2 + 6(66 - 73)^2 = 516$$

$\text{MSTR} = \text{SSTR}/(k-1) = 516/2 = 258$

$s_1^2 = 34 \quad s_2^2 = 20 \quad s_3^2 = 32$

$$\text{SSE} = \sum_{j=1}^{k} (n_j - 1)s_j^2 = 5(34) + 5(20) + 5(32) = 430$$

$\text{MSE} = \text{SSE}/(n_T - k) = 430/(18 - 3) = 28.67$

$F = \text{MSTR}/\text{MSE} = 258/28.67 = 9.00$

Source of Variation	Sum of Squares	Degrees of Freedom	Mean Square	F	p-value
Treatments	516	2	258	9.00	.003
Error	430	15	28.67		
Total	946	17			

Using F table (2 degrees of freedom numerator and 15 denominator), p-value is less than .01

Using Excel or Minitab the p-value corresponding to $F = 9.00$ is .003.

Because $p\text{-value} \le \alpha = .05$, we reject the null hypothesis that the means for the three plants are equal. In other words, analysis of variance supports the conclusion that the population mean examination score at the three NCP plants are not equal.

35.

	50°	60°	70°
Sample Mean	33	29	28
Sample Variance	32	17.5	9.5

$\bar{\bar{x}} = (33 + 29 + 28)/3 = 30$

$$\text{SSTR} = \sum_{j=1}^{k} n_j \left(\bar{x}_j - \bar{\bar{x}} \right)^2 = 5(33 - 30)^2 + 5(29 - 30)^2 + 5(28 - 30)^2 = 70$$

$\text{MSTR} = \text{SSTR}/(k - 1) = 70/2 = 35$

$$\text{SSE} = \sum_{j=1}^{k} (n_j - 1)s_j^2 = 4(32) + 4(17.5) + 4(9.5) = 236$$

$\text{MSE} = \text{SSE}/(n_T - k) = 236/(15 - 3) = 19.67$

$F = \text{MSTR}/\text{MSE} = 35/19.67 = 1.78$

Using F table (2 degrees of freedom numerator and 12 denominator), p-value is greater than .10

Using Excel or Minitab the p-value corresponding to $F = 1.78$ is .2104.

Because p-value $> \alpha = .05$, we cannot reject the null hypothesis that the mean yields for the three temperatures are equal.

36.

	Direct Experience	Indirect Experience	Combination
Sample Mean	17.0	20.4	25.0
Sample Variance	5.01	6.26	4.01

$\bar{\bar{x}} = (17 + 20.4 + 25)/3 = 20.8$

$$\text{SSTR} = \sum_{j=1}^{k} n_j \left(\bar{x}_j - \bar{\bar{x}} \right)^2 = 7(17 - 20.8)^2 + 7(20.4 - 20.8)^2 + 7(25 - 20.8)^2 = 225.68$$

$\text{MSTR} = \text{SSTR}/(k - 1) = 225.68/2 = 112.84$

$$\text{SSE} = \sum_{j=1}^{k} (n_j - 1)s_j^2 = 6(5.01) + 6(6.26) + 6(4.01) = 91.68$$

$\text{MSE} = \text{SSE}/(n_T - k) = 91.68/(21 - 3) = 5.09$

$F = \text{MSTR}/\text{MSE} = 112.84/5.09 = 22.17$

Using F table (2 degrees of freedom numerator and 18 denominator), p-value is less than .01

Using Excel or Minitab the p-value corresponding to $F = 22.17$ is .0000.

Because $p\text{-value} \le \alpha = .05$, we reject the null hypothesis that the means for the three groups are equal.

37.

	Paint 1	Paint 2	Paint 3	Paint 4
Sample Mean	13.3	139	136	144
Sample Variance	47.5	.50	21	54.5

$\bar{\bar{x}} = (133 + 139 + 136 + 144)/3 = 138$

$$\text{SSTR} = \sum_{j=1}^{k} n_j \left(\bar{x}_j - \bar{\bar{x}} \right)^2 = 5(133 - 138)^2 + 5(139 - 138)^2 + 5(136 - 138)^2 + 5(144 - 138)^2 = 330$$

$\text{MSTR} = \text{SSTR}/(k-1) = 330/3 = 110$

$$\text{SSE} = \sum_{j=1}^{k} (n_j - 1) s_j^2 = 4(47.5) + 4(50) + 4(21) + 4(54.5) = 692$$

$\text{MSE} = \text{SSE}/(n_T - k) = 692/(20 - 4) = 43.25$

$F = \text{MSTR}/\text{MSE} = 110/43.25 = 2.54$

Using F table (3 degrees of freedom numerator and 16 denominator), $p\text{-value}$ is between .05 and .10

Using Excel or Minitab the $p\text{-value}$ corresponding to $F = 2.54$ is .0931.

Because $p\text{-value} > \alpha = .05$, we cannot reject the null hypothesis that the mean drying times for the four paints are equal.

38.

	Italian	Seafood	Steakhouse
Sample Mean	17	19	24
Sample Variance	14.857	13.714	14.000

$\bar{\bar{x}} = (17 + 19 + 24)/3 = 20$

$$\text{SSTR} = \sum_{j=1}^{k} n_j \left(\bar{x}_j - \bar{\bar{x}} \right)^2 = 8(17 - 20)^2 + 8(19 - 20)^2 + 8(24 - 20)^2 = 208$$

$\text{MSTR} = \text{SSTR}/(k-1) = 208/2 = 104$

$$\text{SSE} = \sum_{j=1}^{k} (n_j - 1) s_j^2 = 7(14.857) + 7(13.714) + 7(14.000) = 298$$

$\text{MSE} = \text{SSE}/(n_T - k) = 298/(24 - 3) = 14.19$

$F = \text{MSTR}/\text{MSE} = 104/14.19 = 7.33$

Using the F table (2 degrees of freedom numerator and 21 denominator), the $p\text{-value}$ is less than .01.

Using Excel or Minitab the p-value corresponding to $F = 7.33$ is .0038.

Because p-value $\leq \alpha = .05$, we reject the null hypothesis that the mean meal prices are the same for the three types of restaurants.

39. a. $\bar{x}_1 = \dfrac{\Sigma x_i}{n_1} = \dfrac{569,460}{40} = 14,236.5$ 2009 Corolla XRS Sedans that have navigation systems

$\bar{x}_2 = \dfrac{\Sigma x_i}{n_2} = \dfrac{721,490}{50} = 14,429.8$ 2009 Corolla XRS Sedans that do not have navigation systems

So the point estimate of the difference between the population mean prices for 2009 Corolla XRS Sedans that have navigation systems and 2009 Corolla XRS Sedans that do not have navigation systems is $\bar{x}_1 - \bar{x}_2 = 14,236.5 - 14,429.8 = -193.3$

Using sample mean prices, the resale price of 2009 Corolla XRS Sedans that have navigation systems is \$193.30 less than for 2009 Corolla XRS Sedans that do not have navigation systems.

b.   The margin of error $= z_{.025}\sqrt{\dfrac{\sigma_1^2}{n_1} + \dfrac{\sigma_2^2}{n_2}} = 1.96\sqrt{\dfrac{2000^2}{40} + \dfrac{2000^2}{50}} = 1.96(424.26) = 831.56$

c.   The 95% confidence interval is -193.3 ± 831.56 or $(-1024.86$ to $638.26)$. We are 95% confident that the difference in the resale prices of 2009 Corolla XRS Sedans that have navigation systems and 2009 Corolla XRS Sedans that do not have navigation systems is between $-\$1024.86$ to \$638.26.

40. $H_0\colon \mu_1 - \mu_2 = 0$
$H_a\colon \mu_1 - \mu_2 \neq 0$

$z = \dfrac{(\bar{x}_1 - \bar{x}_2) - D_0}{\sqrt{\dfrac{\sigma_1^2}{n_1} + \dfrac{\sigma_2^2}{n_2}}} = \dfrac{(4.1 - 3.4) - 0}{\sqrt{\dfrac{(2.2)^2}{120} + \dfrac{(1.5)^2}{100}}} = 2.79$

p-value $= 2(1.0000 - .9974) = .0052$

p-value $\leq .05$, reject H_0. A difference exists with system B having the lower mean checkout time.

41. a. $\bar{x}_1 = \dfrac{\Sigma x_i}{n_1} = \dfrac{3850}{14} = 275$ anesthesiologists from east of the Mississippi River

$\bar{x}_2 = \dfrac{\Sigma x_i}{n_2} = \dfrac{4522}{14} = 323$ anesthesiologists from west of the Mississippi River

The point estimate of the difference between the population incomes for anesthesiologists east of the Mississippi River and west of the Mississippi River is $\bar{x}_1 - \bar{x}_2 = 275 - 323 = -48$

Using sample mean prices, annual income for anesthesiologists from east of the Mississippi River is \$48,000 less than the annual income for anesthesiologists from west of the Mississippi.

b. The sample standard deviations of incomes for anesthesiologists from east of the Mississippi River is

$$s_1 = \sqrt{\frac{\Sigma(x_i - \overline{x}_1)^2}{n_1 - 1}} = 39.00$$

The sample standard deviations of incomes for anesthesiologists from west of the Mississippi River is

$$s_2 = \sqrt{\frac{\Sigma(x_i - \overline{x}_2)^2}{n_2 - 1}} = 53.55$$

The degrees of freedom is

$$df = \frac{\left(\dfrac{s_1^2}{n_1} + \dfrac{s_2^2}{n_2}\right)^2}{\dfrac{1}{n_1 - 1}\left(\dfrac{s_1^2}{n_1}\right)^2 + \dfrac{1}{n_2 - 1}\left(\dfrac{s_2^2}{n_2}\right)^2} = \frac{\left(\dfrac{39.00^2}{14} + \dfrac{53.55^2}{14}\right)^2}{\dfrac{1}{13}\left(\dfrac{39.00^2}{14}\right)^2 + \dfrac{1}{13}\left(\dfrac{53.55^2}{14}\right)^2} = 23.76$$

Rounding down, use a t distribution with 23 degrees of freedom. From the t table $t_{.005} = 2.807$ The 99% confidence interval estimate of the difference between the population mean incomes for anesthesiologists east of the Mississippi River and west of the Mississippi River is

$$(\overline{x}_1 - \overline{x}_2) \pm t_{.005}\sqrt{\frac{s_1^2}{n_1} + \frac{s_2^2}{n_2}} = -48 \pm 2.807\sqrt{\frac{39.00^2}{14} + \frac{53.55^2}{14}} = -48\ 48 \pm 49.7 \text{ or } (-97.7 \text{ to } 1.7)$$

We are 99% confident that the difference in the annual income for anesthesiologists east of the Mississippi River and the annual income for anesthesiologists from west of the Mississippi is between –\$97,700 and \$1,700.

c. To answer this question, conduct a one-tailed hypothesis test.

μ_1 = population mean annual income for anesthesiologists east of the Mississippi River

μ_2 = population mean annual income for anesthesiologists west of the Mississippi River

$H_0 : \mu_1 - \mu_2 \geq 0$
$H_a : \mu_1 - \mu_2 < 0$

$$t = \frac{\overline{x}_1 - \overline{x}_2}{\sqrt{\dfrac{s_1^2}{n_1} + \dfrac{s_2^2}{n_2}}} = \frac{-48}{\sqrt{\dfrac{39.00^2}{14} + \dfrac{53.55^2}{14}}} = -2.71$$

For $t = -2.71$ and $df = 23$, the p-value = .0062. Because the p-value is less than .01 we reject the null hypothesis that the annual income of anesthesiologists east of the Mississippi River is less than annual incomes of anesthesiologists west of the Mississippi.

42. a. $H_0 : \mu_1 - \mu_2 \le 0$

   $H_a : \mu_1 - \mu_2 > 0$

   b. $n_1 = 30$ $n_2 = 30$

   $\bar{x}_1 = 16.23$ $\bar{x}_2 = 15.70$

   $s_1 = 3.52$ $s_2 = 3.31$

$$t = \frac{(\bar{x}_1 - \bar{x}_2) - D_0}{\sqrt{\dfrac{s_1^2}{n_1} + \dfrac{s_2^2}{n_2}}} = \frac{(16.23 - 15.70) - 0}{\sqrt{\dfrac{(3.52)^2}{30} + \dfrac{(3.31)^2}{30}}} = .60$$

$$df = \frac{\left(\dfrac{s_1^2}{n_1} + \dfrac{s_2^2}{n_2}\right)^2}{\dfrac{1}{n_1-1}\left(\dfrac{s_1^2}{n_1}\right)^2 + \dfrac{1}{n_2-1}\left(\dfrac{s_2^2}{n_2}\right)^2} = \frac{\left(\dfrac{3.52^2}{30} + \dfrac{3.31^2}{30}\right)^2}{\dfrac{1}{29}\left(\dfrac{3.52^2}{30}\right)^2 + \dfrac{1}{29}\left(\dfrac{3.31^2}{30}\right)^2} = 57.8$$

Use $df = 57$

Using t table, p-value is greater than .20

Exact p-value corresponding to $t = .60$ is .2754

p-value $> .05$, do not reject H_0. Cannot conclude that the mutual funds with a load have a greater mean rate of return.

43. a. $n_1 = 10$ $n_2 = 8$

   $\bar{x}_1 = 21.2$ $\bar{x}_2 = 22.8$

   $s_1 = 2.70$ $s_2 = 3.55$

   $\bar{x}_1 - \bar{x}_2 = 21.2 - 22.8 = -1.6$

   Kitchens are less expensive by $1600.

   b. $$df = \frac{\left(\dfrac{s_1^2}{n_1} + \dfrac{s_2^2}{n_2}\right)^2}{\dfrac{1}{n_1-1}\left(\dfrac{s_1^2}{n_1}\right)^2 + \dfrac{1}{n_2-1}\left(\dfrac{s_2^2}{n_2}\right)^2} = \frac{\left(\dfrac{2.70^2}{10} + \dfrac{3.55^2}{8}\right)^2}{\dfrac{1}{9}\left(\dfrac{2.70^2}{10}\right)^2 + \dfrac{1}{7}\left(\dfrac{3.55^2}{8}\right)^2} = 12.9$$

Use $df = 12$, $t_{.05} = 1.782$

$$-1.6 \pm 1.782 \sqrt{\frac{2.70^2}{10} + \frac{3.55^2}{8}}$$

-1.6 ± 2.7 (-4.3 to 1.1)

44. a.

January 1	April 30	d_i	$(d_i - \bar{d})$	$(d_i - \bar{d})^2$
10.13	12.21	-2.08	-4.53	20.5209
28.33	25.48	2.85	0.40	0.1600
73.97	66.10	7.87	5.42	29.3764
16.30	19.32	-3.02	-5.47	29.9209
45.27	43.05	2.22	-0.23	0.0529
16.88	15.46	1.42	-1.03	1.0609
2.29	5.98	-3.69	-6.14	37.6996
16.20	12.65	3.55	1.10	1.2100
59.83	52.36	7.47	5.02	25.2004
31.53	33.00	-1.47	-3.92	15.3664
19.44	20.26	-0.82	-3.27	10.6929
17.73	19.34	-1.61	-4.06	16.4836
17.71	13.36	4.35	1.90	3.6100
43.51	36.18	7.33	4.88	23.8144
61.82	49.44	12.38	9.93	98.6049
	Sum	36.75		313.7742

$$\bar{d} = \frac{\sum d_i}{n} = \frac{36.75}{15} = 2.45 \qquad \text{The mean price per share declined \$2.45 over the four months.}$$

b. $\quad s_d = \sqrt{\dfrac{\sum (d_i - \bar{d})^2}{n-1}} = \sqrt{\dfrac{313.7742}{14}} = 4.73$

$df = n - 1 = 14, \quad t_{.05} = 1.761$

$$\bar{d} \pm t_{.05} \frac{s_d}{\sqrt{n}} \;=\; 2.45 \pm 1.761 \frac{4.73}{\sqrt{15}}$$

$2.45 \pm 2.15 \qquad (\$.30 \text{ to } \$4.60)$

We are 90% confident that the population mean price per share has decreased between \$.30 and \$4.60 over the four month period.

c. Sample mean price per share January 1: $\quad \bar{x} = \dfrac{\sum x_i}{n} = \dfrac{460.94}{15} = \$30.73$

Percentage decrease over the 4 months: $\dfrac{2.45}{30.73}(100) = 8\%$

d. Mean price per share December 31, 2009 = \$30.73(.92)(.92)(.92) = \$23.93. This is a decline of \$30.73 − 23.93 = \$6.80 per share for the year.

45.

	Lawyer	Physical Therapist	Cabinet Maker	Systems Analyst
Sample Mean	50.0	63.7	69.1	61.2
Sample Variance	124.22	164.68	105.88	136.62

$$\overline{\overline{x}} = \frac{50.0 + 63.7 + 69.1 + 61.2}{4} = 61$$

$$SSTR = \sum_{j=1}^{k} n_j \left(\overline{x}_j - \overline{\overline{x}} \right)^2 = 10(50.0 - 61)^2 + 10(63.7 - 61)^2 + 10(69.1 - 61)^2 + 10(61.2 - 61)^2 =$$

1939.4

MSTR = SSTR $/(k - 1)$ = 1939.4 /3 = 646.47

$$SSE = \sum_{j=1}^{k} (n_j - 1)s_j^2 = 9(124.22) + 9(164.68) + 9(105.88) + 9(136.62) = 4,782.60$$

MSE = SSE $/(n_T - k)$ = 4782.6 /(40 − 4) = 132.85

F = MSTR /MSE = 646.47 /132.85 = 4.87

Using F table (3 degrees of freedom numerator and 36 denominator), p-value is less than .01

Using Excel or Minitab, the p-value corresponding to $F = 4.87$ is .0061.

Because p-value $\leq \alpha = .05$, we reject the null hypothesis that the mean job satisfaction rating is the same for the four professions.

46.   The blocks correspond to the 10 dates on which the data were collected (Date) and the treatments correspond to the four cities (City).

The Minitab two-way ANOVA output follows.

Source	DF	SS	MS	F	P
Date	9	903.02	100.336	4.55	0.001
City	3	160.08	53.358	2.42	0.088
Error	27	595.68	22.062		
Total	39	1658.78			

Because the p-value for City (.0888) is greater than $\alpha = .05$, there is no significant difference in the mean ozone level among the four cities. But, if the level of significance was $\alpha = .10$, the difference would have been significant.

47.   The Minitab output is shown below:

One-way ANOVA: Midwest, Northeast, South, West

Source	DF	SS	MS	F	P
Factor	3	376.9	125.6	7.41	0.000
Error	71	1203.3	16.9		
Total	74	1580.1			

S = 4.117   R-Sq = 23.85%   R-Sq(adj) = 20.63%

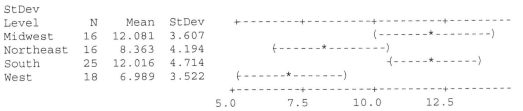

```
                                          Individual 95% CIs For Mean Based on Pooled
StDev
Level        N    Mean   StDev   +---------+---------+---------+---------
Midwest     16  12.081   3.607                              (-------*--------)
Northeast   16   8.363   4.194         (------*--------)
South       25  12.016   4.714                        (-----*------)
West        18   6.989   3.522   (------*-------)
                                 +---------+---------+---------+---------
                                5.0       7.5      10.0      12.5

Pooled StDev = 4.117
```

Because the *p*-value = .000 is less than α = .05, we reject the null hypothesis that the mean rental vacancy rate is the same for each geographic region. The mean vacancy rates were highest (over 12%) in the Midwest and the South.

48.

	Method A	Method B	Method C
Sample Mean	90	84	81
Sample Variance	98.00	168.44	159.78

$\bar{\bar{x}} = (90 + 84 + 81) / 3 = 85$

$\text{SSTR} = \sum_{j=1}^{k} n_j \left(\bar{x}_j - \bar{\bar{x}} \right)^2 = 10(90 - 85)^2 + 10(84 - 85)^2 + 10(81 - 85)^2 = 420$

$\text{MSTR} = \text{SSTR} / (k - 1) = 420 / 2 = 210$

$\text{SSE} = \sum_{j=1}^{k} (n_j - 1) s_j^2 = 9(98.00) + 9(168.44) + 9(159.78) = 3,836$

$\text{MSE} = \text{SSE} / (n_T - k) = 3,836 / (30 - 3) = 142.07$

$F = \text{MSTR} / \text{MSE} = 210 / 142.07 = 1.48$

Using *F* table (2 degrees of freedom numerator and 27 denominator), *p*-value is greater than .10

Using Excel or Minitab, the *p*-value corresponding to *F* = 1.48 is .2455.

Because *p*-value > α = .05, we cannot reject the null hypothesis that the means are equal.

49. a.

	Nonbrowser	Light Browser	Heavy Browser
Sample Mean	4.25	5.25	5.75
Sample Variance	1.07	1.07	1.36

$\bar{\bar{x}} = (4.25 + 5.25 + 5.75) / 3 = 5.08$

$\text{SSTR} = \sum_{j=1}^{k} n_j \left(\bar{x}_j - \bar{\bar{x}} \right)^2 = 8(4.25 - 5.08)^2 + 8(5.25 - 5.08)^2 + 8(5.75 - 5.08)^2 = 9.33$

$\text{MSTR} = \text{SSTR} / (k - 1) = 9.33 / 2 = 4.67$

$$\text{SSE} = \sum_{j=1}^{k} (n_j - 1)s_j^2 = 7(1.07) + 7(1.07) + 7(1.36) = 24.5$$

$$\text{MSE} = \text{SSE} / (n_T - k) = 24.5 / (24 - 3) = 1.17$$

$$F = \text{MSTR} / \text{MSE} = 4.67 / 1.17 = 3.99$$

Using F table (2 degrees of freedom numerator and 21 denominator), p-value is between .025 and .05

Using Excel or Minitab, the p-value corresponding to $F = 3.99$ is .0340.

Because p-value $\leq \alpha = .05$, we reject the null hypothesis that the mean comfort scores are the same for the three groups.

b. $$\text{LSD} = t_{\alpha/2} \sqrt{\text{MSE}\left(\frac{1}{n_i} + \frac{1}{n_j}\right)} = 2.080 \sqrt{1.17\left(\frac{1}{8} + \frac{1}{8}\right)} = 1.12$$

Since the absolute value of the difference between the sample means for nonbrowsers and light browsers is $|4.25 - 5.25| = 1$, we cannot reject the null hypothesis that the two population means are equal.

Chapter 11
Comparisons Involving Proportions and a Test of Independence

Learning Objectives

1. Be able to develop interval estimates and conduct hypothesis tests about the difference between the proportions of two populations.

2. Know the properties of the sampling distribution of the difference between two proportions $(\bar{p}_1 - \bar{p}_2)$.

3. Be able to conduct hypothesis tests about the difference between the proportions of three or more populations.

4. Be able to use the Marascuilo procedure to do multiple pairwise comparisons tests for three or more population proportions.

5. For a test of independence, be able to set up a contingency table, determine the observed and expected frequencies, and determine if the two variables are independent.

6. Understand the role of the chi-square distribution in conducting the tests in this chapter and be able to compute the chi-square test statistic for each application.

Solutions:

1. a. $\bar{p}_1 - \bar{p}_2 = .48 - .36 = .12$

   b. $\bar{p}_1 - \bar{p}_2 \pm z_{.05} \sqrt{\dfrac{\bar{p}_1(1-\bar{p}_1)}{n_1} + \dfrac{\bar{p}_2(1-\bar{p}_2)}{n_2}}$

   $.12 \pm 1.645 \sqrt{\dfrac{.48(1-.48)}{400} + \dfrac{.36(1-.36)}{300}}$

   $.12 \pm .0614 \qquad (.0586 \text{ to } .1814)$

   c. $.12 \pm 1.96 \sqrt{\dfrac{.48(1-.48)}{400} + \dfrac{.36(1-.36)}{300}}$

   $.12 \pm .0731 \qquad (.0469 \text{ to } .1931)$

2. a. $\bar{p} = \dfrac{n_1\bar{p}_1 + n_2\bar{p}_2}{n_1 + n_2} = \dfrac{100(.28) + 140(.20)}{100 + 140} = .2333$

   b. $z = \dfrac{\bar{p}_1 - \bar{p}_2}{\sqrt{\bar{p}(1-\bar{p})\left(\dfrac{1}{n_1} + \dfrac{1}{n_2}\right)}} = \dfrac{.28 - .20}{\sqrt{.2333(1-.2333)\left(\dfrac{1}{100} + \dfrac{1}{140}\right)}} = 1.44$

   $p\text{-value} = 2(1 - .9251) = .1498$

   c. p-value $> .05$; do not reject H_0. We cannot conclude that the two population proportions differ.

3. a. $\bar{p} = \dfrac{n_1\bar{p}_1 + n_2\bar{p}_2}{n_1 + n_2} = \dfrac{200(.22) + 300(.16)}{200 + 300} = .1840$

   $z = \dfrac{\bar{p}_1 - \bar{p}_2}{\sqrt{\bar{p}(1-\bar{p})\left(\dfrac{1}{n_1} + \dfrac{1}{n_2}\right)}} = \dfrac{.22 - .16}{\sqrt{.1840(1-.1840)\left(\dfrac{1}{200} + \dfrac{1}{300}\right)}} = 1.70$

   $p\text{-value} = 1.0000 - .9554 = .0446$

   b. p-value $\leq .05$; reject H_0. Conclude that the proportion for population 1 is greater than the proportion for population 2.

4. $\bar{p}_1 = 220/400 = .55 \qquad \bar{p}_2 = 192/400 = .48$

   $\bar{p}_1 - \bar{p}_2 \pm z_{.025} \sqrt{\dfrac{\bar{p}_1(1-\bar{p}_1)}{n_1} + \dfrac{\bar{p}_2(1-\bar{p}_2)}{n_2}}$

$$.55 - .48 \pm 1.96 \sqrt{\frac{.55(1-.55)}{400} + \frac{.48(1-.48)}{400}}$$

$.07 \pm .0691$ $(.0009 \text{ to } .1391)$

7% more executives are predicting an increase in full-time jobs. The confidence interval shows the difference may be from 0% to 14%.

5.   a.   The point estimate of the proportion of women who trust recommendations made on Pinterest is $\bar{p}_1$ = 117/150 = .78

    b.   The point estimate of the proportion of men who trust recommendations made on Pinterest is $\bar{p}_2$ = 102/170 = .60

    c. $\bar{p}_1 - \bar{p}_2 = .78 - .60 = .18$

$$.18 \pm z_{.025} \sqrt{\frac{\bar{p}_1(1-\bar{p}_1)}{n_1} + \frac{\bar{p}_2(1-\bar{p}_2)}{n_2}}$$

$$.18 \pm 1.96 \sqrt{\frac{.78(.22)}{150} + \frac{.60(.40)}{170}}$$

$.18 \pm .0991$ $(.0809 \text{ to } .2791)$

The 95% confidence interval estimate of the difference between the proportion of women and men who trust recommendations made on Pinterest is $.18 \pm .0991$ or $(.0809 \text{ to } .2791)$.

6.   Let p_1 = the population proportion of tuna that is mislabeled
            p_2 = the population proportion of mahi mahi that is mislabeled

    a.   The point estimate of the proportion of tuna that is mislabeled is $\bar{p}_1$ = 99/220 = .45

    b.   The point estimate of the proportion of mahi mahi that is mislabeled is $\bar{p}_2$ = 56/160 = .35

    c. $\bar{p}_1 - \bar{p}_2 = .45 - .35 = .10$

$$.10 \pm z_{.025} \sqrt{\frac{\bar{p}_1(1-\bar{p}_1)}{n_1} + \frac{\bar{p}_2(1-\bar{p}_2)}{n_2}}$$

$$.10 \pm 1.96 \sqrt{\frac{.45(.55)}{220} + \frac{.35(.65)}{160}}$$

$.10 \pm .0989$ $(.0011 \text{ to } .1989)$

The 95% confidence interval estimate of the difference between the proportion of tuna and mahi mahi that is mislabeled is $.10 \pm .0989$ or $(.0011 \text{ to } .1989)$.

7.   Let p_1 = the population proportion of voters in rural Minnesota voted in the 2012 election
         p_2 = the population proportion of voters in urban Minnesota voted in the 2012 election

    a. H_0: $p_1 \leq p_2$

       H_a: $p_1 > p_2$

    b. $\bar{p}_1$ = 663/884 = .75 75% of voters in rural Minnesota voted in the 2012 election

    c. $\bar{p}_2$ = 414/575 = .72 72% of voters in urban Minnesota voted in the 2012 election

    d. $\bar{p} = \dfrac{n_1\bar{p}_1 + n_2\bar{p}_2}{n_1 + n_2} = \dfrac{663 + 414}{884 + 575} = .7382$

$$z = \frac{\bar{p}_1 - \bar{p}_2}{\sqrt{\bar{p}(1-\bar{p})\left(\dfrac{1}{n_1} + \dfrac{1}{n_2}\right)}} = \frac{.75 - .72}{\sqrt{.7382(1-.7382)\left(\dfrac{1}{884} + \dfrac{1}{575}\right)}} = 1.27$$

Upper tail p-value is the area to the right of the test statistic

Using normal table with $z = 1.27$: p-value = 1 - .8980 = .1020

p-value > α ; do not reject H_0

We cannot conclude that voters from rural Minnesota voted more frequently than voters from urban Minnesota in the 2012 Presidential election.

8.   Let p_1 = the population proportion of wells drilled in 2005 that were dry
         p_2 = the population proportion of wells drilled in 2012 that were dry

    a. H_0: $p_1 - p_2 \leq 0$

       H_a: $p_1 - p_2 > 0$

    b. $\bar{p}_1$ = 24/119 = .2017

    c. $\bar{p}_2$ = 21/162 = .1111

    d. $\bar{p} = \dfrac{n_1\bar{p}_1 + n_2\bar{p}_2}{n_1 + n_2} = \dfrac{24 + 18}{119 + 162} = .1495$

$$z = \frac{\bar{p}_1 - \bar{p}_2}{\sqrt{\bar{p}(1-\bar{p})\left(\dfrac{1}{n_1} + \dfrac{1}{n_2}\right)}} = \frac{.2017 - .1111}{\sqrt{.1495(1-.1495)\left(\dfrac{1}{119} + \dfrac{1}{162}\right)}} = 2.10$$

Upper tail p-value is the area to the right of the test statistic

Using normal table with $z = 2.10$: p-value = 1 - .9821 = .0179.

p-value $<.05$, so reject H_0 and conclude that wells drilled in 2005 were dry more frequently than wells drilled in 2012. That is, the frequency of dry wells has decreased over the eight years from 2005 to 2012.

9. a. Let $p_1 =$ population proportion of men expecting to get a raise or promotion this year

   $p_2 =$ population proportion of women expecting to get a raise or promotion this year

   $H_0: p_1 - p_2 \leq 0$
   $H_a: p_1 - p_2 > 0$

   b. $\bar{p}_1 = 104/200 = .52$ (52%)

   $\bar{p}_2 = 74/200 = .37$ (37%)

   c. $\bar{p} = \dfrac{n_1\bar{p}_1 + n_2\bar{p}_2}{n_1 + n_2} = \dfrac{104 + 74}{200 + 200} = .445$

   $z = \dfrac{\bar{p}_1 - \bar{p}_2}{\sqrt{\bar{p}(1-\bar{p})\left(\dfrac{1}{n_1}+\dfrac{1}{n_2}\right)}} = \dfrac{.52 - .37}{\sqrt{.445(1-.445)\left(\dfrac{1}{200}+\dfrac{1}{200}\right)}} = 3.02$

   p-value $= 1.0000 - .9987 = .0013$

   Reject H_0. There is a significant difference between the population proportions with a great proportion of men expecting to get a raise or a promotion this year.

10. a. Let $p_1 =$ population proportion of rooms occupied for current year

    $p_2 =$ population proportion of rooms occupied for previous year

    $H_0: p_1 - p_2 \leq 0$

    $H_a: p_1 - p_2 > 0$

    b. $\bar{p}_1 = 1470/1750 = .84$ (current year)

    $\bar{p}_2 = 1458/1800 = .81$ (previous year)

    c. $\bar{p} = \dfrac{n_1\bar{p}_1 + n_2\bar{p}_2}{n_1 + n_2} = \dfrac{1750(.84) + 1800(.81)}{1750 + 1800} = .8248$

    $z = \dfrac{\bar{p}_1 - \bar{p}_2}{\sqrt{\bar{p}(1-\bar{p})\left(\dfrac{1}{n_1}+\dfrac{1}{n_2}\right)}} = \dfrac{.84 - .81}{\sqrt{.8248(1-.8248)\left(\dfrac{1}{1750}+\dfrac{1}{1800}\right)}} = 2.35$

    p-value is are in the upper tail at $z = 2.35$

    p-value $= 1.0000 - .9906 = .0094$

    p-value $\leq .05$, reject H_0. There has been an increase in the hotel occupancy rate.

d. $\bar{p}_1 - \bar{p}_2 \pm z_{.025} \sqrt{\dfrac{\bar{p}_1(1-\bar{p}_1)}{n_1} + \dfrac{\bar{p}_2(1-\bar{p}_2)}{n_2}}$

$.84 - .81 \pm 1.96 \sqrt{\dfrac{.84(1-.84)}{1750} + \dfrac{.81(1-.81)}{1800}}$

$.03 \pm .025$ (.005 to .055)

Officials would likely be pleased with the occupancy statistics. The trend for the current year is an increase in hotel occupancy rates compared to last year. The point estimate is a 3% increase with a 95% confidence interval from .5% to 5.5%.

11. $H_0: p_1 = p_2 = p_3$

H_a: Not all population proportions are equal

Observed Frequencies (f_{ij})

	1	2	3	Total
Yes	150	150	96	396
No	100	150	104	354
Total	250	300	200	750

Expected Frequencies (e_{ij})

	1	2	3	Total
Yes	132.0	158.4	105.6	396
No	118.0	141.6	94.4	354
Total	250	300	200	750

Chi Square Calculations $(f_{ij} - e_{ij})^2 / e_{ij}$

	1	2	3	Total
Yes	2.45	.45	.87	3.77
No	2.75	.50	.98	4.22

$$\chi^2 = 7.99$$

Degrees of freedom $= k - 1 = (3 - 1) = 2$

Using the χ^2 table with $df = 2$, $\chi^2 = 7.99$ shows the p-value is between .025 and .01

Using Excel or Minitab, the p-value corresponding to $\chi^2 = 7.99$ is .0184

p-value $\le .05$, reject H_0. Conclude not all population proportions are equal.

12. a. $\bar{p}_1 = 150 / 250 = .60$

$\bar{p}_2 = 150 / 300 = .50$

$\bar{p}_3 = 96 / 200 = .48$

b. Multiple comparisons

For 1 vs. 2

$$CV_{12} = \sqrt{\chi_\alpha^2} \sqrt{\frac{\bar{p}_1(1-\bar{p}_1)}{n_1} + \frac{\bar{p}_2(1-\bar{p}_2)}{n_2}} = \sqrt{5.991}\sqrt{\frac{.60(1-.60)}{250} + \frac{.50(1-.50)}{300}} = .1037$$

$df = k-1 = 3-1 = z$ $\chi_{.05}^2 = 5.991$

Comparison	p_i	p_j	Difference	n_i	n_j	Critical Value	Significant Diff > CV
1 vs. 2	.60	.50	.10	250	300	.1037	
1 vs. 3	.60	.48	.12	250	200	.1150	Yes
2 vs. 3	.50	.48	.02	300	200	.1117	

Only one comparison is significant, 1 vs. 3. The others are not significant. We can conclude that the population proportions differ for populations 1 and 3.

13. a. $H_0: p_1 = p_2 = p_3$

H_a: Not all population proportions are equal

b.   Observed Frequencies (f_{ij})

Flight	Delta	United	US Airways	Total
Delayed	39	51	56	146
On Time	261	249	344	854
Total	300	300	400	1000

Expected Frequencies (e_{ij})

Flight	Delta	United	US Airways	Total
Delayed	43.8	43.8	58.4	146
On Time	256.2	256.2	341.6	854
Total	300	300	400	1000

Chi Square Calculations $(f_{ij} - e_{ij})^2 / e_{ij}$

Flight	Delta	United	US Airways	Total
Delayed	.53	1.18	.10	1.81
On Time	.09	.20	.02	.31
				$\chi^2 = 2.12$

Degrees of freedom = $k - 1 = (3 - 1) = 2$

Using the χ^2 table with $df = 2$, $\chi^2 = 2.12$ shows the p–value is greater than .10

Using Excel or Minitab, the p–value corresponding to $\chi^2 = 2.12$ is .3465

p–value > .05, do not reject H_0. We are unable to reject the null hypothesis that the population proportions are the same.

c. $\bar{p}_1 = 39 / 300 = .13$

$\bar{p}_2 = 51 / 300 = .17$

$\bar{p}_3 = 56 / 400 = .14$

Overall $\bar{p} = 146 / 1000 = .146$

14. a. $H_0: p_1 = p_2 = p_3$

H_a: Not all population proportions are equal

b. Observed Frequencies (f_{ij})

Component	A	B	C	Total
Defective	15	20	40	75
Good	485	480	460	1425
Total	500	500	500	1500

Expected Frequencies (e_{ij})

Component	A	B	C	Total
Defective	25	25	25	75
Good	475	475	475	1425
Total	500	500	500	1500

Chi Square Calculations $(f_{ij} - e_{ij})^2 / e_{ij}$

Component	A	B	C	Total
Defective	4.00	1.00	9.00	14.00
Good	.21	.05	.47	0.74

$$\chi^2 = 14.74$$

Degrees of freedom = $k - 1 = (3 - 1) = 2$

Using the χ^2 table with $df = 2$, $\chi^2 = 14.74$ shows the p–value is less than .01

Using Excel or Minitab, the p–value corresponding to $\chi^2 = 14.74$ is .0006

p–value $\leq .05$, reject H_0. Conclude that the three suppliers do not provide equal proportions of defective components.

c. $\bar{p}_1 = 15 / 500 = .03$

$\bar{p}_2 = 20 / 500 = .04$

$\bar{p}_3 = 40 / 500 = .08$

Multiple comparisons

For Supplier A vs. Supplier B

$df = k - 1 = 3 - 1 = 2z \qquad \chi^2_{.05} = 5.991$

$$CV_{ij} = \sqrt{\chi_\alpha^2} \sqrt{\frac{\bar{p}_i(1-\bar{p}_i)}{n_i} + \frac{\bar{p}_j(1-\bar{p}_j)}{n_j}} = \sqrt{5.991} \sqrt{\frac{.03(1-.03)}{500} + \frac{.04(1-.04)}{500}} = .0284$$

Comparison	p_i	p_j	Difference	n_i	n_j	Critical Value	Significant Diff > CV
A vs. B	.03	.04	.01	500	500	.0284	
A vs. C	.03	.08	.05	500	500	.0351	Yes
B vs. C	.04	.08	.04	500	500	.0366	Yes

Supplier A and supplier B are both significantly different from supplier C. Supplier C can be eliminated on the basis of a significantly higher proportion of defective components. Since suppliers A and supplier B are not significantly different in terms of the proportion defective components, both of these suppliers should remain candidates for use by Benson.

15. a. $H_0: p_1 = p_2 = p_3 = p_4$

H_a: Not all population proportions are equal

Observed Frequencies (f_{ij})

Gender	A	B	C	D	Total
Male	49	44	49	39	181
Female	41	46	36	44	167
Total	90	90	85	83	348

Expected Frequencies (e_{ij})

Gender	A	B	C	D	Total
Male	46.81	46.81	44.21	43.17	181
Female	43.19	43.19	40.79	39.83	167
Total	90	90	85	83	348

Chi Square Calculations $(f_{ij} - e_{ij})^2 / e_{ij}$

Gender	A	B	C	D	Total
Male	.10	.17	.52	.40	1.19
Female	.11	.18	.56	.44	1.29
					$\chi^2 = 2.49$

Degrees of freedom = $k - 1 = (4 - 1) = 3$

Using the χ^2 table with $df = 3$, $\chi^2 = 2.49$ shows the p–value is greater than .10

Using Excel or Minitab, the p–value corresponding to $\chi^2 = 2.49$ is .4771

p–value > .05, do not reject H_0. Conclude that we are unable to reject the hypothesis that the population proportion of male fish is equal in all four locations.

b. No. There is no evidence that differences in agricultural contaminants found at the four locations have altered the gender proportions of the fish populations.

16. a. $\bar{p}_1 = 35/250 = .14$ 14% error rate

   $\bar{p}_2 = 27/300 = .09$ 9% error rate

   b. $H_0: p_1 - p_2 = 0$

   $H_a: p_1 - p_2 \neq 0$

   Observed Frequencies (f_{ij})

Return	Office 1	Office 2	Total
Error	35	27	62
Correct	215	273	488
Total	250	300	550

   Expected Frequencies (e_{ij})

Return	Office 1	Office 2	Total
Error	28.18	33.82	62
Correct	221.82	266.18	488
Total	250	300	550

   Chi Square Calculations $(f_{ij} - e_{ij})^2 / e_{ij}$

Return	Office 1	Office 2	Total
Error	1.65	1.37	3.02
Correct	.21	.17	.38
			$\chi^2 = 3.41$

   $df = k - 1 = (2 - 1) = 1$

   Using the χ^2 table with $df = 1$, $\chi^2 = 3.41$ shows the p–value is between .10 and .05

   Using Excel or Minitab, the p–value corresponding to $\chi^2 = 3.41$ is .0648

   p–value $\leq .10$, reject H_0. Conclude that the two offices do not have the same population proportion error rates.

   c. With two populations, a chi–square test for equal population proportions has 1 degree of freedom. In this case the test statistic χ^2 is always equal to z^2. This relationship between the two test statistics always provides the same p–value and the same conclusion when the null hypothesis involves equal population proportions. However, the use of the z test statistic provides options for one–tailed hypothesis tests about two population proportions while the chi–square test is limited a two–tailed hypothesis tests about the equality of the two population proportions.

17. a. $H_0: p_1 = p_2 = p_3 = p_4$

   H_a: Not all population proportions are equal

   Observed Frequencies (f_{ij})

Social Net	Great Britain	Israel	Russia	USA	Total
Yes	344	265	301	500	1410
No	456	235	399	500	1590
Total	800	500	700	1000	3000

   Expected Frequencies (e_{ij})

Social Net	Great Britain	Israel	Russia	USA	Total
Yes	376	235	329	470	1410
No	424	265	371	530	1590
Total	800	500	700	1000	3000

   Chi Square Calculations $(f_{ij} - e_{ij})^2 / e_{ij}$

Social Net	Great Britain	Israel	Russia	USA	Total
Yes	2.72	3.83	2.38	1.91	10.85
No	2.42	3.40	2.11	1.70	9.62

   $$\chi^2 = 20.47$$

   Degrees of freedom = $df = k - 1 = (4 - 1) = 3$

   Using the χ^2 table with $df = 3$, $\chi^2 = 20.47$ shows the p–value is less than .01

   Using Excel or Minitab, the p–value corresponding to $\chi^2 = 20.47$ is .0001

   p–value $\leq$ .05, reject H_0. Conclude the population proportions are not all equal.

b.
Great Britain	344/800 = .43	
Israel	265/500 = .53	(Largest with 53% of adults)
Russia	301/700 = .43	
United States	500/1000 = .50	

c. Multiple pairwise comparisons

   $$CV_{ij} = \sqrt{\chi_\alpha^2} \sqrt{\frac{\bar{p}_i(1 - \bar{p}_i)}{n_i} + \frac{\bar{p}_j(1 - \bar{p}_j)}{n_j}}$$

   where $df = k - 1 = 4 - 1 = 3$ and $\chi_{.05}^2 = 7.815$

Comparison	p_i	p_j	Difference	n_i	n_j	CV_{ij}	Diff > CV_{ij}
GB vs I	0.43	0.53	0.10	800	500	0.0793	Yes
GB v R	0.43	0.43	0.00	800	700	0.0716	
GB vs USA	0.43	0.50	0.07	800	1000	0.0659	Yes
I vs R	0.53	0.43	0.10	500	700	0.0814	Yes
I vs USA	0.53	0.50	0.03	500	1000	0.0765	
R vs USA	0.43	0.50	0.07	700	1000	0.0685	Yes

Only two comparisons are not significant: Great Britain and Russia and then Israel and United States. All other comparisons show a significant difference.

18. H_0: The distribution of defects is the same for all suppliers

H_a: The distribution of defects is not the same all suppliers

Observed Frequencies (f_{ij})

Part Tested	A	B	C	Total
Minor Defect	15	13	21	49
Major Defect	5	11	5	21
Good	130	126	124	380
Total	150	150	150	450

Expected Frequencies (e_{ij})

Part Tested	A	B	C	Total
Minor Defect	16.33	16.33	16.33	49
Major Defect	7.00	7.00	7.00	21
Good	126.67	126.67	126.67	380
Total	150	150	150	450

Chi Square Calculations $(f_{ij} - e_{ij})^2 / e_{ij}$

Part Tested	A	B	C	Total
Minor Defect	.11	.68	1.33	2.12
Major Defect	.57	2.29	.57	3.43
Good	.09	.00	.06	.15
				$\chi^2 = 5.70$

Degrees of freedom = $(r - 1)(k - 1) = (3 - 1)(3 - 1) = 4$

Using the χ^2 table with $df = 4$, $\chi^2 = 5.70$ shows the p–value is greater than .10

Using Excel or Minitab, the p–value corresponding to $\chi^2 = 5.70$ is .2227

p–value > .05, do not reject H_0. Conclude that we are unable to reject the hypothesis that the population distribution of defects is the same for all three suppliers. There is no evidence that quality of parts from one suppliers is better than either of the others two suppliers.

19. H_0: The column variable is independent of the row variable

H_a: The column variable is not independent of the row variable

Observed Frequencies (f_{ij})

	A	B	C	Total
P	20	44	50	114
Q	30	26	30	86
Total	50	70	80	200

Expected Frequencies (e_{ij})

	A	B	C	Total
P	28.5	39.9	45.6	114
Q	21.5	30.1	34.4	86
Total	50	70	80	200

Chi–Square Calculations $(f_{ij} - e_{ij})^2 / e_{ij}$

	A	B	C	Total
P	2.54	.42	.42	3.38
Q	3.36	.56	.56	4.48

$$\chi^2 = 7.86$$

Degrees of freedom = $(2-1)(3-1) = 2$

Using the χ^2 table with $df = 2$, $\chi^2 = 7.86$ shows the p–value is between .01 and .025.

Using Excel or Minitab, the p–value corresponding to $\chi^2 = 7.86$ is .0196.

p–value $\leq$ .05, reject H_0. Conclude that there is an association between the column variable and the row variable. The variables are not independent.

20. H_0: The column variable is independent of the row variable

H_a: The column variable is dependent on the row variable

Observed Frequencies (f_{ij})

	A	B	C	Total
P	20	30	20	70
Q	30	60	25	115
R	10	15	30	55
Total	60	105	75	240

Expected Frequencies (e_{ij})

	A	B	C	Total
P	17.50	30.63	21.88	70
Q	28.75	50.31	35.94	115
R	13.75	24.06	17.19	55
Total	60	105	75	240

Chi–Square Calculations $(f_{ij} - e_{ij})^2 / e_{ij}$

	A	B	C	Total
P	.36	.01	.16	.53
Q	.05	1.87	3.33	5.25
R	1.02	3.41	9.55	13.99

$$\chi^2 = 19.77$$

Degrees of freedom $= (r - 1)(c - 1) = (3 - 1)(3 - 1) = 4$

Using the χ^2 table with $df = 4$, $\chi^2 = 19.77$ shows the p–value is less than .005.

Using Excel or Minitab, the p–value corresponding to $\chi^2 = 19.77$ is .0006.

p–value $\leq$ .05, reject H_0. Conclude that the column variable is not independent of the row variable.

21. a. H_0: Type of ticket purchased is independent of the type of flight

H_a: Type of ticket purchased is not independent of the type of flight

Expected Frequencies:

e_{11} = 35.59 e_{12} = 15.41
e_{21} = 150.73 e_{22} = 65.27
e_{31} = 455.68 e_{32} = 197.32

Ticket	Flight	Observed Frequency (f_i)	Expected Frequency (e_i)	Chi–square $(f_i - e_i)^2 / e_i$
First	Domestic	29	35.59	1.22
First	International	22	15.41	2.82
Business	Domestic	95	150.73	20.61
Business	International	121	65.27	47.59
Full Fare	Domestic	518	455.68	8.52
Full Fare	International	135	197.32	19.68
	Totals:	920		$\chi^2 = 100.43$

Degrees of freedom $= (r - 1)(c - 1) = (3 - 1)(2 - 1) = 2$

Using the χ^2 table with $df = 2$, $\chi^2 = 100.43$ shows the p–value is less than .005.

Using Excel or Minitab, the p–value corresponding to $\chi^2 = 100.43$ is .0000.

p–value $\leq$ .05, reject H_0. Conclude that the type of ticket purchased is not independent of the type of flight. We can expect the type of ticket purchased to depend upon whether the flight is domestic or international.

b. Column Percentages

Type of Ticket	Type of Flight Domestic	International
First Class	4.5%	7.9%
Business Class	14.8%	43.5%
Economy Class	80.7%	48.6%

A higher percentage of first class and business class tickets are purchased for international flights compared to domestic flights. Economy class tickets are purchased more for domestic flights. The first class or business class tickets are purchased for more than 50% of the international flights; 7.9% + 43.5% = 51.4%.

22. a. H_0: Employment plan is independent of the type of company

   H_a: Employment plan is not independent of the type of company

   Observed Frequency (f_{ij})

Employment Plan	Private	Public	Total
Add Employees	37	32	69
No Change	19	34	53
Lay Off Employees	16	42	58
Total	72	108	180

   Expected Frequency (e_{ij})

Employment Plan	Private	Public	Total
Add Employees	27.6	41.4	69
No Change	21.2	31.8	53
Lay Off Employees	23.2	34.8	58
Total	72.0	108.0	180

   Chi Square Calculations $(f_{ij} - e_{ij})^2 / e_{ij}$

Employment Plan	Private	Public	Total
Add Employees	3.20	2.13	5.34
No Change	0.23	0.15	0.38
Lay Off Employees	2.23	1.49	3.72

   $$\chi^2 = 9.44$$

   Degrees of freedom = $(r-1)(c-1) = (3-1)(2-1) = 2$

   Using the χ^2 table with $df = 2$, $\chi^2 = 9.44$ shows the p–value is less than .01

   Using Excel or Minitab, the p–value corresponding to $\chi^2 = 9.44$ is .0089

   p–value $\leq$ .05, reject H_0. Conclude the employment plan is not independent of the type of company. Thus, we expect employment plan to differ for private and public companies.

   b.   Column probabilities – For example, 37/72 = .5139

Employment Plan	Private	Public
Add Employees	.5139	.2963
No Change	.2639	.3148
Lay Off Employees	.2222	.3889

   Employment opportunities look to be much better for private companies with over 50% of private companies planning to add employees (51.39%). Public companies have the greater proportions of no change and lay off employees planned. 38.89% of public companies are planning to lay off employees over the next 12 months. 69/180 = .3833, or 38.33% of the companies in the survey are planning to hire and add employees during the next 12 months.

23. a. H_0: Having health insurance is independent of the size of the company

H_a: Having health insurance is not independent of the size of the company

Observed Frequencies (f_{ij})

Health Insurance	Small	Medium	Large	Total
Yes	36	65	88	189
No	14	10	12	36
Total	50	75	100	225

Expected Frequencies (e_{ij})

Health Insurance	Small	Medium	Large	Total
Yes	42	63	84	189
No	8	12	16	36
Total	50	75	100	225

Chi–Square Calculations $(f_{ij} - e_{ij})^2 / e_{ij}$

Health Insurance	Small	Medium	Large	Total
Yes	.86	.06	.19	1.11
No	4.50	.33	1.00	5.83

$$\chi^2 = 6.94$$

Degrees of freedom $= (r - 1)(c - 1) = (2 - 1)(3 - 1) = 2$

Using the χ^2 table with $df = 2$, $\chi^2 = 6.94$ shows the p–value is between .025 and .05.

Using Excel or Minitab, the p–value corresponding to $\chi^2 = 6.94$ is .0311.

p–value $\leq$ .05, reject H_0. Conclude health insurance coverage is not independent of the size of the company. Health coverage is expected to vary depending on the size of the company.

b. Percentage of no coverage by company size

Small   14/50   = 28%
Medium 10/75   = 13%
Large   12/100 = 12%

More than twice as many small companies do not provide health insurance coverage when compared to medium and large companies.

24. a. H_0: Quality rating is independent of the education of the owner

H_a: Quality rating is not independent of the education of the owner

Observed Frequencies (f_{ij})

Quality Rating	Some HS	HS Grad	Some College	College Grad	Total
Average	35	30	20	60	145
Outstanding	45	45	50	90	230
Exceptional	20	25	30	50	125
Total	100	100	100	200	500

Expected Frequencies (e_{ij})

Quality Rating	Some HS	HS Grad	Some College	College Grad	Total
Average	29	29	29	58	145
Outstanding	46	46	46	92	230
Exceptional	25	25	25	50	125
Total	100	100	100	200	500

Chi Square Calculations $(f_{ij} - e_{ij})^2 / e_{ij}$

Quality Rating	Some HS	HS Grad	Some College	College Grad	Total
Average	1.24	.03	2.79	.07	4.14
Outstanding	.02	.02	.35	.04	.43
Exceptional	1.00	.00	1.00	.00	2.00

$$\chi^2 = 6.57$$

Degrees of freedom = $(r - 1)(c - 1) = (3 - 1)(4 - 1) = 6$

Using the χ^2 table with $df = 6$, $\chi^2 = 6.57$ shows the p–value is greater than .10

Using Excel or Minitab, the p–value corresponding to $\chi^2 = 6.57$ is .3624

p–value > .05, do not reject H_0. We are unable to conclude that the quality rating is not independent of the education of the owner. Thus, quality ratings are not expected to differ with the education of the owner.

b. Average: 145/500 = 29%

Outstanding: 230/500 = 46%

Exceptional: 125/500 = 25%

New owners look to be pretty satisfied with their new automobiles with almost 50% rating the quality outstanding and over 70% rating the quality outstanding or exceptional.

25. a. H_0: Quality of Management is independent of the Reputation of the Company

H_a: Quality of Management is not independent of the Reputation of the Company

Observed Frequencies (f_{ij})

Quality of Management	Excellent	Good	Fair	Total
Excellent	40	25	5	70
Good	35	35	10	80
Fair	25	10	15	50
Total	100	70	30	200

Expected Frequencies (e_{ij})

Quality of Management	Excellent	Good	Fair	Total
Excellent	35.0	24.5	10.5	70
Good	40.0	28.0	12.0	80
Fair	25.0	17.5	7.5	50
Total	100	70	30	200

Chi Square Calculations $(f_{ij} - e_{ij})^2 / e_{ij}$

Quality of Management	Excellent	Good	Fair	Total
Excellent	.71	.01	2.88	3.61
Good	.63	1.75	.33	2.71
Fair	.00	3.21	7.50	10.71

$$\chi^2 = 17.03$$

Degrees of freedom = $(r - 1)(c - 1) = (3 - 1)(3 - 1) = 4$

Using the χ^2 table with $df = 4$, $\chi^2 = 17.03$ shows the p-value is less than .005

Using Excel or Minitab, the p-value corresponding to $\chi^2 = 17.03$ is .0019

p-value $\leq .05$, reject H_0. Conclude that the rating for the quality of management is not independent of the rating for the reputation of the company.

b. Using the highest column probabilities, if the reputation of the company is

Excellent: There is a 40/100 = .40 chance the quality of management will also be excellent.

Good: There is a 35/70 = .50 chance the quality of management will also be good.

Fair: There is a 15/30 = .50 chance the quality of management will also be fair.

The highest probabilities are that the two variables will have the same ratings. Thus, the two rating are associated.

26. a. Observed Frequency (f_{ij})

Actress	Age of Respondent				
	18-30	31-44	45-58	Over 58	Totals
Jessica Chastain	51	50	41	42	184
Jennifer Lawrence	63	55	37	50	205
Emmanuelle Riva	15	44	56	74	189
Quvenzhané Wallis	48	25	22	31	126
Naomi Watts	36	65	62	33	196
Totals	213	239	218	230	900

The sample size is 900.

b. The sample proportion of movie fans who prefer each actress is

$$\bar{p}_1 = \frac{184}{900} = .2044, \ \bar{p}_2 = \frac{205}{900} = .2278, \ \bar{p}_3 = \frac{189}{900} = .2100, \ \bar{p}_4 = \frac{126}{900} = .1400, \ \bar{p}_5 = \frac{196}{900} = .2178$$

The movie fans favored Jennifer Lawrence, but three other nominees (Jessica Chastain, Emmanuelle Riva, and Naomi Watts) each were favored by almost as many of the fans.

c. Expected Frequency (e_{ij})

		Age of Respondent			
Actress	18-30	31-44	45-58	Over 58	Totals
Jessica Chastain	43.5	48.9	44.6	47.0	184
Jennifer Lawrence	48.5	54.4	49.7	52.4	205
Emmanuelle Riva	44.7	50.2	45.8	48.3	189
Quvenzhané Wallis	29.8	33.5	30.5	32.2	126
Naomi Watts	46.4	52.0	47.5	50.1	196
Totals	213	239	218	230	900

Calculate $\dfrac{(f_{ij}-e_{ij})^2}{e_{ij}}$ for each cell in the table.

		Age of Respondent			
Actress	18-30	31-44	45-58	Over 58	Totals
Jessica Chastain	1.28	0.03	0.29	0.54	2.12
Jennifer Lawrence	4.32	0.01	3.23	0.11	7.66
Emmanuelle Riva	19.76	0.76	2.28	13.67	36.48
Quvenzhané Wallis	11.08	2.14	2.38	0.04	15.65
Naomi Watts	2.33	3.22	4.44	5.83	15.82
Totals	38.77	6.16	12.61	20.20	77.74

$$\chi^2 = \sum_i \sum_j \frac{(f_{ij}-e_{ij})^2}{e_{ij}} = 77.74$$

With (5-1)(4-1) = 12 degrees of freedom, the p-value is approximately 0.

p-value ≤ .05, so reject H_0. Attitude toward the actress who was most deserving of the 2013 Academy Award for actress in a leading role is not independent of age.

27. a. H_0: Hours of sleep per night is independent of age

   H_a: Hours of sleep per night is not independent of age

   Observed Frequencies (f_{ij})

Hours of Sleep	39 or younger	40 or older	Total
Fewer than 6	38	36	74
6 to 6.9	60	57	117
7 to 7.9	77	75	152
8 or more	65	92	157
Total	240	260	500

   Expected Frequencies (e_{ij})

Hours of Sleep	39 or younger	40 or older	Total
Fewer than 6	35.52	38.48	74
6 to 6.9	56.16	60.84	117
7 to 7.9	72.96	79.04	152
8 or more	75.36	81.64	157
Total	240	260	500

   Chi Square Calculations $(f_{ij} - e_{ij})^2 / e_{ij}$

Hours of Sleep	39 or younger	40 or older	Total
Fewer than 6	.17	.16	.33
6 to 6.9	.26	.24	.50
7 to 7.9	.22	.21	.43
8 or more	1.42	1.31	2.74
			$\chi^2 = 4.01$

   Degrees of freedom $= (r - 1)(c - 1) = (4 - 1)(2 - 1) = 3$

   Using the χ^2 table with $df = 3$, $\chi^2 = 4.01$ shows the p–value is greater than .10.

   Using Excel or Minitab, the p–value corresponding to $\chi^2 = 4.01$ is .2604.

   p–value > .05, do not reject H_0. Cannot reject the assumption that age and hours of sleep are independent.

   b. Since age does not appear to have an association on hours of sleep, use the overall row percentages.

Fewer than 6	74/500 = .148	14.8%
6 to 6.9	117/500 = .234	23.4%
7 to 7.9	152/500 = .304	30.4%
8 or more	157/500 = .314	31.4%

   30.4% + 31.4% = 61.8% of individuals get seven or more hours of sleep a night.

28.   Expected Frequencies:

$e_{11} = 11.81$ $e_{12} = 8.44$ $e_{13} = 24.75$
$e_{21} = 8.40$ $e_{22} = 6.00$ $e_{23} = 17.60$
$e_{31} = 21.79$ $e_{32} = 15.56$ $e_{33} = 45.65$

Host A	Host B	Observed Frequency (f_i)	Expected Frequency (e_i)	Chi Square $(f_i - e_i)^2 / e_i$
Con	Con	24	11.81	12.57
Con	Mixed	8	8.44	.02
Con	Pro	13	24.75	5.58
Mixed	Con	8	8.40	.02
Mixed	Mixed	13	6.00	8.17
Mixed	Pro	11	17.60	2.48
Pro	Con	10	21.79	6.38
Pro	Mixed	9	15.56	2.77
Pro	Pro	64	45.65	7.38

$$\chi^2 = 45.36$$

Degrees of freedom $= (r - 1)(c - 1) = (3 - 1)(3 - 1) = 4$

Using the χ^2 table with $df = 2$, $\chi^2 = 45.36$ shows the p–value is less than .005.

Using Excel or Minitab, the p–value corresponding to $\chi^2 = 45.36$ is .0000.

p–value $\le .01$, reject H_0. Conclude that the ratings of the two hosts are not independent. The host responses are more similar than different and they tend to agree or be close in their ratings.

29.   Let $p_1 =$ population proportion of men who worked Sodoku puzzles
       $p_2 =$ population proportion of women who worked Sodoku puzzles

a. $H_0: p_1 - p_2 = 0$
      $H_a: p_1 - p_2 \neq 0$

b. $\bar{p}_1 = 312/1200 = .26$
      $\bar{p}_2 = 512/1600 = .32$

c. $\bar{p} = \dfrac{n_1 \bar{p}_1 + n_2 \bar{p}_2}{n_1 + n_2} = \dfrac{1200(.26) + 1600(.32)}{1200 + 1600} = .2943$

$$z = \frac{\bar{p}_1 - \bar{p}_2}{\sqrt{\bar{p}(1-\bar{p})\left(\dfrac{1}{n_1} + \dfrac{1}{n_2}\right)}} = \frac{(.26 - .32)}{\sqrt{.2943(1-.2943)\left(\dfrac{1}{1200} + \dfrac{1}{1600}\right)}} = -3.45$$

p-value is approximately 0

p-value $\le .05$, so reject H_0. Conclude the population proportions are not equal. The proportion is higher for women.

d. $\bar{p}_1 - \bar{p}_2 \pm z_{.025} \sqrt{\dfrac{\bar{p}_1(1-\bar{p}_1)}{n_1} + \dfrac{\bar{p}_2(1-\bar{p}_2)}{n_2}}$

$(.26 - .32) \pm 1.96 \sqrt{\dfrac{.26(1-.26)}{1200} + \dfrac{.32(1-.32)}{1600}}$

$-.06 \pm .0337$

Margin of Error = .0337

95% Confidence Interval $(-.0937$ to $-.0263)$

30. a. $\bar{p}_1 = 76/400 = .19$

$\bar{p}_2 = 90/900 = .10$

$\bar{p} = \dfrac{n_1\bar{p}_1 + n_2\bar{p}_2}{n_1 + n_2} = \dfrac{76+90}{400+900} = .1277$

$z = \dfrac{\bar{p}_1 - \bar{p}_2}{\sqrt{\bar{p}(1-\bar{p})\left(\dfrac{1}{n_1} + \dfrac{1}{n_2}\right)}} = \dfrac{.19-.10}{\sqrt{.1277(1-.1277)\left(\dfrac{1}{400} + \dfrac{1}{900}\right)}} = 4.49$

p-value ≈ 0

Reject H_0; there is a difference between claim rates.

b. $\bar{p}_1 - \bar{p}_2 \pm z_{.025} \sqrt{\dfrac{\bar{p}_1(1-\bar{p}_1)}{n_1} + \dfrac{\bar{p}_2(1-\bar{p}_2)}{n_2}}$

$.19 - .10 \pm 1.96 \sqrt{\dfrac{.19(1-.19)}{400} + \dfrac{.10(1-.10)}{900}}$

$.09 \pm .0432$ $(.0468$ to $.1332)$

Claim rates are higher for single males.

31. $\bar{p}_1 = 9/142 = .0634$
$\bar{p}_2 = 5/268 = .0187$
$\bar{p} = \dfrac{n_1\bar{p}_1 + n_2\bar{p}_2}{n_1 + n_2} = \dfrac{9+5}{142+268} = .0341$

$z = \dfrac{\bar{p}_1 - \bar{p}_2}{\sqrt{\bar{p}(1-\bar{p})\left(\dfrac{1}{n_1} + \dfrac{1}{n_2}\right)}} = \dfrac{.0634-.0187}{\sqrt{.0341(1-.0341)\left(\dfrac{1}{142} + \dfrac{1}{268}\right)}} = 2.37$

p-value = $2(1.0000 - .9911) = .0178$

p-value $\le .02$, reject H_0. There is a significant difference in drug resistance between the two states. New Jersey has the higher drug resistance rate.

32. a. March 2007: $\bar{p}_1 = 70/200 = .35$

   March 2008: $\bar{p}_2 = 70/150 = .4667$

   b. Using $\bar{p}_2 - \bar{p}_1$ to express the difference as an increase for March 2008,

   $\bar{p}_2 - \bar{p}_1 = .4667 - .35 = .1167$

   $$s_{\bar{p}_1 - \bar{p}_2} = \sqrt{\frac{.35(1-.35)}{200} + \frac{.4667(1-.4667)}{150}} = .0529$$

   Confidence interval: $.1167 \pm 1.96(.0529)$ or $.1167 \pm .1037$ $(.0130$ to $.2204)$

   c. Because the confidence interval in part (b) does not include 0, conclude that occupancy rates are higher in the first week of March 2008 than in the first week of March 2007. On the basis of this, we would expect occupancy rates to be higher in March 2008.

33. $\bar{p}_1 = .276$
      $\bar{p}_2 = .487$ One week earlier
      $\bar{p}_3 = .397$ One month earlier

   a. Point estimate: $\bar{p}_1 - \bar{p}_2 = .276 - .487 = -.211$

   Margin of error: $z_{.025}\sqrt{\frac{\bar{p}_1(1-\bar{p}_1)}{n_1} + \frac{\bar{p}_2(1-\bar{p}_2)}{n_2}} = 1.96\sqrt{\frac{.276(1-.276)}{240} + \frac{.487(1-.487)}{240}} = .085$

   95% confidence interval: $-.211 \pm .085$ $(-.296, -.126)$

   b. H_0: $p_1 - p_3 \ge 0$
      H_a: $p_1 - p_3 < 0$

   c. $\bar{p} = \dfrac{n_1\bar{p}_1 + n_2\bar{p}_3}{n_1 + n_3} = \dfrac{(240)(.276) + (240)(.397)}{240 + 240} = .3365$

   $$s_{\bar{p}_1 - \bar{p}_2} = \sqrt{\bar{p}(1-\bar{p})\left(\frac{1}{n_1} + \frac{1}{n_2}\right)} = \sqrt{(.3365)(1-.3365)\left(\frac{1}{240} + \frac{1}{240}\right)} = .0431$$

   $$z = \frac{.276 - .397}{.0431} = -2.81$$

   p-value $= .0025$

   With p-value $\le .01$, reject H_0 and conclude that bullish sentiment has declined over the one- month period.

34. a. $\bar{p}_1 = 44 / 500 = .088$

$\bar{p}_2 = 35 / 300 = .117$

$\bar{p}_3 = 36 / 400 = .090$

$\bar{p}_4 = 34 / 400 = .085$

Bridgeport 8.8%, Los Alamos 11.7%, Naples 9%, Washington DC 8.5%

b. H_0: $p_1 = p_2 = p_3 = p_4$

H_a: Not all population proportions are equal

Observed Frequencies (f_{ij})

Millionaire	Bridgeport	Los' Alamos	Naples	Washington	Total
Yes	44	35	36	34	149
No	456	265	364	366	1451
Total	500	300	400	400	1600

Expected Frequencies (e_{ij})

Millionaire	Bridgeport	Los' Alamos	Naples	Washington	Total
Yes	46.56	27.94	37.25	37.25	149
No	453.44	272.06	362.75	362.75	1451
Total	500	300	400	400	1600

Chi Square Calculations $(f_{ij} - e_{ij})^2 / e_{ij}$

Millionaire	Bridgeport	Los' Alamos	Naples	Washington	Total
Yes	.14	1.79	.04	.28	2.25
No	.01	.18	.00	.03	.23

$$\chi^2 = 2.48$$

Degrees of freedom = $k - 1 = (4 - 1) = 3$

Using the χ^2 table with $df = 3$, $\chi^2 = 2.48$ shows the p–value is greater than .10

Using Excel or Minitab, the p–value corresponding to $\chi^2 = 2.48$ is .4789

p–value $>$ .05, do not reject H$_0$. Cannot conclude that there is a difference among the population proportion of millionaires for these four cities.

35. a. H_0: $p_1 = p_2 = p_3$

H_a: Not all population proportions are equal

Observed Frequencies (f_{ij})

Quality	First	Second	Third	Total
Good	285	368	176	829
Defective	15	32	24	71
Total	300	400	200	900

Expected Frequencies (e_{ij})

Quality	First	Second	Third	Total
Good	276.33	368.44	184.22	829
Defective	23.67	31.56	15.78	71
Total	300	400	200	900

Chi Square Calculations $(f_{ij} - e_{ij})^2 / e_{ij}$

Quality	First	Second	Third	Total
Good	.27	.00	.37	.64
Defective	3.17	.01	4.28	7.46

$$\chi^2 = 8.10$$

Degrees of freedom = $k - 1 = (3 - 1) = 2$

Using the χ^2 table with $df = 2$, $\chi^2 = 8.10$ shows the p–value is between .025 and .01.

Using Excel or Minitab, the p–value corresponding to $\chi^2 = 8.10$ is .0174

p–value $\leq$ .05, reject H_0. Conclude the population proportion of good parts is not equal for all three shifts. The shifts differ in terms of production quality.

b. $\bar{p}_1 = 285 / 300 = .95$

$\bar{p}_2 = 368 / 400 = .92$

$\bar{p}_3 = 176 / 200 = .88$

$df = k - 1 = 3 - 1 = 2$ $\chi^2_{.05} = 5.991$

Comparison	p_i	p_j	Difference	n_i	n_j	Critical Value	Significant Diff > CV
1 vs. 2	.95	.92	.03	300	400	.0453	
1 vs. 3	.95	.88	.07	300	200	.0641	Yes
2 vs. 3	.92	.88	.04	400	200	.0653	

Shifts 1 and 3 differ significantly with shift 1 producing better quality (95%) than shift 3 (88%). The study cannot identify shift 2 (92%) as better or worse quality than the other two shifts. Shift 3, at 7% more defectives than shift 1 should be studied to determine how to improve its production quality.

36. Let p_1 = population proportion of on-time arrivals for American Airlines
p_2 = population proportion of on-time arrivals for Continental Airlines
p_3 = population proportion of on-time arrivals for Delta Air Lines
p_4 = population proportion of on-time arrivals for JetBlue Airways
p_5 = population proportion of on-time arrivals for Southwest Airlines
p_6 = population proportion of on-time arrivals for United Airlines
p_7 = population proportion of on-time arrivals for US Airways

a. Point estimates of the population proportion of on-time arrivals for each of these seven airlines are

$\bar{p}_1 = 83/99 = .8384$ is the point estimate of the population proportion of on-time arrivals for American Airlines

$\overline{p}_2 = 54/72 = .75$ is the point estimate of the population proportion of on-time arrivals for Continental Airlines

$\overline{p}_3 = 96/117 = .8205$ is the point estimate of the population proportion of on-time arrivals for Delta Air Lines

$\overline{p}_4 = 60/82 = .7317$ is the point estimate of the population proportion of on-time arrivals for JetBlue Airways

$\overline{p}_5 = 69/92 = .75$ is the point estimate of the population proportion of on-time arrivals for Southwest Airlines

$\overline{p}_6 = 66/81 = .8148$ is the point estimate of the population proportion of on-time arrivals for United Airlines

$\overline{p}_7 = 68/80 = .85$ is the point estimate of the population proportion of on-time arrivals for US Airways

b. $H_0: p_1 = p_2 = p_3 = p_4 = p_5 = p_6 = p_7$
H_a: Not all population proportions are equal

Observed Frequency (f_{ij})

	American Airlines	Continental Airlines	Delta Air Lines	JetBlue Airways	Southwest Airlines	United Airlines	US Airways	Total
On-Time Arrivals	83	54	96	60	69	66	68	496
Late Arrivals	16	18	21	22	23	15	12	1277
Totals	99	72	117	82	92	81	80	623

Expected Frequency (e_{ij})

	American Airlines	Continental Airlines	Delta Air Lines	JetBlue Airways	Southwest Airlines	United Airlines	US Airways	Total
On-Time Arrivals	78.8	57.3	93.1	65.3	73.2	64.5	63.7	496
Late Arrivals	20.2	14.7	23.9	16.7	18.8	16.5	16.3	127
Totals	99	72	117	82	92	81	80	623

Chi Square $(f_{ij} - e_{ij})^2 / e_{ij}$

	American Airlines	Continental Airlines	Delta Air Lines	JetBlue Airways	Southwest Airlines	United Airlines	US Airways	Total
On-Time Arrivals	0.22	0.19	0.09	0.43	0.25	0.04	0.29	1.50
Late Arrivals	0.87	0.75	0.34	1.67	0.96	0.14	1.14	5.87

$$\chi^2 = 7.37$$

Degrees of freedom $= k - 1 = 7 - 1 = 6$

Using the χ^2 table with $df = 6$, $\chi^2 = 7.37$ shows the p–value is greater than .10.

Using Excel or Minitab, the p–value corresponding to $\chi^2 = 7.37$ is .2880.

p–value > .05, so do not reject H_0. We cannot conclude that the population proportion of on-time flights in 2012 differs for these seven airlines.

37. Let p_1 = population proportion of visitors who rate the Musée du Louvre as spectacular
   p_2 = population proportion of visitors who rate the Metropolitan Museum of Art as spectacular
   p_3 = population proportion of visitors who rate the British Museum as spectacular
   p_4 = population proportion of visitors who rate the National Gallery as spectacular
   p_5 = population proportion of visitors who rate the Tate Modern as spectacular

   a. Point estimates of the population proportion of visitors who rated each of these museums as spectacular are

   $\bar{p}_1 = 113/150 = .7533$ is the point estimate of the population proportion of visitors who rated the Musée du Louvre as spectacular

   $\bar{p}_2 = 94/140 = .6714$ is the point estimate of the population proportion of visitors who rated the Metropolitan Museum of Art as spectacular

   $\bar{p}_3 = 96/160 = .60$ is the point estimate of the population proportion of visitors who rated the British Museum as spectacular

   $\bar{p}_4 = 78/120 = .65$ is the point estimate of the population proportion of visitors who rated the National Gallery as spectacular

   $\bar{p}_5 = 88/110 = .80$ is the point estimate of the population proportion of visitors who rated the Tate Modern as spectacular

   b. $H_0: p_1 = p_2 = p_3 = p_4 = p_5$
   H_a: Not all population proportions are equal

Observed Frequency (f_{ij})

	Musée du Louvre	Metropolitan Museum of Art	British Museum	National Gallery	Tate Modern	Totals
Rated Spectacular	113	94	96	78	88	469
Did Not Rate Spectacular	37	46	64	42	22	211
Totals	150	140	160	120	110	680

Expected Frequency (e_{ij})

	Musée du Louvre	Metropolitan Museum of Art	British Museum	National Gallery	Tate Modern	Totals
Rated Spectacular	103.5	96.6	110.4	82.8	75.9	469
Did Not Rate Spectacular	46.5	43.4	49.6	37.2	34.1	211
Totals	150	140	160	120	110	680

Chi Square $(f_{ij} - e_{ij})^2 / e_{ij}$

	Musée du Louvre	Metropolitan Museum of Art	British Museum	National Gallery	Tate Modern	Totals
Rated Spectacular	0.88	0.07	1.87	0.27	1.94	5.03
Did Not Rate Spectacular	1.96	0.15	4.15	0.61	4.31	11.18

$$\chi^2 = 16.21$$

Degrees of freedom = $k - 1 = 5 - 1 = 4$

Using the χ^2 table with $df = 4$, $\chi^2 = 16.21$ shows the p–value is less than .005.

Using Excel or Minitab, the p–value corresponding to $\chi^2 = 16.21$ is .0027.

p–value $\leq .05$, reject H_0. We conclude that the population proportion of visitors who rated the museum as spectacular differs for these five museums.

38.　　Let　p_1 = population proportion of truck drivers who rate Rochester, NY as satisfactory in keeping its streets clear of snow

　　　　　p_2 = population proportion of truck drivers who rate Salt Lake City, UT as satisfactory in keeping its streets clear of snow

　　　　　p_3 = population proportion of truck drivers who rate Madison, WI as satisfactory in keeping its streets clear of snow

　　　　　p_4 = population proportion of truck drivers who rate Bridgeport, CT as satisfactory in keeping its streets clear of snow

a. Point estimates of the population proportion of truck drivers who rated each of these cities as satisfactory in keeping its roads clear of snow are

$\bar{p}_1 = 27/48 = .5625$ is the point estimate of the population proportion of truck drivers who rated Rochester, NY as satisfactory in keeping its streets clear of snow

$\bar{p}_2 = 35/56 = .625$ is the point estimate of the population proportion of truck drivers who rated Salt Lake City, UT as satisfactory in keeping its streets clear of snow

$\bar{p}_3 = 29/47 = .617$ is the point estimate of the population proportion of truck drivers who rated Madison, WI as satisfactory in keeping its streets clear of snow

$\bar{p}_4 = 24/45 = .5333$ is the point estimate of the population proportion of truck drivers who rated Bridgeport, CT as satisfactory in keeping its streets clear of snow

b. H_0: $p_1 = p_2 = p_3 = p_4$
H_a: Not all population proportions are equal

Observed Frequency (f_{ij})

	Rochester, NY	Salt Lake City, UT	Madison, WI	Bridgeport, CT	Totals
Satisfactory	27	35	29	24	115
Not Satisfactory	21	21	18	21	81
Totals	48	56	47	45	196

Expected Frequency (e_{ij})

	Rochester, NY	Salt Lake City, UT	Madison, WI	Bridgeport, CT	Totals
Satisfactory	28.2	32.9	27.6	26.4	115
Not Satisfactory	19.8	23.1	19.4	18.6	81
Totals	48	56	47	45	196

Chi Square $(f_{ij} - e_{ij})^2 / e_{ij}$

	Rochester, NY	Salt Lake City, UT	Madison, WI	Bridgeport, CT	Totals
Satisfactory	0.05	0.14	0.07	0.22	0.48
Not Satisfactory	0.07	0.20	0.10	0.31	0.68

$$\chi^2 = 1.16$$

Degrees of freedom = $k - 1 = 4 - 1 = 3$

Using the χ^2 table with $df = 3$, $\chi^2 = 1.16$ shows the p–value is greater than .10.

Using Excel or Minitab, the p–value corresponding to $\chi^2 = 1.16$ is .7626.

p–value > .05, so do not reject H_0. We cannot conclude that the he population proportion of truck drivers who rate whether the city does a satisfactory job of keeping its streets clear of snow differs for these four cities.

39.   Expected Frequencies:

	Quality	
Shift	Good	Defective
1st	368.44	31.56
2nd	276.33	23.67
3rd	184.22	15.78

$$\chi^2 = 8.10$$

Degrees of freedom = $(3 - 1)(2 - 1) = 2$

Using the χ^2 table with $df = 2$, $\chi^2 = 8.10$ shows the p-value is between .01 and .025.

Using Excel or Minitab, the p-value corresponding to $\chi^2 = 8.10$ is .0174.

p-value $\leq$ .05, reject H_0. Conclude that shift and quality are not independent.

40.   Expected Frequencies:

e_{11}	=	1046.19	e_{12}	=	632.81
e_{21}	=	28.66	e_{22}	=	17.34
e_{31}	=	258.59	e_{32}	=	156.41
e_{41}	=	516.55	e_{42}	=	312.40

Employment	Region	Observed Frequency (f_i)	Expected Frequency (e_i)	$(f_i - e_i)^2 / e_i$
Full-Time	Eastern	1105	1046.19	3.31
Full-time	Western	574	632.81	5.46
Part-Time	Eastern	31	28.66	0.19
Part-Time	Western	15	17.34	0.32
Self-Employed	Eastern	229	258.59	3.39
Self-Employed	Western	186	156.41	5.60
Not Employed	Eastern	485	516.55	1.93
Not Employed	Western	344	312.45	3.19
	Totals:	2969		23.37

Degrees of freedom = (4 - 1)(2 - 1) = 3

Using the χ^2 table with $df = 3$, $\chi^2 = 23.37$ shows the p-value is less than .005.

Using Excel or Minitab, the p-value corresponding to $\chi^2 = 23.37$ is .0000.

p-value $\leq$ .05, reject H_0. Conclude that employment status is not independent of region.

41. Expected frequencies:

	Loan Approval Decision	
Loan Offices	Approved	Rejected
Miller	24.86	15.14
McMahon	18.64	11.36
Games	31.07	18.93
Runk	12.43	7.57

$\chi^2 = 2.21$

Degrees of freedom = (4 - 1)(2 - 1) = 3

Using the χ^2 table with $df = 3$, $\chi^2 = 1.21$ shows the p-value is greater than .10.

Using Excel or Minitab, the p-value corresponding to $\chi^2 = 2.21$ is .5300.

p-value > .05, do not reject H_0. The loan decision does not appear to be dependent on the officer.

42. a. Column totals: Slower 213, No Preference 21, and Faster 66.

Percentage preferring a slower pace = (213/300)(100) = 71%

Percentage preferring a faster pace = (66/300)(100) = 22%

The combined samples of men and women show a majority would rather live in a place with a slower pace of life.

b. Observed Frequency (f_{ij})

Respondent	Preferred Pace of Life			
	Slower	No Pref	Faster	Total
Men	102	9	39	150
Woman	111	12	27	150
Total	213	21	66	300

Expected Frequency (e_{ij})

Respondent	Preferred Pace of Life			
	Slower	No Pref	Faster	Total
Men	106.5	10.5	33	150
Woman	106.5	10.5	33	150
Total	213	21	66	300

Chi Square $(f_{ij} - e_{ij})^2 / e_{ij}$

Respondent	Preferred Pace of Life			
	Slower	No Pref	Faster	Total
Men	.19	.21	1.09	1.495
Woman	.19	..21	1.09	1.495
				$\chi^2 = 2.99$

Degrees of freedom = (2-1)(3-1) = 2

Using the χ^2 table with $df = 2$, $\chi^2 = 2.99$ shows the p-value is greater than .10.

Using Excel or Minitab, the p-value corresponding to $\chi^2 = 2.99$ is .2242.

p-value > .05, do not reject H_0. We cannot reject the assumption that the preferred pace of life is independent of the respondent being a man or a woman. That is, there is no statistical evidence to conclude men and women differ with respected to the preferred pace of life.

This is a good example of where it would be desirable to study this further before drawing a conclusion. Including a larger number of men and women in the sample and repeating the analysis should be considered.

43. Observed Frequencies

Flavor	Age of Consumer					Totals
	Under 18	18-30	31-44	45-58	Over 58	
Vanilla	155	108	99	100	129	591
Chocolate	39	53	47	28	30	197
Butter Pecan	12	15	21	20	43	111
Strawberry	23	14	13	17	34	101
Total	229	190	180	165	236	1000

Expected Frequencies

Flavor	Age of Consumer					Totals
	Under 18	18-30	31-44	45-58	Over 58	
Vanilla	135.3	112.3	106.4	97.5	139.5	591
Chocolate	45.1	37.4	35.5	32.5	46.5	197
Butter Pecan	25.4	21.1	20.0	18.3	26.2	111
Strawberry	23.1	19.2	18.2	16.7	23.8	101
Totals	229	190	180	165	236	1000

Chi Square

Flavor	Age of Consumer					Totals
	Under 18	18-30	31-44	45-58	Over 58	
Vanilla	2.86	0.16	0.51	0.06	0.79	4.38
Chocolate	0.83	6.48	3.76	0.62	5.85	17.54
Butter Pecan	7.08	1.76	0.05	0.16	10.78	19.83
Strawberry	0.00	1.40	1.48	0.01	4.33	7.22

$$\chi^2 = 48.97$$

Degrees of freedom = (4-1)(5-1)=12

Using the χ^2 table with $df = 12$, $\chi^2 = 48.97$ shows the p-value is less than .005.

Using Excel or Minitab, the p-value corresponding to $\chi^2 = 48.97$ is approximately 0.

p-value $\leq$ .05, reject H_0. Conclude that consumer preference for these four flavors of ice cream and age of the consumer are not independent.

If we calculate the column percentages, we gain insight into the relationship between age of the consumer and the preferred ice cream flavor.

Flavor	Age of Consumer					Totals
	Under 18	18-30	31-44	45-58	Over 58	
Vanilla	.68	.57	.55	.61	.55	.59
Chocolate	.17	.28	.26	.17	.13	.20
Butter Pecan	.05	.08	.12	.12	.18	.11
Strawberry	.10	.07	.07	.10	.14	.10

The proportion of consumers who prefer butter pecan is much higher in the Over 58 group that (.18) than in the entire sample (.11), and the proportion of consumers who prefer butter pecan is much lower in the Under 18 group (.05). There is also a great deal of difference in reference for chocolate between some of these groups; the proportion of consumers who chocolate is much lower in the Over 58 group that (.13) than in the entire sample (.20), and the proportion of consumers who prefer chocolate is much higher in the 18 -30 group (.28) and the 31-44 group (.26). Butter pecan ice cream is favored by older consumers, while chocolate is favored by consumers who are between 18 and 44 years old.

44. Expected Frequencies:

	Los Angeles	San Diego	San Francisco	San Jose	Totals
Occupied	165.7	124.3	186.4	165.7	642
Vacant	34.3	25.7	38.6	34.3	133
Totals	200.0	150.0	225.0	200.0	775

$$\chi^2 = \frac{(160-165.7)^2}{165.7} + \frac{(116-124.3)^2}{124.3} + \cdots + \frac{(26-34.3)^2}{34.3} = 7.75$$

Degrees of freedom = (2 - 1)(4 - 1) = 3

Using the χ^2 table with $df = 3$, $\chi^2 = 7.75$ shows the p-value between .05 and .10.

Using Excel or Minitab, the p-value corresponding to $\chi^2 = 7.75$ is .0515.

p-value > .05, do not reject H_0. We cannot conclude that office vacancies are dependent on metropolitan area, but it is close: the p-value is slightly larger than .05.

Chapter 12
Simple Linear Regression

Learning Objectives

1. Understand how regression analysis can be used to develop an equation that estimates mathematically how two variables are related.

2. Understand the differences between the regression model, the regression equation, and the estimated regression equation.

3. Know how to fit an estimated regression equation to a set of sample data based upon the least-squares method.

4. Be able to determine how good a fit is provided by the estimated regression equation and compute the sample correlation coefficient from the regression analysis output.

5. Understand the assumptions necessary for statistical inference and be able to test for a significant relationship.

6. Know how to develop confidence interval estimates of y given a specific value of x in both the case of a mean value of y and an individual value of y.

7. Learn how to use a residual plot to make a judgement as to the validity of the regression assumptions.

8. Know the definition of the following terms:

   independent and dependent variable
   simple linear regression
   regression model
   regression equation and estimated regression equation
   scatter diagram
   coefficient of determination
   standard error of the estimate
   confidence interval
   prediction interval
   residual plot

Solutions:

1 a.

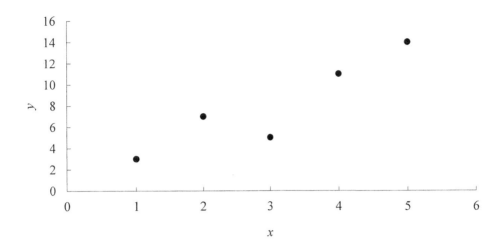

b. There appears to be a positive linear relationship between x and y.

c. Many different straight lines can be drawn to provide a linear approximation of the relationship between x *and* y; in part (d) we will determine the equation of a straight line that "best" represents the relationship according to the least squares criterion.

d. $\bar{x} = \dfrac{\Sigma x_i}{n} = \dfrac{15}{5} = 3$ $\bar{y} = \dfrac{\Sigma y_i}{n} = \dfrac{40}{5} = 8$

$\Sigma(x_i - \bar{x})(y_i - \bar{y}) = 26$ $\Sigma(x_i - \bar{x})^2 = 10$

$b_1 = \dfrac{\Sigma(x_i - \bar{x})(y_i - \bar{y})}{\Sigma(x_i - \bar{x})^2} = \dfrac{26}{10} = 2.6$

$b_0 = \bar{y} - b_1\bar{x} = 8 - (2.6)(3) = 0.2$

$\hat{y} = 0.2 + 2.6x$

e. $\hat{y} = 0.2 + 2.6(4) = 10.6$

2. a.

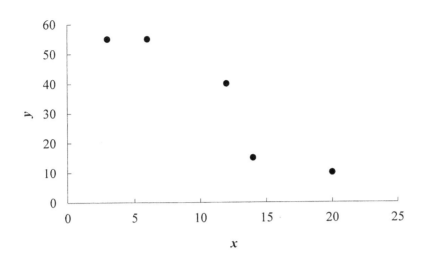

b. There appears to be a negative linear relationship between x and y.

c. Many different straight lines can be drawn to provide a linear approximation of the relationship between x and y; in part (d) we will determine the equation of a straight line that "best" represents the relationship according to the least squares criterion.

d. $\bar{x} = \dfrac{\Sigma x_i}{n} = \dfrac{55}{5} = 11 \qquad \bar{y} = \dfrac{\Sigma y_i}{n} = \dfrac{175}{5} = 35$

$\Sigma(x_i - \bar{x})(y_i - \bar{y}) = -540 \qquad \Sigma(x_i - \bar{x})^2 = 180$

$b_1 = \dfrac{\Sigma(x_i - \bar{x})(y_i - \bar{y})}{\Sigma(x_i - \bar{x})^2} = \dfrac{-540}{180} = -3$

$b_0 = \bar{y} - b_1\bar{x} = 35 - (-3)(11) = 68$

$\hat{y} = 68 - 3x$

e. $\hat{y} = 68 - 3(10) = 38$

3.   a.

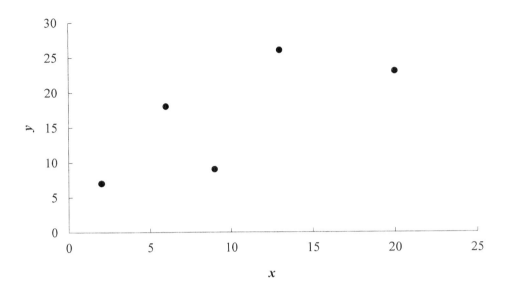

b. $\bar{x} = \dfrac{\Sigma x_i}{n} = \dfrac{50}{5} = 10$ $\bar{y} = \dfrac{\Sigma y_i}{n} = \dfrac{83}{5} = 16.6$

$\Sigma(x_i - \bar{x})(y_i - \bar{y}) = 171$ $\Sigma(x_i - \bar{x})^2 = 190$

$b_1 = \dfrac{\Sigma(x_i - \bar{x})(y_i - \bar{y})}{\Sigma(x_i - \bar{x})^2} = \dfrac{171}{190} = 0.9$

$b_0 = \bar{y} - b_1\bar{x} = 16.6 - (0.9)(10) = 7.6$

$\hat{y} = 7.6 + 0.9x$

c. $\hat{y} = 7.6 + 0.9(6) = 13$

4. a.

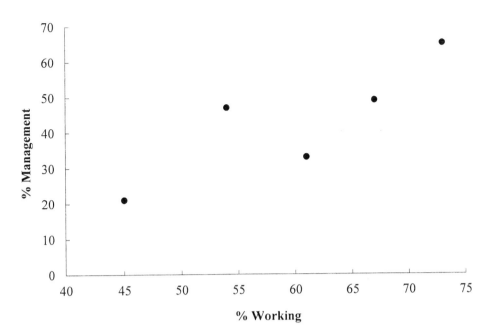

b. There appears to be a positive linear relationship between the percentage of women working in the five companies (x) and the percentage of management jobs held by women in that company (y)

c. Many different straight lines can be drawn to provide a linear approximation of the relationship between x and y; in part (d) we will determine the equation of a straight line that "best" represents the relationship according to the least squares criterion.

d. $\bar{x} = \dfrac{\Sigma x_i}{n} = \dfrac{300}{5} = 60 \qquad \bar{y} = \dfrac{\Sigma y_i}{n} = \dfrac{215}{5} = 43$

$\Sigma(x_i - \bar{x})(y_i - \bar{y}) = 624 \qquad \Sigma(x_i - \bar{x})^2 = 480$

$b_1 = \dfrac{\Sigma(x_i - \bar{x})(y_i - \bar{y})}{\Sigma(x_i - \bar{x})^2} = \dfrac{624}{480} = 1.3$

$b_0 = \bar{y} - b_1\bar{x} = 43 - 1.3(60) = -35$

$\hat{y} = -35 + 1.3x$

e. $\hat{y} = -35 + 1.3x = -35 + 1.3(60) = 43\%$

12 - 5

5. a.

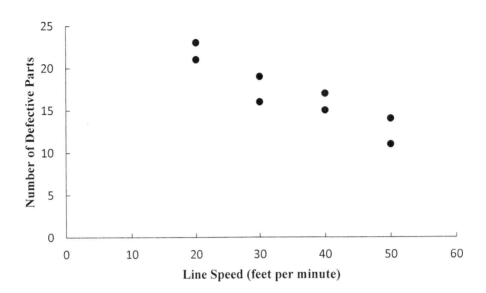

b. There appears to be a negative relationship between line speed (feet per minute) and the number of defective parts.

c. Let x = line speed (feet per minute) and y = number of defective parts.

$$\bar{x} = \frac{\Sigma x_i}{n} = \frac{280}{8} = 35 \quad \bar{y} = \frac{\Sigma y_i}{n} = \frac{136}{8} = 17$$

$$\Sigma(x_i - \bar{x})(y_i - \bar{y}) = -300 \quad \Sigma(x_i - \bar{x})^2 = 1000$$

$$b_1 = \frac{\Sigma(x_i - \bar{x})(y_i - \bar{y})}{\Sigma(x_i - \bar{x})^2} = \frac{-300}{1000} = -.3$$

$$b_0 = \bar{y} - b_1\bar{x} = 17 - (-.3)(35) = 27.5$$

$$\hat{y} = 27.5 - .3x$$

d. $\hat{y} = 27.5 - .3x = 27.5 - .3(25) = 20$

6. a.

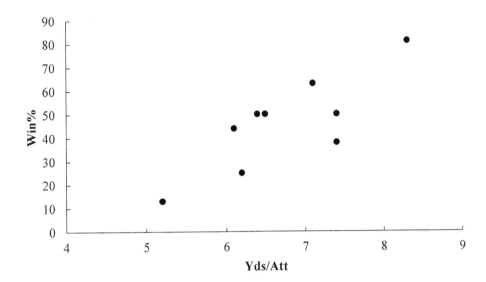

b. The scatter diagram indicates a positive linear relationship between x = average number of passing yards per attempt and y = the percentage of games won by the team.

c. $\bar{x} = \Sigma x_i / n = 680 / 10 = 6.8 \quad \bar{y} = \Sigma y_i / n = 464 / 10 = 46.4$

   $\Sigma(x_i - \bar{x})(y_i - \bar{y}) = 121.6 \quad \Sigma(x_i - \bar{x})^2 = 7.08$

   $b_1 = \dfrac{\Sigma(x_i - \bar{x})(y_i - \bar{y})}{\Sigma(x_i - \bar{x})^2} = \dfrac{121.6}{7.08} = 17.1751$

   $b_0 = \bar{y} - b_1\bar{x} = 46.4 - (17.1751)(6.8) = -70.391$

   $\hat{y} = -70.391 + 17.1751x$

d. The slope of the estimated regression line is approximately 17.2. So, for every increase of one yard in the average number of passes per attempt, the percentage of games won by the team increases by 17.2%.

e. With an average number of passing yards per attempt of 6.2, the predicted percentage of games won is $\hat{y}$ = -70.391 + 17.175(6.2) = 36%. With a record of 7 wins and 9 loses, the percentage of wins that the Kansas City Chiefs won is 43.8 or approximately 44%. Considering the small data size, the prediction made using the estimated regression equation is not too bad.

7.   a.

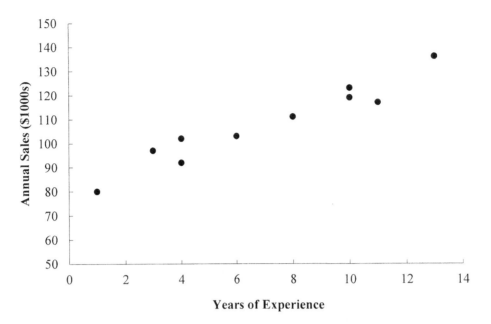

Years of Experience

b.   Let x = years of experience and y = annual sales ($1000s)

$$\bar{x} = \frac{\Sigma x_i}{n} = \frac{70}{10} = 7 \qquad \bar{y} = \frac{\Sigma y_i}{n} = \frac{1080}{10} = 108$$

$$\Sigma(x_i - \bar{x})(y_i - \bar{y}) = 568 \qquad \Sigma(x_i - \bar{x})^2 = 142$$

$$b_1 = \frac{\Sigma(x_i - \bar{x})(y_i - \bar{y})}{\Sigma(x_i - \bar{x})^2} = \frac{568}{142} = 4$$

$$b_0 = \bar{y} - b_1\bar{x} = 108 - (4)(7) = 80$$

$$\hat{y} = 80 + 4x$$

c. $\hat{y} = 80 + 4x = 80 + 4(9) = 116$ or $116,000

8.   a.

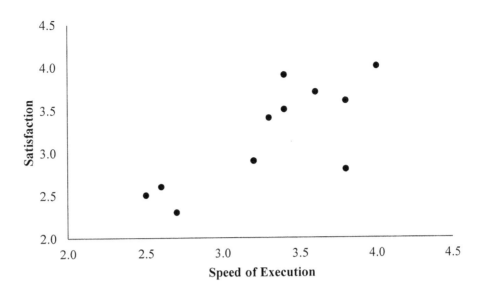

b.   The scatter diagram indicates a positive linear relationship between x = speed of execution rating and y = overall satisfaction rating for electronic trades.

c. $\bar{x} = \Sigma x_i / n = 36.3 / 11 = 3.3$ $\bar{y} = \Sigma y_i / n = 35.2 / 11 = 3.2$

$\Sigma(x_i - \bar{x})(y_i - \bar{y}) = 2.4$ $\Sigma(x_i - \bar{x})^2 = 2.6$

$b_1 = \dfrac{\Sigma(x_i - \bar{x})(y_i - \bar{y})}{\Sigma(x_i - \bar{x})^2} = \dfrac{2.4}{2.6} = .9077$

$b_0 = \bar{y} - b_1\bar{x} = 3.2 - (.9077)(3.3) = .2046$

$\hat{y} = .2046 + .9077x$

d.   The slope of the estimated regression line is approximately .9077. So, a one unit increase in the speed of execution rating will increase the overall satisfaction rating by approximately .9 points.

e.   The average speed of execution rating for the other brokerage firms is 3.4. Using this as the new value of x for Zecco.com, we can use the estimated regression equation developed in part (c) to estimate the overall satisfaction rating corresponding to $x = 3.4$.

$\hat{y} = .2046 + .9077x = .2046 + .9077(3.4) = 3.29$

Thus, an estimate of the overall satisfaction rating when $x = 3.4$ is approximately 3.3.

9. a.

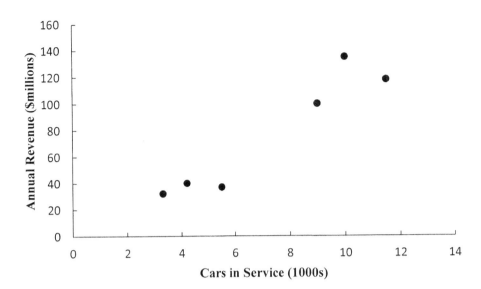

b. The scatter diagram indicates a positive linear relationship between x = cars in service (1000s) and y = annual revenue ($millions).

c. $\bar{x} = \Sigma x_i / n = 43.5 / 6 = 7.25$ $\bar{y} = \Sigma y_i / n = 462 / 6 = 77$

$\Sigma(x_i - \bar{x})(y_i - \bar{y}) = 734.6$ $\Sigma(x_i - \bar{x})^2 = 56.655$

$$b_1 = \frac{\Sigma(x_i - \bar{x})(y_i - \bar{y})}{\Sigma(x_i - \bar{x})^2} = \frac{734.6}{56.655} = 12.9662$$

$$b_0 = \bar{y} - b_1\bar{x} = 77 - (12.9662)(7.25) = -17.005$$

$$\hat{y} = -17.005 + 12.966x$$

d. For every additional 1000 cars placed in service annual revenue will increase by 12.966 ($millions) or $12,966,000. Therefor every additional car placed in service will increase annual revenue by $12,966.

e. $\hat{y} = -17.005 + 12.966x = -17.005 + 12.966(11) = 125.621$

A prediction of annual revenue for Fox Rent A Car is approximately $126 million.

10. a.

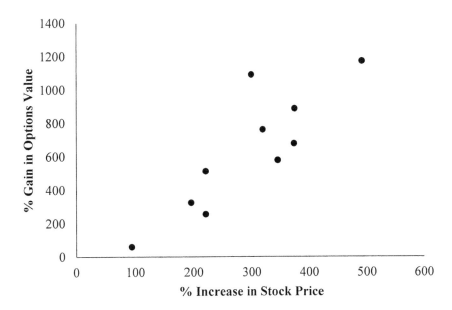

b. The scatter diagram indicates a positive linear relationship between x = percentage increase in the stock price and y = percentage gain in options value. In other words, options values increase as stock prices increase.

c. $\bar{x} = \Sigma x_i / n = 2939 / 10 = 293.9$ $\bar{y} = \Sigma y_i / n = 6301 / 10 = 630.1$

   $\Sigma(x_i - \bar{x})(y_i - \bar{y}) = 314,501.1$ $\Sigma(x_i - \bar{x})^2 = 115,842.9$

   $b_1 = \dfrac{\Sigma(x_i - \bar{x})(y_i - \bar{y})}{\Sigma(x_i - \bar{x})^2} = \dfrac{314,501.1}{115,842.9} = 2.7149$

   $b_0 = \bar{y} - b_1\bar{x} = 630.1 - (2.1749)(293.9) = -167.81$

   $\hat{y} = -167.81 + 2.7149x$

d. The slope of the estimated regression line is approximately 2.7. So, for every percentage increase in the price of the stock the options value increases by 2.7%.

e. The rewards for the CEO do appear to be based upon performance increases in the stock value. While the rewards may seem excessive, the executive is being rewarded for his/her role in increasing the value of the company. This is why such compensation schemes are devised for CEOs by boards of directors. A compensation scheme where an executive got a big salary increase when the company stock went down would be bad. And, if the stock price for a company had gone down during the periods in question, the value of the CEOs options would also go down.

11. a.

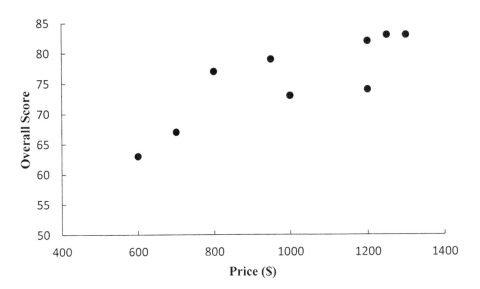

b. The scatter diagram indicates a positive linear relationship between x = price ($) and y = overall score.

c. $\bar{x} = \Sigma x_i / n = 10,200 / 10 = 1020$ $\bar{y} = \Sigma y_i / n = 755 / 10 = 75.5$

$\Sigma (x_i - \bar{x})(y_i - \bar{y}) = 11,900$ $\Sigma (x_i - \bar{x})^2 = 561,000$

$$b_1 = \frac{\Sigma (x_i - \bar{x})(y_i - \bar{y})}{\Sigma (x_i - \bar{x})^2} = \frac{11,900}{561,000} = .021212$$

$b_0 = \bar{y} - b_1 \bar{x} = 75.5 - (.021212)(1020) = 53.864$

$\hat{y} = 53.864 + .0212x$

d. The slope of .0212 means that spending an additional $100 in price will increase the overall score by approximately 2 points.

e. A prediction of the overall score is $\hat{y} = 53.864 + .0212x = 53.864 + .0212(700) = 68.7$

12. a.

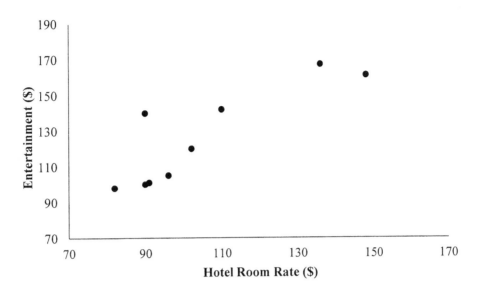

b. The scatter diagram indicates a positive linear relationship between x = hotel room rate and the amount spent on entertainment.

c. $\bar{x} = \Sigma x_i / n = 945/9 = 105$ $\quad \bar{y} = \Sigma y_i / n = 1134/9 = 126$

   $\Sigma(x_i - \bar{x})(y_i - \bar{y}) = 4237$ $\quad \Sigma(x_i - \bar{x})^2 = 4100$

   $b_1 = \dfrac{\Sigma(x_i - \bar{x})(y_i - \bar{y})}{\Sigma(x_i - \bar{x})^2} = \dfrac{4237}{4100} = 1.0334$

   $b_0 = \bar{y} - b_1\bar{x} = 126 - (1.0334)(105) = 17.49$

   $\hat{y} = 17.49 + 1.0334x$

d. With a value of x = \$128, the predicted value of y for Chicago is

   $\hat{y} = 17.49 + 1.0334x = 17.49 + 1.0334(128) = 150$

   Note: In The Wall Street Journal article the entertainment expense for Chicago was \$146. Thus, the estimated regression equation provided a good estimate of entertainment expenses for Chicago.

13. a.

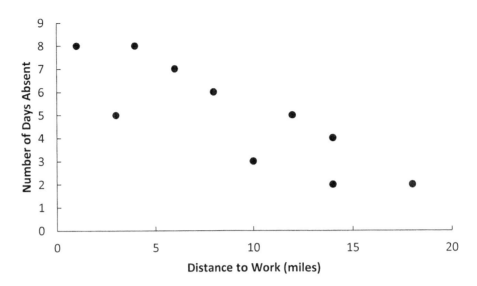

The scatter diagram indicates a negative linear relationship between x = distance to work and y = number of days absent.

b. $\bar{x} = \Sigma x_i / n = 90 / 10 = 9$ $\bar{y} = \Sigma y_i / n = 50 / 10 = 5$

$\Sigma(x_i - \bar{x})(y_i - \bar{y}) = -95$ $\Sigma(x_i - \bar{x})^2 = 276$

$b_1 = \dfrac{\Sigma(x_i - \bar{x})(y_i - \bar{y})}{\Sigma(x_i - \bar{x})^2} = \dfrac{-95}{276} = -.3442$

$b_0 = \bar{y} - b_1\bar{x} = 5 - (-.3442)(9) = 8.0978$

$\hat{y} = 8.0978 - .3442x$

c.   A prediction of the number of days absent is $\hat{y} = 8.0978 - .3442(5) = 6.4$ or approximately 6 days.

14. a.

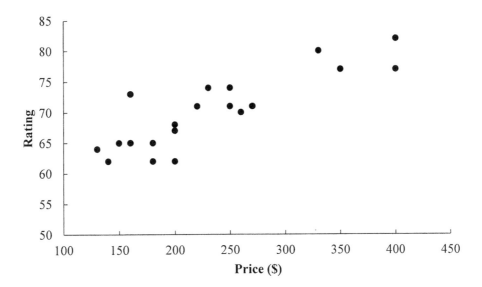

b. The scatter diagram indicates a positive linear relationship between x = price ($) and y = overall rating.

c. $\bar{x} = \Sigma x_i / n = 4660 / 20 = 233 \quad \bar{y} = \Sigma y_i / n = 1400 / 20 = 70$

$\Sigma(x_i - \bar{x})(y_i - \bar{y}) = 8100 \quad \Sigma(x_i - \bar{x})^2 = 127,420$

$b_1 = \dfrac{\Sigma(x_i - \bar{x})(y_i - \bar{y})}{\Sigma(x_i - \bar{x})^2} = \dfrac{8100}{127,420} = .06357$

$b_0 = \bar{y} - b_1\bar{x} = 70 - (.06357)(233) = 55.188$

$\hat{y} = 55.188 + .06357x$

d. We can use the estimated regression equation developed in part (c) to estimate the overall satisfaction rating corresponding to $x = 200$.

$\hat{y} = 55.188 + .06357x = 55.188 + .06357(200) = 67.9$

Thus, an estimate of the overall rating when x = $200 is approximately 70.

15. a. The estimated regression equation and the mean for the dependent variable are:

$\hat{y}_i = 0.2 + 2.6x_i \qquad \bar{y} = 8$

The sum of squares due to error and the total sum of squares are

$SSE = \Sigma(y_i - \hat{y}_i)^2 = 12.40 \qquad SST = \Sigma(y_i - \bar{y})^2 = 80$

Thus, SSR = SST - SSE = 80 - 12.4 = 67.6

b. $r^2 = \text{SSR/SST} = 67.6/80 = .845$

The least squares line provided a very good fit; 84.5% of the variability in y has been explained by the least squares line.

c. $r_{xy} = \sqrt{.845} = +.9192$

16. a. The estimated regression equation and the mean for the dependent variable are:

$$\hat{y}_i = 68 - 3x \qquad \bar{y} = 35$$

The sum of squares due to error and the total sum of squares are

$$\text{SSE} = \Sigma(y_i - \hat{y}_i)^2 = 230 \qquad \text{SST} = \Sigma(y_i - \bar{y})^2 = 1850$$

Thus, SSR = SST - SSE = 1850 - 230 = 1620

b. $r^2 = \text{SSR/SST} = 1620/1850 = .876$

The least squares line provided an excellent fit; 87.6% of the variability in y has been explained by the estimated regression equation.

c. $r_{xy} = \sqrt{.876} = -.936$

Note: the sign for r is negative because the slope of the estimated regression equation is negative. ($b_1 = -3$)

17. The estimated regression equation and the mean for the dependent variable are:

$$\hat{y}_i = 7.6 + .9x \qquad \bar{y} = 16.6$$

The sum of squares due to error and the total sum of squares are

$$\text{SSE} = \Sigma(y_i - \hat{y}_i)^2 = 127.3 \qquad \text{SST} = \Sigma(y_i - \bar{y})^2 = 281.2$$

Thus, SSR = SST - SSE = 281.2 - 127.3 = 153.9

$r^2 = \text{SSR/SST} = 153.9/281.2 = .547$

We see that 54.7% of the variability in y has been explained by the least squares line.

$r_{xy} = \sqrt{.547} = +.740$

18. a. $\bar{x} = \Sigma x_i / n = 600 / 6 = 100 \qquad \bar{y} = \Sigma y_i / n = 330 / 6 = 55$

$\text{SST} = \Sigma(y_i - \bar{y})^2 = 1800 \qquad \text{SSE} = \Sigma(y_i - \hat{y}_i)^2 = 287.624$

$\text{SSR} = \text{SST} - \text{SSR} = 1800 - 287.624 = 1512.376$

b. $r^2 = \dfrac{\text{SSR}}{\text{SST}} = \dfrac{1512.376}{1800} = .84$

c. $r = \sqrt{r^2} = \sqrt{.84} = .917$

19. a. The estimated regression equation and the mean for the dependent variable are:

$$\hat{y} = 80 + 4x \qquad\qquad \bar{y} = 108$$

The sum of squares due to error and the total sum of squares are

$$SSE = \Sigma(y_i - \hat{y}_i)^2 = 170 \qquad SST = \Sigma(y_i - \bar{y})^2 = 2442$$

Thus, SSR = SST - SSE = 2442 - 170 = 2272

b. $r^2 = SSR/SST = 2272/2442 = .93$

We see that 93% of the variability in y has been explained by the least squares line.

c. $r_{xy} = \sqrt{.93} = +.96$

20. a. $\bar{x} = \Sigma x_i / n = 160/10 = 16 \quad \bar{y} = \Sigma y_i / n = 55,500/10 = 5550$

$$\Sigma(x_i - \bar{x})(y_i - \bar{y}) = -31,284 \quad \Sigma(x_i - \bar{x})^2 = 21.74$$

$$b_1 = \frac{\Sigma(x_i - \bar{x})(y_i - \bar{y})}{\Sigma(x_i - \bar{x})^2} = \frac{-31,284}{21.74} = -1439$$

$$b_0 = \bar{y} - b_1\bar{x} = 5550 - (-1439)(16) = 28,574$$

$$\hat{y} = 28,574 - 1439x$$

b. SST = 52,120,800 $\quad$ SSE = 7,102,922.54

SSR = SST – SSR = 52,120,800 - 7,102,922.54 = 45,017,877

$r^2 = SSR/SST = 45,017,877/52,120,800 = .864$

The estimated regression equation provided a very good fit.

c. $\hat{y} = 28,574 - 1439x = 28,574 - 1439(15) = 6989$

Thus, an estimate of the price for a bike that weighs 15 pounds is $6989.

21. a. $\bar{x} = \dfrac{\Sigma x_i}{n} = \dfrac{3450}{6} = 575 \quad \bar{y} = \dfrac{\Sigma y_i}{n} = \dfrac{33,700}{6} = 5616.67$

$$\Sigma(x_i - \bar{x})(y_i - \bar{y}) = 712,500 \qquad \Sigma(x_i - \bar{x})^2 = 93,750$$

$$b_1 = \frac{\Sigma(x_i - \bar{x})(y_i - \bar{y})}{\Sigma(x_i - \bar{x})^2} = \frac{712,500}{93,750} = 7.6$$

$$b_0 = \bar{y} - b_1\bar{x} = 5616.67 - (7.6)(575) = 1246.67$$

$$\hat{y} = 1246.67 + 7.6x$$

b. $7.60

c. The sum of squares due to error and the total sum of squares are:

$$SSE = \Sigma(y_i - \hat{y}_i)^2 = 233,333.33 \qquad SST = \Sigma(y_i - \bar{y})^2 = 5,648,333.33$$

Thus, SSR = SST - SSE = 5,648,333.33 - 233,333.33 = 5,415,000

r^2 = SSR/SST = 5,415,000/5,648,333.33 = .9587

We see that 95.87% of the variability in y has been explained by the estimated regression equation.

d. $\hat{y} = 1246.67 + 7.6x = 1246.67 + 7.6(500) = \$5046.67$

22 a. SSE = 1043.03

$$\bar{y} = \Sigma y_i / n = 462/6 = 77 \qquad SST = \Sigma(y_i - \bar{y})^2 = 10,568$$

SSR = SST − SSR = 10,568 − 1043.03 = 9524.97

$$r^2 = \frac{SSR}{SST} = \frac{9524.97}{10,568} = .9013$$

b. The estimated regression equation provided a very good fit; approximately 90% of the variability in the dependent variable was explained by the linear relationship between the two variables.

c. $r = \sqrt{r^2} = \sqrt{.9013} = .95$

This reflects a strong linear relationship between the two variables.

23. a. s^2 = MSE = SSE / $(n-2)$ = 12.4 / 3 = 4.133

b. $s = \sqrt{MSE} = \sqrt{4.133} = 2.033$

c. $\Sigma(x_i - \bar{x})^2 = 10$

$$s_{b_1} = \frac{s}{\sqrt{\Sigma(x_i - \bar{x})^2}} = \frac{2.033}{\sqrt{10}} = 0.643$$

d. $t = \dfrac{b_1}{s_{b_1}} = \dfrac{2.6}{.643} = 4.044$

Using t table (3 degrees of freedom), area in tail is between .01 and .025

p-value is between .02 and .05

Using Excel or Minitab, the p-value corresponding to $t = 4.04$ is .0272.

Because p-value $\leq \alpha$, we reject H_0: $\beta_1 = 0$

e. MSR $=$ SSR $/ 1 = 67.6$

$F =$ MSR $/$ MSE $= 67.6 / 4.133 = 16.36$

Using F table (1 degree of freedom numerator and 3 denominator), p-value is between .025 and .05

Using Excel or Minitab, the p-value corresponding to $F = 16.36$ is .0272.

Because p-value $\leq \alpha$, we reject H_0: $\beta_1 = 0$

Source of Variation	Sum of Squares	Degrees of Freedom	Mean Square	F	p-value
Regression	67.6	1	67.6	16.36	.0272
Error	12.4	3	4.133		
Total	80.0	4			

24. a. $s^2 =$ MSE $=$ SSE$/(n - 2) = 230/3 = 76.6667$

b. $s = \sqrt{\text{MSE}} = \sqrt{76.6667} = 8.7560$

c. $\Sigma(x_i - \bar{x})^2 = 180$

$$s_{b_1} = \frac{s}{\sqrt{\Sigma(x_i - \bar{x})^2}} = \frac{8.7560}{\sqrt{180}} = 0.6526$$

d. $t = \dfrac{b_1}{s_{b_1}} = \dfrac{-3}{.653} = -4.59$

Using t table (3 degrees of freedom), area in tail is less than .01; p-value is less than .02

Using Excel or Minitab, the p-value corresponding to $t = -4.59$ is .0193.

Because p-value $\leq \alpha$, we reject H_0: $\beta_1 = 0$

e. MSR $=$ SSR$/1 = 1620$

$F =$ MSR$/$MSE $= 1620/76.6667 = 21.13$

Using F table (1 degree of freedom numerator and 3 denominator), p-value is less than .025

Using Excel or Minitab, the p-value corresponding to $F = 21.13$ is .0193.

Because p-value $\leq \alpha$, we reject H_0: $\beta_1 = 0$

Source of Variation	Sum of Squares	Degrees of Freedom	Mean Square	F	p-value
Regression	1620	1	1620	21.13	.0193
Error	230	3	76.6667		
Total	1850	4			

25. a. $s^2 = \text{MSE} = \text{SSE}/(n-2) = 127.3/3 = 42.4333$

       $s = \sqrt{\text{MSE}} = \sqrt{42.4333} = 6.5141$

   b. $\Sigma(x_i - \bar{x})^2 = 190$

       $s_{b_1} = \dfrac{s}{\sqrt{\Sigma(x_i - \bar{x})^2}} = \dfrac{6.5141}{\sqrt{190}} = 0.4726$

       $t = \dfrac{b_1}{s_{b_1}} = \dfrac{.9}{.4726} = 1.90$

       Using t table (3 degrees of freedom), area in tail is between .05 and .10

       p-value is between .10 and .20

       Using Excel or Minitab, the p-value corresponding to $t = 1.90$ is .1530.

       Because p-value $> \alpha$, we cannot reject H_0: $\beta_1 = 0$; x and y do not appear to be related.

   c. $\text{MSR} = \text{SSR}/1 = 153.9/1 = 153.9$

       $F = \text{MSR}/\text{MSE} = 153.9/42.4333 = 3.63$

       Using F table (1 degree of freedom numerator and 3 denominator), p-value is greater than .10

       Using Excel or Minitab, the p-value corresponding to $F = 3.63$ is .1530.

       Because p-value $> \alpha$, we cannot reject H_0: $\beta_1 = 0$; x and y do not appear to be related.

26. a.   In the statement of exercise 18, $\hat{y} = 23.194 + .318x$

       In solving exercise 18, we found SSE = 287.624

       $s^2 = \text{MSE} = \text{SSE}/(n-2) = 287.624 / 4 = 71.906$

       $s = \sqrt{\text{MSE}} = \sqrt{71.906} = 8.4797$

       $\sum(x - \bar{x})^2 = 14,950$

       $s_{b_1} = \dfrac{s}{\sqrt{\sum(x - \bar{x})^2}} = \dfrac{8.4797}{\sqrt{14,950}} = .0694$

$$t = \frac{b_1}{s_{b_1}} = \frac{.318}{.0694} = 4.58$$

Using t table (4 degrees of freedom), area in tail is between .005 and .01

p-value is between .01 and .02

Using Excel, the p-value corresponding to $t = 4.58$ is .010.

Because p-value $\leq \alpha$, we reject H_0: $\beta_1 = 0$; there is a significant relationship between price and overall score

b. In exercise 18 we found SSR = 1512.376

MSR = SSR/1 = 1512.376/1 = 1512.376

F = MSR/MSE = 1512.376/71.906 = 21.03

Using F table (1 degree of freedom numerator and 4 denominator), p-value is between .025 and .01

Using Excel, the p-value corresponding to $F = 11.74$ is .010.

Because p-value $\leq \alpha$, we reject H_0: $\beta_1 = 0$

c.

Source of Variation	Sum of Squares	Degrees of Freedom	Mean Square	F	p-value
Regression	1512.376	1	1512.376	21.03	.010
Error	287.624	4	71.906		
Total	1800	5			

27. a. Let x = number of megapixels and y = price ($)

$$\bar{x} = \frac{\Sigma x_i}{n} = \frac{95}{10} = 9.5 \quad \bar{y} = \frac{\Sigma y_i}{n} = \frac{2190}{10} = 219$$

$$\Sigma(x_i - \bar{x})(y_i - \bar{y}) = 2165 \quad \Sigma(x_i - \bar{x})^2 = 56.5$$

$$b_1 = \frac{\Sigma(x_i - \bar{x})(y_i - \bar{y})}{\Sigma(x_i - \bar{x})^2} = \frac{2165}{56.5} = 38.31858$$

$$b_0 = \bar{y} - b_1\bar{x} = 219 - (38.31858)(9.5) = -145.0265$$

$$\hat{y} = -145.0265 + 38.31858x$$

b. SSE = $\Sigma(y_i - \hat{y}_i)^2 = 20,730.27$ SST = $\Sigma(y_i - \bar{y})^2 = 103,690$

Thus, SSR = SST - SSE = 103,690 − 20,730.27 = 82,959.73

MSR = SSR/1 = 82,959.73

$$\text{MSE} = \text{SSE}/(n-2) = 20{,}730.27/8 = 2591.28$$

$$F = \text{MSR}/\text{MSE} = 82{,}959.73/2591.28 = 32.015$$

Using F table (1 degree of freedom numerator and 8 denominator), p-value is less than .01

Using Excel, the p-value corresponding to $F = 32.015$ is .000.

Because p-value $\leq \alpha$, we reject H_0: $\beta_1 = 0$

Number of megapixels and price are related.

c. $r^2 = \text{SSR}/\text{SST} = 82{,}959.73/103{,}690 = .80$

The estimated regression equation provided a good fit; we should feel comfortable using the estimated regression equation to estimate the price given the number of megapixels.

d. $\hat{y} = -145.0265 + 38.31858(10) = 238.16$ or approximately \$238

28.   The sum of squares due to error and the total sum of squares are

$$\text{SSE} = \Sigma(y_i - \hat{y}_i)^2 = 1.4379 \qquad \text{SST} = \Sigma(y_i - \overline{y})^2 = 3.5800$$

Thus, SSR = SST - SSE = 3.5800 – 1.4379 = 2.1421

$$s^2 = \text{MSE} = \text{SSE}/(n-2) = 1.4379/9 = .1598$$

$$s = \sqrt{\text{MSE}} = \sqrt{.1598} = .3997$$

We can use either the t test or F test to determine whether speed of execution and overall satisfaction are related.

We will first illustrate the use of the t test.

$$\Sigma(x_i - \overline{x})^2 = 2.6$$

$$s_{b_1} = \frac{s}{\sqrt{\Sigma(x_i - \overline{x})^2}} = \frac{.3997}{\sqrt{2.6}} = .2479$$

$$t = \frac{b_1}{s_{b_1}} = \frac{.9077}{.2479} = 3.66$$

Using t table (9 degrees of freedom), area in tail is less than .005; p-value is less than .01

Using Excel or Minitab, the p-value corresponding to $t = 3.66$ is .000.

Because p-value $\leq \alpha$, we reject H_0: $\beta_1 = 0$

Because we can reject H_0: $\beta_1 = 0$ we conclude that speed of execution and overall satisfaction are related.

Next we illustrate the use of the F test.

$MSR = SSR / 1 = 2.1421$

$F = MSR / MSE = 2.1421 / .1598 = 13.4$

Using F table (1 degree of freedom numerator and 9 denominator), p-value is less than .01

Using Excel or Minitab, the p-value corresponding to $F = 13.4$ is .000.

Because p-value $\leq \alpha$, we reject H_0: $\beta_1 = 0$

Because we can reject H_0: $\beta_1 = 0$ we conclude that speed of execution and overall satisfaction are related.

The ANOVA table is shown below.

Source of Variation	Sum of Squares	Degrees of Freedom	Mean Square	F	p-value
Regression	2.1421	1	2.1421	13.4	.000
Error	1.4379	9	.1598		
Total	3.5800	10			

29. $SSE = \Sigma(y_i - \hat{y}_i)^2 = 233,333.33$ $SST = \Sigma(y_i - \overline{y})^2 = 5,648,333.33$

Thus, $SSR = SST - SSE = 5,648,333.33 - 233,333.33 = 5,415,000$

$MSE = SSE/(n - 2) = 233,333.33/(6 - 2) = 58,333.33$

$MSR = SSR/1 = 5,415,000$

$F = MSR / MSE = 5,415,000 / 58,333.25 = 92.83$

Source of Variation	Sum of Squares	Degrees of Freedom	Mean Square	F	p-value
Regression	5,415,000.00	1	5,415,000	92.83	.0006
Error	233,333.33	4	58,333.33		
Total	5,648,333.33	5			

Using F table (1 degree of freedom numerator and 4 denominator), p-value is less than .01

Using Excel or Minitab, the p-value corresponding to $F = 92.83$ is .0006.

Because p-value $\leq \alpha$, we reject H_0: $\beta_1 = 0$. Production volume and total cost are related.

30. $SSE = \Sigma(y_i - \hat{y}_i)^2 = 1043.03$ $SST = \Sigma(y_i - \overline{y})^2 = 10,568$

Thus, $SSR = SST - SSE = 10,568 - 1043.03 = 9524.97$

$s^2 = MSE = SSE/(n-2) = 1043.03/4 = 260.7575$

$s = \sqrt{260.7575} = 16.1480$

$\Sigma(x_i - \overline{x})^2 = 56.655$

$$s_{b_1} = \frac{s}{\sqrt{\sum(x_i - \bar{x})^2}} = \frac{16.148}{\sqrt{56.655}} = 2.145$$

$$t = \frac{b_1}{s_{b_1}} = \frac{12.966}{2.145} = 6.045$$

Using t table (4 degrees of freedom), area in tail is less than .005

p-value is less than .01

Using Excel or Minitab, the p-value corresponding to $t = 6.045$ is .004.

Because p-value $\le \alpha$, we reject H_0: $\beta_1 = 0$

There is a significant relationship between cars in service and annual revenue.

31. SST = 52,120,800   SSE = 7,102,922.54

SSR = SST – SSR = 52,120,800 - 7,102,922.54 = 45,017,877

MSR = SSR/1 = 45,017,877

MSE = SSE/(n - 2) = 7,102,922.54/8 = 887,865.3

F = MSR / MSE = 45,017,877/887,865.3 = 50.7

Using F table (1 degree of freedom numerator and 8 denominator), p-value is less than .01

Using Excel, the p-value corresponding to $F = 32.015$ is .000.

Because p-value $\le \alpha$, we reject H_0: $\beta_1 = 0$

Weight and price are related.

32. a. $s = 2.033$

$\bar{x} = 3$ $\Sigma(x_i - \bar{x})^2 = 10$

$$s_{\hat{y}^*} = s\sqrt{\frac{1}{n} + \frac{(x^* - \bar{x})^2}{\Sigma(x_i - \bar{x})^2}} = 2.033\sqrt{\frac{1}{5} + \frac{(4-3)^2}{10}} = 1.11$$

b. $\hat{y}^* = .2 + 2.6 x^* = .2 + 2.6(4) = 10.6$

$\hat{y}^* \pm t_{\alpha/2} s_{\hat{y}^*}$

$10.6 \pm 3.182 (1.11) = 10.6 \pm 3.53$

or 7.07 to 14.13

c. $$s_{\text{pred}} = s\sqrt{1 + \frac{1}{n} + \frac{(x^* - \bar{x})^2}{\Sigma(x_i - \bar{x})^2}} = 2.033\sqrt{1 + \frac{1}{5} + \frac{(4-3)^2}{10}} = 2.32$$

d. $\hat{y}^* \pm t_{\alpha/2} s_{\text{pred}}$

$10.6 \pm 3.182 \, (2.32) = 10.6 \pm 7.38$

or 3.22 to 17.98

33. a. $s = 8.7560$

b. $\bar{x} = 11 \quad \Sigma(x_i - \bar{x})^2 = 180$

$s_{\hat{y}^*} = s \sqrt{\dfrac{1}{n} + \dfrac{(x^* - \bar{x})^2}{\Sigma(x_i - \bar{x})^2}} = 8.7560 \sqrt{\dfrac{1}{5} + \dfrac{(8-11)^2}{180}} = 4.3780$

$\hat{y}^* = 0.2 + 2.6x^* = 0.2 + 2.6(4) = 10.6$

$\hat{y}^* \pm t_{\alpha/2} s_{\hat{y}^*}$

$44 \pm 3.182 \, (4.3780) = 44 \pm 13.93$

or 30.07 to 57.93

c. $s_{\text{pred}} = s \sqrt{1 + \dfrac{1}{n} + \dfrac{(x^* - \bar{x})^2}{\Sigma(x_i - \bar{x})^2}} = 8.7560 \sqrt{1 + \dfrac{1}{5} + \dfrac{(8-11)^2}{180}} = 9.7895$

d. $\hat{y}^* \pm t_{\alpha/2} s_{\text{pred}}$

$44 \pm 3.182(9.7895) = 44 \pm 31.15$

or 12.85 to 75.15

34. $s = 6.5141$

$\bar{x} = 10 \quad \Sigma(x_i - \bar{x})^2 = 190$

$s_{\hat{y}^*} = s \sqrt{\dfrac{1}{n} + \dfrac{(x^* - \bar{x})^2}{\Sigma(x_i - \bar{x})^2}} = 6.5141 \sqrt{\dfrac{1}{5} + \dfrac{(12-10)^2}{190}} = 3.0627$

$\hat{y}^* = 7.6 + .9x^* = 7.6 + .9(12) = 18.40$

$\hat{y}^* \pm t_{\alpha/2} s_{\hat{y}^*}$

$18.40 \pm 3.182(3.0627) = 18.40 \pm 9.75$

or 8.65 to 28.15

$s_{\text{pred}} = s \sqrt{1 + \dfrac{1}{n} + \dfrac{(x^* - \bar{x})^2}{\Sigma(x_i - \bar{x})^2}} = 6.5141 \sqrt{1 + \dfrac{1}{5} + \dfrac{(12-10)^2}{190}} = 7.1982$

$\hat{y}^* \pm t_{\alpha/2} s_{\text{pred}}$

$18.40 \pm 3.182(7.1982) = 18.40 \pm 22.90$

or -4.50 to 41.30

The two intervals are different because there is more variability associated with predicting an individual value than there is a mean value.

35. a. $\hat{y}^* = 2090.5 + 581.1x^* = 2090.5 + 581.1(3) = 3833.8$

   b. $s = \sqrt{\text{MSE}} = \sqrt{21,284} = 145.89 \; s = 145.89$

   $\bar{x} = 3.2 \quad \Sigma(x_i - \bar{x})^2 = 0.74$

   $s_{\hat{y}^*} = s\sqrt{\dfrac{1}{n} + \dfrac{(x^* - \bar{x})^2}{\Sigma(x_i - \bar{x})^2}} = 145.89\sqrt{\dfrac{1}{6} + \dfrac{(3 - 3.2)^2}{0.74}} = 68.54$

   $\hat{y}^* \pm t_{\alpha/2} s_{\hat{y}^*}$

   $3833.8 \pm 2.776\,(68.54) = 3833.8 \pm 190.27$

   or \$3643.53 to \$4024.07

   c. $s_{\text{pred}} = s\sqrt{1 + \dfrac{1}{n} + \dfrac{(x^* - \bar{x})^2}{\Sigma(x_i - \bar{x})^2}} = 145.89\sqrt{1 + \dfrac{1}{6} + \dfrac{(3 - 3.2)^2}{0.74}} = 161.19$

   $\hat{y}^* \pm t_{\alpha/2} s_{\text{pred}}$

   $3833.8 \pm 2.776\,(161.19) = 3833.8 \pm 447.46$

   or \$3386.34 to \$4281.26

   d. As expected, the prediction interval is much wider than the confidence interval. This is due to the fact that it is more difficult to predict the starting salary for one new student with a GPA of 3.0 than it is to estimate the mean for all students with a GPA of 3.0.

36. a. $s_{\hat{y}^*} = s\sqrt{\dfrac{1}{n} + \dfrac{(x^* - \bar{x})^2}{\Sigma(x_i - \bar{x})^2}} = 4.6098\sqrt{\dfrac{1}{10} + \dfrac{(9 - 7)^2}{142}} = 1.6503$

   $\hat{y}^* \pm t_{\alpha/2} s_{\hat{y}^*}$

   $\hat{y}^* = 80 + 4x^* = 80 + 4(9) = 116$

   $116 \pm 2.306(1.6503) = 116 \pm 3.8056$

   or 112.19 to 119.81 (\$112,190 to \$119,810)

b. $s_{pred} = s\sqrt{1 + \dfrac{1}{n} + \dfrac{(x^* - \overline{x})^2}{\Sigma(x_i - \overline{x})^2}} = 4.6098\sqrt{1 + \dfrac{1}{10} + \dfrac{(9-7)^2}{142}} = 4.8963$

$\hat{y}^* \pm t_{\alpha/2} s_{pred}$

$116 \pm 2.306(4.8963) = 116 \pm 11.2909$

or 104.71 to 127.29 ($104,710 to $127,290)

c. As expected, the prediction interval is much wider than the confidence interval. This is due to the fact that it is more difficult to predict annual sales for one new salesperson with 9 years of experience than it is to estimate the mean annual sales for all salespersons with 9 years of experience.

37. The point estimate of $\hat{y}^*$ is given by $\hat{y}^* = 27.5 - .3 x^* = 27.5 - .3(25) = 20$

We now compute the margin of error.

$\overline{x} = 35 \quad \Sigma(x_i - \overline{x})^2 = 1000$

$s^2 = SSE/(n-2) = 16/6 = 2.6667 \quad s = 1.633$

$s_{\hat{y}^*} = s\sqrt{\dfrac{1}{n} + \dfrac{(x^* - \overline{x})^2}{\Sigma(x_i - \overline{x})^2}} = 1.633\sqrt{\dfrac{1}{8} + \dfrac{(25-35)^2}{1000}} = 0.7746$

Margin of error $= t_{.025} s_{\hat{y}^*} = 2.447(.7746) = 1.8954$

The confidence interval is

$20 \pm 1.8954 = 18.1046$ to 21.8954 or 18 to 22

38. a. $\hat{y}^* = 1246.67 + 7.6(500) = \$5046.67$

b. $\overline{x} = 575 \quad \Sigma(x_i - \overline{x})^2 = 93,750$

$s^2 = MSE = 58,333.33 \quad s = 241.52$

$s_{pred} = s\sqrt{1 + \dfrac{1}{n} + \dfrac{(x^* - \overline{x})^2}{\Sigma(x_i - \overline{x})^2}} = 241.52\sqrt{1 + \dfrac{1}{6} + \dfrac{(500-575)^2}{93,750}} = 267.50$

$\hat{y}^* \pm t_{\alpha/2} s_{pred}$

$5046.67 \pm 4.604 (267.50) = 5046.67 \pm 1231.57$

or $3815.10 to $6278.24

c. Based on one month, $6000 is not out of line since $3815.10 to $6278.24 is the prediction interval. However, a sequence of five to seven months with consistently high costs should cause concern.

39. a. With $x^* = 89$, $\hat{y}^* = 17.49 + 1.0334x^* = 17.49 + 1.0334(89) = \$109.46$

   b. $s^2 = \text{MSE} = \text{SSE}/(n-2) = 1541.4/7 = 220.2$

   $s = \sqrt{220.2} = 14.391$

   $s_{\hat{y}^*} = s\sqrt{\dfrac{1}{n} + \dfrac{(x^* - \bar{x})^2}{\Sigma(x_i - \bar{x})^2}} = 14.8391\sqrt{\dfrac{1}{9} + \dfrac{(89-105)^2}{4100}} = 6.1819$

   $\hat{y}^* \pm t_{.025}s_{\hat{y}^*} = 109.46 \pm 2.365(6.1819) = 109.46 \pm 14.6202$

   or $94.84 to $124.08

   c. $\hat{y}^* = 17.49 + 1.0334x = 17.49 + 1.0334(128) = \$149.77$

   $s_{\text{pred}} = s\sqrt{1 + \dfrac{1}{n} + \dfrac{(x^* - \bar{x})^2}{\Sigma(x_i - \bar{x})^2}} = 14.8391\sqrt{1 + \dfrac{1}{9} + \dfrac{(128-105)^2}{4100}} = 16.525$

   $\hat{y}^* \pm t_{\alpha/2}s_{\text{pred}}$

   $149.77 \pm 2.365(16.525) = 149.77 \pm 39.08$

   or $110.69 to $188.85

40. a. 9

   b. $\hat{y} = 20.0 + 7.21x$

   c. 1.3626

   d. $\text{SSE} = \text{SST} - \text{SSR} = 51,984.1 - 41,587.3 = 10,396.8$

   $\text{MSE} = 10,396.8/7 = 1,485.3$

   $F = \text{MSR}/\text{MSE} = 41,587.3/1,485.3 = 28.00$

   Using F table (1 degree of freedom numerator and 7 denominator), p-value is less than .01

   Using Excel or Minitab, the p-value corresponding to $F = 28.00$ is .0011.

   Because p-value $\leq \alpha = .05$, we reject H_0: $B_1 = 0$.

   Selling price is related to annual gross rents.

   e. $\hat{y} = 20.0 + 7.21(50) = 380.5$ or $380,500

41. a. $\hat{y} = 6.1092 + .8951x$

   b. $t = \dfrac{b_1 - B_1}{s_{b_1}} = \dfrac{.8951 - 0}{.149} = 6.01$

Using the t table (8 degrees of freedom), area in tail is less than .005
p-value is less than .01

Using Excel or Minitab, the p-value corresponding to $t = 6.01$ is .0003.

Because p-value $\leq \alpha = .05$, we reject H_0: $B_1 = 0$

Maintenance expense is related to usage.

   c. $\hat{y} = 6.1092 + .8951(25) = 28.49$ or $28.49 per month

42 a. $\hat{y} = 80.0 + 50.0x$

   b.   30

   c. $F = \text{MSR} / \text{MSE} = 6828.6/82.1 = 83.17$

Using F table (1 degree of freedom numerator and 28 denominator), p-value is less than .01

Using Excel or Minitab, the p-value corresponding to $F = 83.17$ is .000.

Because p-value $< \alpha = .05$, we reject H_0: $B_1 = 0$.

Annual sales is related to the number of salespersons.

   d. $\hat{y} = 80 + 50 \,(12) = 680$ or $680,000

43. a.

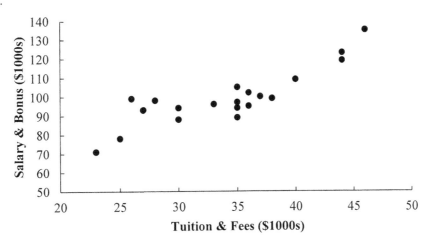

   b.   There appears to be a positive relationship between the two variables. Students that graduate from the schools with higher tuition and fees tend to receive a higher starting salary and bonus.

The Minitab output is shown below:

```
The regression equation is
Salary & Bonus ($1000s) = 33.8 + 1.92 Tuition & Fees ($1000s)
```

```
Predictor                      Coef   SE Coef      T       P
Constant                     33.788     9.340   3.62   0.002
Tuition & Fees ($1000s)      1.9154    0.2689   7.12   0.000


S = 7.60875   R-Sq = 73.8%   R-Sq(adj) = 72.4%


Analysis of Variance

Source             DF      SS      MS      F       P
Regression          1  2937.1  2937.1  50.73   0.000
Residual Error     18  1042.1    57.9
Total              19  3979.2
```

d. The *p*-value = .000 < α = .05 (*t* or *F*); significant relationship

e. r^2 = .738. The least squares line provided a good fit; approximately 74% of the variability in salary and bonus can be explained by the linear relationship with tuition and fees.

f. $\hat{y}$ = 33.788 + 1.9154(43) = 116.15 or approximately $116,000.

Note to Instructor: The average starting salary and bonus reported by U.S. News & World Report for the University of Virginia was $121,000.

44. a. Scatter diagram:

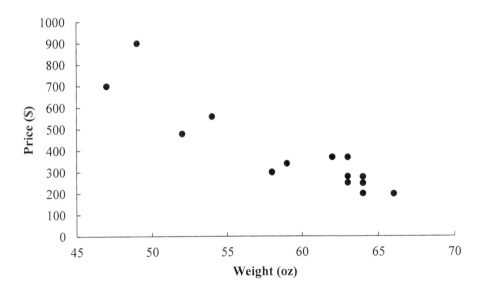

b. There appears to be a negative linear relationship between the two variables. The heavier helmets tend to be less expensive.

c. The Minitab output is shown below:

```
The regression equation is
Price = 2044 - 28.3 Weight
```

```
Predictor      Coef   SE Coef      T      P
Constant      2044.4     226.4   9.03  0.000
Weight       -28.350     3.826  -7.41  0.000


S = 91.8098   R-Sq = 77.4%   R-Sq(adj) = 76.0%


Analysis of Variance

Source            DF      SS       MS      F      P
Regression         1  462761   462761  54.90  0000
Residual Error    16  134865     8429
Total             17  597626
```

$\hat{y} = 2044.4 - 28.35 \text{ Weight}$

d. Significant relationship: p-value = .000 < α = .05

e. $r^2 = 0.774$; A good fit

45. a. $\bar{x} = \dfrac{\Sigma x_i}{n} = \dfrac{70}{5} = 14$ $\bar{y} = \dfrac{\Sigma y_i}{n} = \dfrac{76}{5} = 15.2$

$\Sigma(x_i - \bar{x})(y_i - \bar{y}) = 200$ $\Sigma(x_i - \bar{x})^2 = 126$

$b_1 = \dfrac{\Sigma(x_i - \bar{x})(y_i - \bar{y})}{\Sigma(x_i - \bar{x})^2} = \dfrac{200}{126} = 1.5873$

$b_0 = \bar{y} - b_1\bar{x} = 15.2 - (1.5873)(14) = -7.0222$

$\hat{y} = -7.02 + 1.59x$

b. The residuals are 3.48, -2.47, -4.83, -1.6, and 5.22

c.

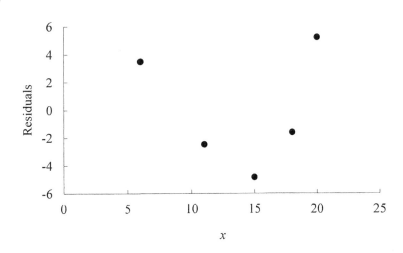

With only 5 observations it is difficult to determine if the assumptions are satisfied.
However, the plot does suggest curvature in the residuals that would indicate that the error

12 - 31

term assumptions are not satisfied. The scatter diagram for these data also indicates that the underlying relationship between x and y may be curvilinear.

46. a. $\hat{y} = 2.32 + .64x$

b.

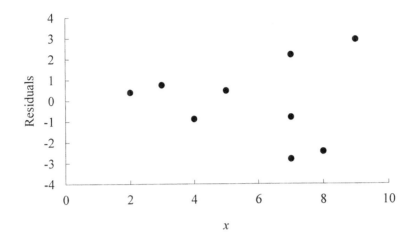

The assumption that the variance is the same for all values of x is questionable. The variance appears to increase for larger values of x.

47. a. Let x = advertising expenditures and y = revenue

$\hat{y} = 29.4 + 1.55x$

b. SST = 1002   SSE = 310.28   SSR = 691.72

MSR = SSR / 1 = 691.72

MSE = SSE / (n - 2) = 310.28/ 5 = 62.0554

F = MSR / MSE = 691.72/ 62.0554= 11.15

Using F table (1 degree of freedom numerator and 5 denominator), p-value is between .01 and .025

Using Excel or Minitab, the p-value corresponding to F = 11.15 is .0206.

Because p-value $\leq \alpha$ = .05, we conclude that the two variables are related.

c.

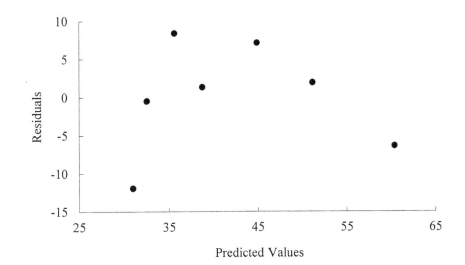

d. The residual plot leads us to question the assumption of a linear relationship between x and y. Even though the relationship is significant at the .05 level of significance, it would be extremely dangerous to extrapolate beyond the range of the data.

48. a. $\hat{y} = 80 + 4x$

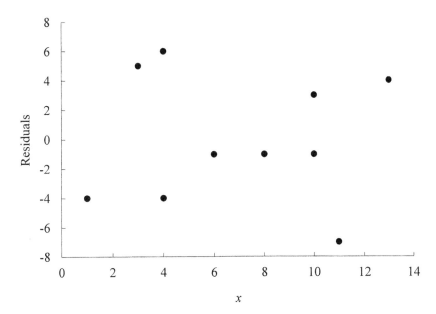

b. The assumptions concerning the error term appear reasonable.

49. a. The Minitab output follows:

```
The regression equation is
Mortgage($) = - 198 + 1.07 Rent($)


Predictor    Coef   SE Coef       T       P
Constant    -198.0     187.7   -1.05   0.322
Rent ($)    1.0699    0.2148    4.98   0.001


S = 78.7819    R-Sq = 75.6%    R-Sq(adj) = 72.6%


Analysis of Variance

Source           DF      SS      MS       F       P
Regression        1  153962  153962   24.81   0.001
Residual Error    8   49653    6207
Total             9  203614
```

b.

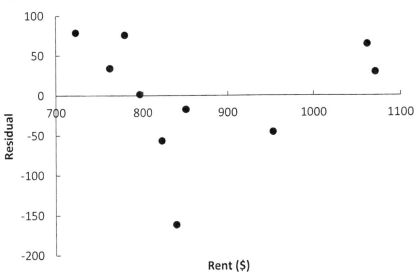

c. The residual plot leads us to question the assumption of a linear relationship between the average asking rent and the monthly mortgage. Therefore, even though the relationship is very significant (*p*-value = .001), using the estimated regression equation to make predictions of the monthly mortgage beyond the range of the data is not recommended.

50. a.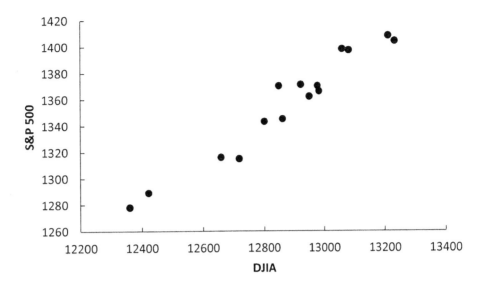

b. A portion of the Minitab output is shown below:

```
The regression equation is
S&P = - 669 + 0.157 DJIA


Predictor      Coef   SE Coef       T       P
Constant      -669.0     130.7   -5.12   0.000
DJIA         0.15727   0.01015   15.49   0.000


S = 9.60811    R-Sq = 94.9%    R-Sq(adj) = 94.5%


Analysis of Variance

Source           DF      SS      MS        F       P
Regression        1   22146   22146   239.89   0.000
Residual Error   13    1200      92
Total            14   23346
```

c. Using the F test, the p-value corresponding to $F = 239.89$ is .000. Because the p-value $\leq \alpha = .05$, we reject $H_0 : \beta_1 = 0$; there is a significant relationship.

d. With R-Sq = 94.9%, the estimated regression equation provided an excellent fit.

e. $\hat{y} = -669.0 + .15727(DJIA) = -669.0 + .15727(13,500) = 1454$

f. The DJIA is not that far beyond the range of the data. With the excellent fit provided by the estimated regression equation, we should not be too concerned about using the estimated regression equation to predict the S&P500.

51. a.   The Minitab output is shown below:

```
The regression equation is
Share Price ($) = - 2.99 + 0.911 Fair Value ($)

Predictor          Coef  SE Coef      T      P
Constant         -2.987    5.791  -0.52  0.610
Fair Value ($)  0.91128  0.09783   9.31  0.000

S = 12.0064   R-Sq = 76.9%   R-Sq(adj) = 76.1%

Analysis of Variance

Source          DF     SS     MS      F      P
Regression       1  12507  12507  86.76  0.000
Residual Error  26   3748    144
Total           27  16255
```

$\hat{y}$ = -2.987 + .91128 Fair Value ($)

b.   Significant relationship: p-value = .000 < α = .05

c. $\hat{y}$ = -2.987 + .91128 Fair Value ($) = -2.987 + .91128(50) = 42.577 or approximately $42.58

d.   The estimated regression equation should provide a good estimate because r^2 = 0.769

52. a.

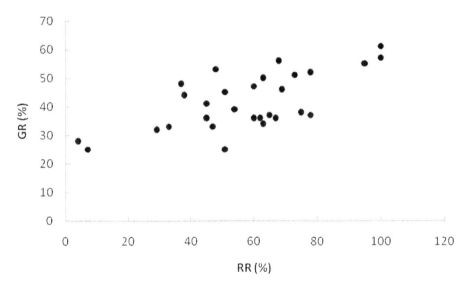

The scatter diagram indicates a positive linear relationship between the two variables. Online universities with higher retention rates tend to have higher graduation rates.

b. The Minitab output follows:

```
The regression equation is
GR(%) = 25.4 + 0.285 RR(%)

Predictor      Coef   SE Coef      T       P
Constant     25.423     3.746    6.79   0.000
RR(%)       0.28453   0.06063    4.69   0.000

S = 7.45610    R-Sq = 44.9%    R-Sq(adj) = 42.9%

Analysis of Variance

Source            DF      SS      MS      F       P
Regression         1  1224.3  1224.3  22.02   0.000
Residual Error    27  1501.0    55.6
Total             28  2725.3

Unusual Observations

Obs  RR(%)  GR(%)    Fit   SE Fit  Residual  St Resid
  2     51  25.00  39.93    1.44    -14.93    -2.04R
  3      4  28.00  26.56    3.52      1.44      0.22 X

R denotes an observation with a large standardized residual.
X denotes an observation whose X value gives it large leverage.
```

c. Because the p-value = .000 < α =.05, the relationship is significant.

d. The estimated regression equation is able to explain 44.9% of the variability in the graduation rate based upon the linear relationship with the retention rate. It is not a great fit, but given the type of data, the fit is reasonably good.

e. In the Minitab output in part (b), South University is identified as an observation with a large standardized residual. With a retention rate of 51% it does appear that the graduation rate of 25% is low as compared to the results for other online universities. The president of South University should be concerned after looking at the data. Using the estimated regression equation, we estimate that the gradation rate at South University should be 25.4 + .285(51) = 40%.

f. In the Minitab output in part (b), the University of Phoenix is identified as an observation whose x value gives it large influence. With a retention rate of only 4%, the president of the University of Phoenix should be concerned after looking at the data.

53. The Minitab output is shown below:

```
The regression equation is
Expense = 10.5 + 0.953 Usage

Predictor        Coef      SE Coef        T        p
Constant       10.528        3.745     2.81    0.023
X              0.9534        0.1382     6.90    0.000

S = 4.250      R-sq = 85.6%      R-sq(adj) = 83.8%
```

```
Analysis of Variance

SOURCE          DF              SS          MS          F          p
Regression      1           860.05      860.05      47.62      0.000
Residual Error  8           144.47       18.06
Total           9          1004.53

   Fit  Stdev.Fit         95% C.I.          95% P.I.
  39.13      1.49    ( 35.69,  42.57)  ( 28.74,  49.52)
```

a. $\hat{y} = 10.528 + .9534$ Usage

b. Since the p-value corresponding to $F = 47.62 = .000 < \alpha = .05$, we reject H_0: $\beta_1 = 0$.

c. The 95% prediction interval is 28.74 to 49.52 or $2874 to $4952

d. Yes, since the expected expense is $\hat{y} = 10.528 + .9534(30) = 39.13$ or $3913.

54. a. The Minitab output is shown below:

```
The regression equation is
Cost = 220 + 132 Age

Predictor        Coef      SE Coef          T          p
Constant       220.00        58.48       3.76      0.006
X              131.67        17.80       7.40      0.000

S = 75.50       R-sq = 87.3%      R-sq(adj) = 85.7%

Analysis of Variance

SOURCE          DF              SS          MS          F          p
Regression      1           312050      312050      54.75      0.000
Residual Error  8            45600        5700
Total           9           357650

   Fit  Stdev.Fit         95% C.I.          95% P.I.
  746.7      29.8    ( 678.0,  815.4)  ( 559.5,  933.9)
```

b. Since the p-value corresponding to $F = 54.75$ is $.000 < \alpha = .05$, we reject H_0: $\beta_1 = 0$.

Maintenance cost and age of bus are related.

c. $r^2 = .873$. The least squares line provided a very good fit.

d. The 95% prediction interval is 559.5 to 933.9 or $559.50 to $933.90

55. a. The Minitab output is shown below:

```
The regression equation is
Horizon = 0.275 + 0.950 S&P 500

Predictor        Coef      SE Coef          T          P
Constant       0.2747       0.9004       0.31      0.768
S&P 500        0.9498       0.3569       2.66      0.029

S = 2.664       R-Sq = 47.0%      R-Sq(adj) = 40.3%
```

Analysis of Variance

Source	DF	SS	MS	F	P
Regression	1	50.255	50.255	7.08	0.029
Residual Error	8	56.781	7.098		
Total	9	107.036			

The market beta for Horizon is $b_1 = .95$

b. Since the p-value $= 0.029$ is less than $\alpha = .05$, the relationship is significant.

c. $r^2 = .470$. The least squares line does not provide a very good fit.

d. Xerox has higher risk with a market beta of 1.22.

56. a.

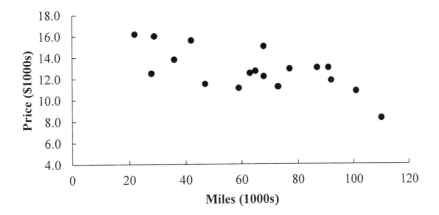

b. There appears to be a negative relationship between the two variables that can be approximated by a straight line. An argument could also be made that the relationship is perhaps curvilinear because at some point a car has so many miles that its value becomes very small.

c. The Minitab output is shown below.

```
The regression equation is
Price ($1000s) = 16.5 - 0.0588 Miles (1000s)

Predictor          Coef   SE Coef      T      P
Constant        16.4698    0.9488  17.36  0.000
Miles (1000s)  -0.05877   0.01319  -4.46  0.000

S = 1.54138   R-Sq = 53.9%   R-Sq(adj) = 51.2%
```

Analysis of Variance

Source	DF	SS	MS	F	P
Regression	1	47.158	47.158	19.85	0.000
Residual Error	17	40.389	2.376		
Total	18	87.547			

d. Significant relationship: p-value $= 0.000 < \alpha = .05$.

e. $r^2 = .539$; a reasonably good fit considering that the condition of the car is also an important factor in what the price is.

f. The slope of the estimated regression equation is -.0558. Thus, a one-unit increase in the value of x coincides with a decrease in the value of y equal to .0558. Because the data were recorded in thousands, every additional 1000 miles on the car's odometer will result in a $55.80 decrease in the predicted price.

g. The predicted price for a 2007 Camry with 60,000 miles is $\hat{y} = 16.5 -.0588(60) = 12.97$ or approximately $13,000. Because of other factors, such as condition and whether the seller is a private party or a dealer, this is probably not the price you would offer for the car. But, it should be a good starting point in figuring out what to offer the seller.

57. a.

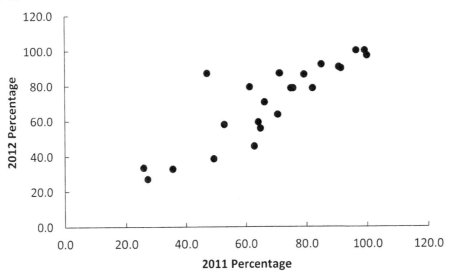

b. There appears to be a positive linear relationship between the two variables.

c. The Minitab output is shown below.

```
The regression equation is
2012 Percentage = 7.39 + 0.928 2011 Percentage


Predictor              Coef   SE Coef      T       P
Constant              7.388     8.212   0.90   0.379
2011 Percentage      0.9276    0.1146   8.09   0.000


S = 11.5916    R-Sq = 75.7%    R-Sq(adj) = 74.6%


Analysis of Variance

Source             DF        SS       MS       F      P
Regression          1    8798.2   8798.2   65.48  0.000
Residual Error     21    2821.7    134.4
Total              22   11619.9
```

d. Significant relationship: p-value = $0.000 < \alpha = .05$.

e. $r^2 = .757$; a good fit.

f.

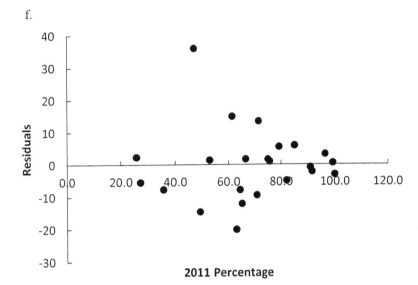

The point with a residual value of approximately 36 clearly stands out as compared to the other points. This point corresponds to the observation for Air Tran Airways. Other than this point, the residual plot does not exhibit a pattern that would suggest a linear model is not appropriate.

Chapter 13
Multiple Regression

Learning Objectives

1. Understand how multiple regression analysis can be used to develop relationships involving one dependent variable and several independent variables.

2. Be able to interpret the coefficients in a multiple regression analysis.

3. Know the assumptions necessary to conduct statistical tests involving the hypothesized regression model.

4. Understand the role of computer packages in performing multiple regression analysis.

5. Be able to interpret and use computer output to develop the estimated regression equation.

6. Be able to determine how good a fit is provided by the estimated regression equation.

7. Be able to test for the significance of the regression equation.

8. Understand how multicollinearity affects multiple regression analysis.

Solutions:

1. a. $b_1 = .5906$ is an estimate of the change in y corresponding to a 1 unit change in x_1 when x_2 is held constant.

    $b_2 = .4980$ is an estimate of the change in y corresponding to a 1 unit change in x_2 when x_1 is held constant.

    b. $\hat{y} = 29.1270 + .5906(180) + .4980(310) = 289.82$

2. a. The estimated regression equation is

    $\hat{y} = 45.06 + 1.94x_1$

    An estimate of y when $x_1 = 45$ is

    $\hat{y} = 45.06 + 1.94(45) = 132.36$

    b. The estimated regression equation is

    $\hat{y} = 85.22 + 4.32x_2$

    An estimate of y when $x_2 = 15$ is

    $\hat{y} = 85.22 + 4.32(15) = 150.02$

    c. The estimated regression equation is

    $\hat{y} = -18.37 + 2.01x_1 + 4.74x_2$

    An estimate of y when $x_1 = 45$ and $x_2 = 15$ is

    $\hat{y} = -18.37 + 2.01(45) + 4.74(15) = 143.18$

3. a. $b_1 = 3.8$ is an estimate of the change in y corresponding to a 1 unit change in x_1 when x_2, x_3, and x_4 are held constant.

    $b_2 = -2.3$ is an estimate of the change in y corresponding to a 1 unit change in x_2 when x_1, x_3, and x_4 are held constant.

    $b_3 = 7.6$ is an estimate of the change in y corresponding to a 1 unit change in x_3 when x_1, x_2, and x_4 are held constant.

    $b_4 = 2.7$ is an estimate of the change in y corresponding to a 1 unit change in x_4 when x_1, x_2, and x_3 are held constant.

    b. $\hat{y} = 17.6 + 3.8(10) - 2.3(5) + 7.6(1) + 2.7(2) = 57.1$

4. a. $\hat{y} = 25 + 10(15) + 8(10) = 255$; sales estimate: $255,000

   b. Sales can be expected to increase by $10 for every dollar increase in inventory investment when advertising expenditure is held constant. Sales can be expected to increase by $8 for every dollar increase in advertising expenditure when inventory investment is held constant.

5. a. The Minitab output is shown below:

```
The regression equation is
Revenue = 88.6 + 1.60 TVAdv

Predictor         Coef      SE Coef           T          P
Constant        88.638        1.582       56.02      0.000
TVAdv           1.6039        0.4778        3.36      0.015

S = 1.215       R-Sq = 65.3%      R-Sq(adj) = 59.5%

Analysis of Variance

Source            DF           SS          MS          F          P
Regression         1       16.640      16.640      11.27      0.015
Residual Error     6        8.860       1.477
Total              7       25.500
```

   b. The Minitab output is shown below:

```
The regression equation is
Revenue = 83.2 + 2.29 TVAdv + 1.30 NewsAdv

Predictor         Coef      SE Coef           T          P
Constant        83.230        1.574       52.88      0.000
TVAdv           2.2902        0.3041        7.53      0.001
NewsAdv         1.3010        0.3207        4.06      0.010

S = 0.6426      R-Sq = 91.9%      R-Sq(adj) = 88.7%

Analysis of Variance

Source            DF           SS          MS          F          P
Regression         2       23.435      11.718      28.38      0.002
Residual Error     5        2.065       0.413
Total              7       25.500
```

   c. No, it is 1.60 in part (a) and 2.29 above. In part (b) it represents the marginal change in revenue due to an increase in television advertising with newspaper advertising held constant.

   d. Revenue = 83.2 + 2.29(3.5) + 1.30(1.8) = $93.56 or $93,560

6. a. The Minitab output is shown below:

```
The regression equation is
Win% = - 58.8 + 16.4 Yds/Att

Predictor    Coef  SE Coef     T      P
Constant   -58.77    26.18  -2.25  0.041
Yds/Att     16.391    3.750   4.37  0.001

S = 15.8732   R-Sq = 57.7%   R-Sq(adj) = 54.7%

Analysis of Variance

Source          DF      SS      MS      F      P
Regression       1  4814.3  4814.3  19.11  0.001
Residual Error  14  3527.4   252.0
Total           15  8341.7

Unusual Observations

Obs  Yds/Att   Win%    Fit  SE Fit  Residual  St Resid
 14     6.50  81.30  47.77    4.24     33.53      2.19R

R denotes an observation with a large standardized residual.
```

b. The Minitab output is shown below:

```
The regression equation is
Win% = 97.5 - 1600 Int/Att

Predictor    Coef  SE Coef     T      P
Constant    97.54    13.86   7.04  0.000
Int/Att   -1600.5    484.6  -3.30  0.005

S = 18.3008   R-Sq = 43.8%   R-Sq(adj) = 39.8%

Analysis of Variance

Source          DF      SS      MS      F      P
Regression       1  3652.8  3652.8  10.91  0.005
Residual Error  14  4688.9   334.9
Total           15  8341.7

Unusual Observations

Obs  Int/Att   Win%    Fit  SE Fit  Residual  St Resid
  8   0.0260  12.50  55.93    4.60    -43.43     -2.45R

R denotes an observation with a large standardized residual.
```

c. The Minitab output is shown below:

```
The regression equation is
Win% = - 5.8 + 12.9 Yds/Att - 1084 Int/Att

Predictor    Coef  SE Coef     T      P
Constant    -5.76    27.15  -0.21  0.835
Yds/Att     12.949    3.186   4.06  0.001
Int/Att   -1083.8    357.1  -3.03  0.010

S = 12.6024   R-Sq = 75.2%   R-Sq(adj) = 71.4%
```

```
Analysis of Variance

Source          DF     SS      MS      F      P
Regression       2   6277.0  3138.5  19.76  0.000
Residual Error  13   2064.7   158.8
Total           15   8341.7

Source   DF   Seq SS
Yds/Att   1   4814.3
Int/Att   1   1462.8

Unusual Observations

Obs  Yds/Att   Win%   Fit   SE Fit  Residual  St Resid
  8    5.60   12.50  38.57   5.32    -26.07    -2.28R

R denotes an observation with a large standardized reidual.
```

d.   The predicted value of Win% for the Kansas City Chiefs is

Win% = - 5.8 + 12.9(6.2) – 1084(.036) = 35%

With 7 wins and 9 loses, the Kansas City Chiefs won 44% of the games they played. The predicted value is somewhat lower than the actual value.

7.   a.   The Minitab output is shown below:

```
The regression equation is
PCW Rating = 66.1 + 0.170 Performance

Predictor       Coef   SE Coef     T       P
Constant      66.062     3.793   17.42   0.000
Performance   0.16989   0.05407   3.14   0.014

S = 2.59221   R-Sq = 55.2%   R-Sq(adj) = 49.6%

Analysis of Variance

Source          DF      SS       MS      F      P
Regression       1    66.343   66.343  9.87   0.014
Residual Error   8    53.757    6.720
Total            9   120.100
```

b.   The Minitab output is shown below:

```
The regression equation is
PCW Rating = 40.0 + 0.113 Performance + 0.382 Features

Predictor       Coef   SE Coef     T       P
Constant      39.982     7.855    5.09   0.001
Performance   0.11338   0.03846   2.95   0.021
Features      0.3820    0.1093    3.49   0.010

S = 1.67285   R-Sq = 83.7%   R-Sq(adj) = 79.0%
```

13 - 5

```
Analysis of Variance

Source            DF        SS        MS        F        P
Regression         2   100.511    50.255    17.96    0.002
Residual Error     7    19.589     2.798
Total              9   120.100
```

c. $\hat{y} = 40.0 + .113(80) + .382(70) = 75.78$ or 76

8. a.   The Minitab output follows.

```
The regression equation is
Overall = 69.3 + 0.235 Shore Excursions

Predictor            Coef   SE Coef       T        P
Constant           69.300     4.799   14.44    0.000
Shore Excursions  0.23476   0.05659    4.15    0.001

S = 1.87028   R-Sq = 48.9%   R-Sq(adj) = 46.0%

Analysis of Variance

Source            DF        SS        MS        F        P
Regression         1    60.202    60.202    17.21    0.001
Residual Error    18    62.963     3.498
Total             19   123.166
```

b.   The Minitab output follows.

```
The regression equation is
Overall = 45.2 + 0.253 Shore Excursions + 0.248 Food/Dining

Predictor            Coef   SE Coef       T        P
Constant           45.178     6.952    6.50    0.000
Shore Excursions  0.25289   0.04189    6.04    0.000
Food/Dining       0.24819   0.06161    4.03    0.001

S = 1.37650   R-Sq = 73.8%   R-Sq(adj) = 70.8%

Analysis of Variance

Source            DF        SS        MS        F        P
Regression         2    90.955    45.477    24.00    0.000
Residual Error    17    32.211     1.895
Total             19   123.166
```

c. $\hat{y} = 45.2 + .253(\text{Shore Excursions}) + .248(\text{Food/Dining}) = 45.2 + .253(80) + .248(90) = 87.76$

Thus, an estimate of the overall score is approximately 88.

9. a.   The Minitab output is shown below.

```
The regression equation is
Total Distance = 125 + 1.39 Club Head Speed

Predictor            Coef   SE Coef       T        P
Constant          124.716     7.409   16.83    0.000
Club Head Speed   1.39425   0.06531   21.35    0.000
```

13 - 6

```
S = 3.70038    R-Sq = 70.8%    R-Sq(adj) = 70.6%

Analysis of Variance

Source              DF      SS      MS       F       P
Regression           1   6241.1  6241.1  455.79  0.000
Residual Error     188   2574.3    13.7
Total              189   8815.3
```

b. The Minitab output is shown below.

```
The regression equation is
Total Distance = 117 + 0.988 Ball Speed

Predictor        Coef   SE Coef       T       P
Constant      117.139     7.022   16.68   0.000
Ball Speed    0.98764   0.04184   23.61   0.000

S = 3.43937    R-Sq = 74.8%    R-Sq(adj) = 74.6%

Analysis of Variance

Source              DF      SS      MS       F       P
Regression           1   6591.4  6591.4  557.21  0.000
Residual Error     188   2223.9     118
Total              189   8815.3
```

c. The following scatter diagram illustrates the relationship between the two variables.

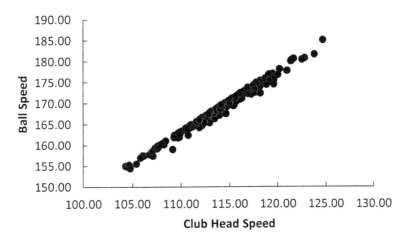

The scatter diagram shows a very strong linear relationship between the two variables. In fact, for these data the coefficient of determination is approximately .99. As a result using both variables in the same model is not recommended because once the linear effect of one variable is accounted for the other variable will be of little additional value. This situation, referred to as multicollinearity, is discussed later in the chapter in the section on testing for significance.

d. The Minitab output is shown below.

```
The regression equation is
Total Distance = 81.6 + 1.09 Ball Speed + 1.65 Launch Angle

Predictor          Coef   SE Coef        T      P
Constant         81.596     6.953    11.74  0.000
Ball Speed      1.09266    0.03644   29.99  0.000
Launch Angle     1.6465     0.1765    9.33  0.000

S = 2.84872    R-Sq = 82.8%    R-Sq(adj) = 82.6%

Analysis of Variance

Source            DF        SS        MS        F      P
Regression         2     7297.8    3648.9   449.64  0.000
Residual Error   187     1517.5       8.1
Total            189     8815.3
```

e. $\hat{y}$ = predicted Total Distance = 81.6 + 1.09 Ball Speed + 1.65 Launch Angle

$\hat{y}$ = 81.6 + 1.09(170) + 1.65(11) = 285 yards

10. a. The Minitab output follows.

```
The regression equation is
R/IP = 0.676 - 0.284 SO/IP

Predictor          Coef   SE Coef        T      P
Constant        0.67575   0.06307    10.71  0.000
SO/IP          -0.28385   0.07869    -3.61  0.002

S = 0.0602733    R-Sq = 42.0%    R-Sq(adj) = 38.7%

Analysis of Variance

Source            DF          SS          MS        F      P
Regression         1    0.047263    0.047263    13.01  0.002
Residual Error    18    0.065392    0.003633
Total             19    0.112655
```

b. The Minitab output follows.

```
The regression equation is
R/IP = 0.308 + 1.35 HR/IP

Predictor          Coef   SE Coef        T      P
Constant        0.30805   0.06036     5.10  0.000
HR/IP            1.3467    0.5407      2.49  0.023

S = 0.0682239    R-Sq = 25.6%    R-Sq(adj) = 21.5%

Analysis of Variance

Source            DF          SS          MS        F      P
Regression         1    0.028874    0.028874     6.20  0.023
Residual Error    18    0.083781    0.004655
Total             19    0.112655
```

```
Unusual Observations

Obs  HR/IP    R/IP     Fit  SE Fit  Residual  St Resid
  1  0.100  0.2900  0.4427  0.0159   -0.1527     -2.30R

R denotes an observation with a large standardized residual.
```

c. The Minitab output follows.

```
The regression equation is
R/IP = 0.537 - 0.248 SO/IP + 1.03 HR/IP

Predictor        Coef  SE Coef      T      P
Constant      0.53651  0.08141   6.59  0.000
SO/IP        -0.24835  0.07181  -3.46  0.003
HR/IP          1.0319   0.4359   2.37  0.030

S = 0.0537850   R-Sq = 56.3%   R-Sq(adj) = 51.2%

Analysis of Variance

Source            DF        SS        MS      F      P
Regression         2  0.063477  0.031738  10.97  0.001
Residual Error    17  0.049178  0.002893
Total             19  0.112655
```

d. Using the estimated regression equation in part (c) we obtain

R/IP = 0.537 - 0.248 SO/IP + 1.03 HR/IP
R/IP = 0.537 - 0.248(.91)+ 1.03(.16)= .48

The predicted value for R/IP was less than the actual value.

e. This suggestion does not make sense. If a pitcher gives up more runs per inning pitched this pitcher's earned run average also has to increase. For these data the sample correlation coefficient between ERA and R/IP is .964. The following Minitab output shows the results for part (c) using ERA as the dependent variable.

```
The regression equation is
ERA = 3.88 + 12.0 HR/IP - 1.84 SO/IP

Predictor      Coef  SE Coef     T      P
Constant     3.8781   0.6466  6.00  0.000
HR/IP        11.993    3.462  3.46  0.003
SO/IP       -1.8428   0.5703 -3.23  0.005

S = 0.427204   R-Sq = 62.5%   R-Sq(adj) = 58.1%

Analysis of Variance

Source            DF      SS      MS      F      P
Regression         2  5.1739  2.5870  14.17  0.000
Residual Error    17  3.1025  0.1825
Total             19  8.2765
```

11. a. SSE = SST - SSR = 6,724.125 - 6,216.375 = 507.75

b. $R^2 = \dfrac{\text{SSR}}{\text{SST}} = \dfrac{6,216.375}{6,724.125} = .924$

c. $R_a^2 = 1 - (1 - R^2)\dfrac{n-1}{n-p-1} = 1 - (1 - .924)\dfrac{10-1}{10-2-1} = .902$

d. The estimated regression equation provided an excellent fit.

12. a. $R^2 = \dfrac{\text{SSR}}{\text{SST}} = \dfrac{14,052.2}{15,182.9} = .926$

b. $R_a^2 = 1 - (1 - R^2)\dfrac{n-1}{n-p-1} = 1 - (1 - .926)\dfrac{10-1}{10-2-1} = .905$

c. Yes; after adjusting for the number of independent variables in the model, we see that 90.5% of the variability in y has been accounted for.

13. a. $R^2 = \dfrac{\text{SSR}}{\text{SST}} = \dfrac{1760}{1805} = .975$

b. $R_a^2 = 1 - (1 - R^2)\dfrac{n-1}{n-p-1} = 1 - (1 - .975)\dfrac{30-1}{30-4-1} = .971$

c. The estimated regression equation provided an excellent fit.

14. a. $R^2 = \dfrac{\text{SSR}}{\text{SST}} = \dfrac{12,000}{16,000} = .75$

b. $R_a^2 = 1 - (1 - R^2)\dfrac{n-1}{n-p-1} = 1 - .25\dfrac{9}{7} = .68$

c. The adjusted coefficient of determination shows that 68% of the variability has been explained by the two independent variables; thus, we conclude that the model does not explain a large amount of variability.

15. a. $R^2 = \dfrac{\text{SSR}}{\text{SST}} = \dfrac{23.435}{25.5} = .919$

$R_a^2 = 1 - (1 - R^2)\dfrac{n-1}{n-p-1} = 1 - (1 - .919)\dfrac{8-1}{8-2-1} = .887$

b. Multiple regression analysis is preferred since both R^2 and R_a^2 show an increased percentage of the variability of y explained when both independent variables are used.

16. a. $r^2 = .577$. Thus, the averages number of passing yards per attempt is able to explain 57.7% of the variability in the percentage of games won. Considering the nature of the data and all the other factors that might be related to the number of games won, this is not too bad a fit.

b. The value of the coefficient of determination increased to $R^2 = .752$, and the adjusted coefficient of determination is $R_a^2 = .714$. Thus, using both independent variables provides a much better fit.

17. a. A portion of the Minitab output is shown below.

```
The regression equation is
Total Distance = 81.6 + 1.09 Ball Speed + 1.65 Launch Angle

Predictor          Coef   SE Coef       T       P
Constant         81.596     6.953   11.74   0.000
Ball Speed      1.09266   0.03644   29.99   0.000
Launch Angle     1.6465    0.1765    9.33   0.000

S = 2.84872    R-Sq = 82.8%    R-Sq(adj) = 82.6%
```

The value of R-Sq = 82.8% and the value of R-Sq (adj) = 82.6% indicate that the estimated regression equation provided a very good fit.

b. The Minitab output is shown below.

```
The regression equation is
Total Distance = 117 + 0.988 Ball Speed

Predictor      Coef   SE Coef       T       P
Constant    117.139     7.022   16.68   0.000
Ball Speed  0.98764   0.04184   23.61   0.000

S = 3.43937    R-Sq = 74.8%    R-Sq(adj) = 74.6%
```

The value of R-Sq = 74.8% indicates that using just ball speed can account for 74.8% of the variability in total distance. The addition of launch angle increases the percentage to almost 83%. Therefore, the estimated regression equation using both ball speed and launch angle will provide better predictions.

18. a. The Minitab output in exercise 10 shows that $R^2 = .563$ and $R_a^2 = .512$.

b. The fit is not great, but considering the nature of the data being able to explain slightly more than 50% of the variability in the number of runs given up per inning pitched using just two independent variables is not too bad.

c. The Minitab output using ERA as the dependent variable follows.

```
The regression equation is
ERA = 3.88 + 12.0 HR/IP - 1.84 SO/IP

Predictor     Coef   SE Coef       T       P
Constant    3.8781    0.6466    6.00   0.000
HR/IP       11.993     3.462    3.46   0.003
SO/IP      -1.8428    0.5703   -3.23   0.005

S = 0.427204    R-Sq = 62.5%    R-Sq(adj) = 58.1%

Analysis of Variance

Source            DF       SS       MS       F       P
Regression         2   5.1739   2.5870   14.17   0.000
Residual Error    17   3.1025   0.1825
Total             19   8.2765
```

The Minitab output shows that $R^2 = .625$ and $R_a^2 = .581$

Approximately 60% of the variability in the ERA can be explained by the linear effect of HR/IP and SO/IP. This is not too bad considering the complexity of predicting pithing performance.

19. a. $MSR = SSR/p = 6{,}216.375/2 = 3{,}108.188$

   $$MSE = \frac{SSE}{n-p-1} = \frac{507.75}{10-2-1} = 72.536$$

   b. $F = MSR/MSE = 3{,}108.188/72.536 = 42.85$

   Using F table (2 degrees of freedom numerator and 7 denominator), p-value is less than .01

   Actual p-value = .0001

   Because p-value $\leq \alpha$ = .05, the overall model is significant.

   c. $t = .5906/.0813 = 7.26$

   Using t table (7 degrees of freedom), area in tail is less than .005; p-value is less than .01

   Actual p-value = .0002

   Because p-value $\leq \alpha$, β_1 is significant.

   d. $t = .4980/.0567 = 8.78$

   Using t table (7 degrees of freedom), area in tail is less than .005; p-value is less than .01

   Actual p-value = .0001

   Because p-value $\leq \alpha$, β_2 is significant.

20.   A portion of the Minitab output is shown below.

```
The regression equation is
Y = - 18.4 + 2.01 X1 + 4.74 X2

Predictor         Coef        SE Coef           T          P
Constant        -18.37          17.97       -1.02      0.341
X1               2.0102        0.2471        8.13      0.000
X2               4.7378        0.9484        5.00      0.002

S = 12.71        R-Sq = 92.6%      R-Sq(adj)  = 90.4%

Analysis of Variance

Source            DF            SS           MS          F          P
Regression         2        14052.2       7026.1      43.50      0.000
Residual Error     7         1130.7        161.5
Total              9        15182.9
```

   a.   Since the p-value corresponding to $F = 43.50$ is $.000 < \alpha = .05$, we reject H_0: $\beta_1 = \beta_2 = 0$; there is a significant relationship.

b. Since the p-value corresponding to $t = 8.13$ is $.000 < \alpha = .05$, we reject H_0: $\beta_1 = 0$; β_1 is significant.

c. Since the p-value corresponding to $t = 5.00$ is $.002 < \alpha = .05$, we reject H_0: $\beta_2 = 0$; β_2 is significant.

21. a. In the two independent variable case the coefficient of x_1 represents the expected change in y corresponding to a one unit increase in x_1 when x_2 is held constant. In the single independent variable case the coefficient of x_1 represents the expected change in y corresponding to a one unit increase in x_1.

b. Yes. If x_1 and x_2 are correlated one would expect a change in x_1 to be accompanied by a change in x_2.

22. a. SSE = SST - SSR = 16000 - 12000 = 4000

$$s^2 = \frac{SSE}{n - p - 1} = \frac{4000}{7} = 571.43$$

$$MSR = \frac{SSR}{p} = \frac{12000}{2} = 6000$$

b. F = MSR/MSE = 6000/571.43 = 10.50

Using F table (2 degrees of freedom numerator and 7 denominator), p-value is less than .01

Actual p-value = .008

Because p-value $\leq \alpha$, we reject H_0. There is a significant relationship among the variables.

23. a. $F = 28.38$

Using F table (2 degrees of freedom numerator and 5 denominator), p-value is less than .01

Actual p-value = .002

Because p-value $\leq \alpha$, there is a significant relationship.

b. $t = 7.53$

Using t table (5 degrees of freedom), area in tail is less than .005; p-value is less than .01

Actual p-value = .001

Because p-value $\leq \alpha$, β_1 is significant and x_1 should not be dropped from the model.

c. $t = 4.06$

Actual p-value = .010

Because p-value $\leq \alpha$, β_2 is significant and x_2 should not be dropped from the model.

24. a. The Minitab output is shown below:

```
The regression equation is
Win% = 60.5 + 0.319 OffPassYds/G- 0.241 DefYds/G

Predictor          Coef  SE Coef       T       P
Constant          60.54    28.36    2.14   0.041
OffPassYds/G    0.31862  0.06256    5.09   0.000
DefYds/G       -0.24134  0.08928   -2.70   0.011

S = 15.3096   R-Sq = 47.6%   R-Sq(adj) = 44.0%

Analysis of Variance

Source            DF       SS       MS       F       P
Regression         2   6179.1   3089.6   13.18   0.000
Residual Error    29   6797.2    234.4
Total             31  12976.3
```

   b. Because the p-value for the F test = .000 < α = .05, there is a significant relationship.

   c. For OffPassYds/G: Because the p-value = .000 < α = .05, OffPassYds/G is significant.

       For DefYds/G: Because the p-value = .011 < α = .05, DefYds/G is significant.

25. a. The Minitab output follows.

```
The regression equation is
Overall = 35.6 + 0.110 Itineraries/Schedule + 0.245 Shore Excursions
          + 0.247 Food/Dining

Predictor                Coef  SE Coef      T       P
Constant                35.62    13.23   2.69   0.016
Itineraries/Schedule   0.1105   0.1297   0.85   0.407
Shore Excursions      0.24454  0.04336   5.64   0.000
Food/Dining           0.24736  0.06212   3.98   0.001

S = 1.38775   R-Sq = 75.0%   R-Sq(adj) = 70.3%

Analysis of Variance

Source            DF       SS       MS       F       P
Regression         3   92.352   30.784   15.98   0.000
Residual Error    16   30.813    1.926
Total             19  123.166


Total             19  123.166
```

   b. Because the p-value corresponding to F = 15.98, 0.000, is less than .05, the level of significance, overall there is a significant relationship.

   c. Because the p-value for Itineraries/Schedule (.407) is greater than the level of significance (.05), Itineraries/Schedule is not significant. Shore Excursions (p-value = .000) and Food/Dining (p-value = .001) are both significant because the p-value for each of these independent variables is less than the level of significance (.05).

d. After removing Itineraries/Schedule from the model, we obtained the following Minitab output.

```
The regression equation is
Overall = 45.2 + 0.253 Shore Excursions + 0.248 Food/Dining

Predictor              Coef   SE Coef     T       P
Constant             45.178     6.952   6.50   0.000
Shore Excursions    0.25289    0.0489   6.04   0.000
Food/Dining         0.24819    0.06161   4.03   0.001


S = 1.37650    R-Sq = 73.8%    R-Sq(adj) = 70.8%

Analysis of Variance

Source            DF        SS       MS       F       P
Regression         2     90.955   45.477   24.00   0.000
Residual Error    17     32.211    1.895
Total             19    123.166
```

With Itineraries/Schedule in the model, the R^2 was .750, while the R^2 after Itineraries/Schedule was removed from the model was .738. Removing Itineraries/Schedule from the model resulted in almost no loss in the model's ability to explain variability in the Overall Score.

26. The Minitab output from part (c) of exercise 10 follows.

```
The regression equation is
R/IP = 0.537 - 0.248 SO/IP + 1.03 HR/IP

Predictor       Coef    SE Coef      T       P
Constant     0.53651    0.08141    6.59   0.000
SO/IP       -0.24835    0.07181   -3.46   0.003
HR/IP         1.0319     0.4359    2.37   0.030


S = 0.0537850    R-Sq = 56.3%    R-Sq(adj) = 51.2%

Analysis of Variance

Source            DF         SS        MS        F      P
Regression         2    0.063477  0.031738   10.97  0.001
Residual Error    17    0.049178  0.002893
Total             19    0.112655
```

a. The p-value associated with $F = 10.97$ is .001. Because the p-value $< .05$, there is a significant overall relationship.

b. For SO/IP, the p-value associated with $t = -3.46$ is .003. Because the p-value $< .05$, SO/IP is significant. For HR/IP, the p-value associated with $t = 2.37$ is .030. Because the p-value $< .05$, HR/IP is also significant.

27. a. $\hat{y} = 29.1270 + .5906(180) + .4980(310) = 289.8150$

b. The point estimate for an individual value is $\hat{y} = 289.8150$, the same as the point estimate of the mean value.

28. a. Using Minitab, the 95% confidence interval is 132.16 to 154.16.

b. Using Minitab, the 95% prediction interval is 111.13 to 175.18.

29. a. $\hat{y} = 83.2 + 2.29(3.5) + 1.30(1.8) = 93.555$ or $93,555

Note: In Exercise 5b, the Minitab output also shows that $b_0 = 83.230$, $b_1 = 2.2902$, and $b_2 = 1.3010$; hence, $\hat{y} = 83.230 + 2.2902x_1 + 1.3010x_2$. Using this estimated regression equation, we obtain

$\hat{y} = 83.230 + 2.2902(3.5) + 1.3010(1.8) = 93.588$ or $93,588

The difference ($93,588 - $93,555 = $33) is simply due to the fact that additional significant digits are used in the computations. From a practical point of view, however, the difference is not enough to be concerned about. In practice, a computer software package is always used to perform the computations and this will not be an issue.

The Minitab output is shown below:

```
      Fit    Stdev.Fit           95% C.I.            95% P.I.
   93.588        0.291     ( 92.840,  94.335)   ( 91.774,  95.401)
```

Note that the value of FIT ($\hat{y}$) is 93.588.

   b. Confidence interval estimate: 92.840 to 94.335 or $92,840 to $94,335

   c. Prediction interval estimate: 91.774 to 95.401 or $91,774 to $95,401

30. a. A prediction of the percentage of games won for these values is

$\hat{y} = 60.5 + .319x_1 - .241x_2 = 60.5 + .319(225) - .241(300) = 59.975\%$

   b. The Minitab output follows.

```
The regression equation is
Win% = 60.5 + 0.319 OffPassYds/G - 0.241 DefYds/G

Predictor          Coef   SE Coef       T       P
Constant          60.54     28.36    2.14   0.041
OffPassYds/G     0.31862   0.06256    5.09   0.000
DefYds/G        -0.24134   0.08928   -2.70   0.011

S = 15.3096    R-Sq = 47.6%    R-Sq(adj) = 44.0%

Analysis of Variance

Source            DF         SS       MS       F       P
Regression         2     6179.1   3089.6   13.18   0.000
Residual Error    29     6797.2    234.4
Total             31    12976.3

Predicted Values for New Observations

New Obs    Fit   SE Fit        95% CI             95% PI
      1   59.83    4.89    (49.83, 69.82)    (26.96, 92.70)
```

The 95% confidence interval is 49.83 to 69.82 or approximately 50% to 70%.

31. a.   A portion of the Minitab output follows.

```
The regression equation is
Satisfaction Electronic Trades = - 0.783 + 0.558 Trade Price
                                + 0.734 Speed of Execution

Predictor                 Coef   SE Coef      T      P
Constant               -0.7835    0.9423  -0.83  0.423
Trade Price             0.5580    0.2332   2.39  0.036
Speed of Execution      0.7342    0.1557   4.71  0.001

S = 0.410845   R-Sq = 68.3%   R-Sq(adj) = 62.5%

Analysis of Variance

Source            DF       SS      MS      F      P
Regression         2   3.9954  1.9977  11.84  0.002
Residual Error    11   1.8567  0.1688
Total             13   5.8521
```

   b.   Satisfaction Electronic Trades = - 0.783 + 0.558(3) + 0.734(3) = 3.093

   c./d. A portion of the Minitab output follows.

```
Predicted Values for New Observations

New Obs    Fit   SE Fit       95% CI            95% PI
      1  3.093    0.111  (2.848, 3.338)  (2.156, 4.030)
```

   For part (c) the 95% confidence interval is 2.848 to 3.338

   For part (d) the 95% prediction interval is 2.156 to 4.030; but, because the highest possible rating is 4, the upper end of the prediction interval is treated as 4.

32. a. $E(y) = \beta_0 + \beta_1 x_1 + \beta_2 x_2$ where

   $x_2 = 0$ if level 1 and 1 if level 2

   b. $E(y) = \beta_0 + \beta_1 x_1 + \beta_2(0) = \beta_0 + \beta_1 x_1$

   c. $E(y) = \beta_0 + \beta_1 x_1 + \beta_2(1) = \beta_0 + \beta_1 x_1 + \beta_2$

   d. $\beta_2 = E(y \mid \text{level 2}) - E(y \mid \text{level 1})$

   β_1 is the change in $E(y)$ for a 1 unit change in x_1 holding x_2 constant.

33. a.   two

   b. $E(y) = \beta_0 + \beta_1 x_1 + \beta_2 x_2 + \beta_3 x_3$ where

x_2	x_3	Level
0	0	1
1	0	2
0	1	3

13 - 17

c. $E(y \mid \text{level 1}) = \beta_0 + \beta_1 x_1 + \beta_2(0) + \beta_3(0) = \beta_0 + \beta_1 x_1$

$E(y \mid \text{level 2}) = \beta_0 + \beta_1 x_1 + \beta_2(1) + \beta_3(0) = \beta_0 + \beta_1 x_1 + \beta_2$

$E(y \mid \text{level 3}) = \beta_0 + \beta_1 x_1 + \beta_2(0) + \beta_3(0) = \beta_0 + \beta_1 x_1 + \beta_3$

$\beta_2 = E(y \mid \text{level 2}) - E(y \mid \text{level 1})$

$\beta_3 = E(y \mid \text{level 3}) - E(y \mid \text{level 1})$

β_1 is the change in $E(y)$ for a 1 unit change in x_1 holding x_2 and x_3 constant.

34. a. $15,300

  b.   Estimate of sales $= 10.1 - 4.2(2) + 6.8(8) + 15.3(0) = 56.1$ or $56,100

  c.   Estimate of sales $= 10.1 - 4.2(1) + 6.8(3) + 15.3(1) = 41.6$ or $41,600

35. a.   Let Type $= 0$ if a mechanical repair
           Type $= 1$ if an electrical repair

  The Minitab output is shown below:

```
The regression equation is
Time = 3.45 + 0.617 Type

Predictor          Coef        SE Coef            T          P
Constant         3.4500         0.5467         6.31      0.000
Type             0.6167         0.7058         0.87      0.408

S = 1.093        R-Sq = 8.7%        R-Sq(adj)  =  0.0%

Analysis of Variance

Source             DF             SS            MS          F          P
Regression          1          0.913         0.913       0.76      0.408
Residual Error      8          9.563         1.195
Total               9         10.476
```

  b.   The estimated regression equation did not provide a good fit. In fact, the p-value of .408 shows that the relationship is not significant for any reasonable value of α.

  c.   Person $= 0$ if Bob Jones performed the service and Person $= 1$ if Dave Newton performed the service. The Minitab output is shown below:

```
The regression equation is
Time = 4.62 - 1.60 Person

Predictor          Coef        SE Coef            T          P
Constant         4.6200         0.3192        14.47      0.000
Person          -1.6000         0.4514        -3.54      0.008

S = 0.7138       R-Sq = 61.1%        R-Sq(adj)  =  56.2%
```

```
Analysis of Variance

Source               DF          SS           MS          F         P
Regression            1      6.4000       6.4000      12.56     0.008
Residual Error        8      4.0760       0.5095
Total                 9     10.4760
```

d. We see that 61.1% of the variability in repair time has been explained by the repair person that performed the service; an acceptable, but not good, fit.

36. a. The Minitab output is shown below:

```
The regression equation is
Time = 1.86 + 0.291 Months + 1.10 Type - 0.609 Person

Predictor          Coef      SE Coef            T          P
Constant         1.8602       0.7286         2.55      0.043
Months          0.29144      0.08360         3.49      0.013
Type             1.1024       0.3033         3.63      0.011
Person          -0.6091       0.3879        -1.57      0.167

S = 0.4174      R-Sq = 90.0%      R-Sq(adj) = 85.0%

Analysis of Variance

Source               DF          SS           MS          F         P
Regression            3      9.4305       3.1435      18.04     0.002
Residual Error        6      1.0455       0.1743
Total                 9     10.4760
```

b. Since the p-value corresponding to $F = 18.04$ is .002 $< \alpha = .05$, the overall model is statistically significant.

c. The p-value corresponding to $t = -1.57$ is .167 $> \alpha = .05$; thus, the addition of Person is not statistically significant. Person is highly correlated with Months (the sample correlation coefficient is -.691); thus, once the effect of Months has been accounted for, Person will not add much to the model.

37. a. A portion of the Minitab output follows:

```
The regression equation is
Score = 69.3 + 0.559 Price

Predictor     Coef  SE Coef       T       P
Constant    69.276    3.400   20.37   0.000
Price       0.5586   0.1769    3.16   0.005

S = 3.02575    R-Sq = 34.4%    R-Sq(adj) = 31.0%

Analysis of Variance

Source            DF       SS       MS       F       P
Regression         1   91.290   91.290    9.97   0.005
Residual Error    19  173.948    9.155
Total             20  265.238
```

b. Because the *p*-value = .005 < α = .05, there is a significant relationship.

c. Let Type_Italian = 1 if the restaurant is an Italian restaurant; 0 otherwise

d. A portion of the Minitab output follows:

```
The regression equation is
Score = 67.4 + 0.573 Price + 3.04 Type_Italian

Predictor        Coef   SE Coef       T       P
Constant       67.405     3.053   22.07   0.000
Price          0.5734    0.1546    3.71   0.002
Type_Italian    3.038     1.155    2.63   0.017

S = 2.64219    R-Sq = 52.6%    R-Sq(adj) = 47.4%

Analysis of Variance

Source          DF        SS       MS       F       P
Regression       2   139.577   69.789   10.00   0.001
Residual Error  18   125.661    6.981
Total           20   265.238
```

e. For the Type_Italian dummy variable, the *p*-value = .017 < α = .05; thus, type of restaurant is a significant factor in overall customer satisfaction.

f. The estimated regression equation computed in part (d) is $\hat{y} = 67.4 + .573(\text{Price}) + 3.04(\text{Type\_Italian})$.

For a seafood/steakhouse Type_Italian = 0 and the estimated score is $\hat{y} = 67.4 + .573(20) + 3.04(0) = 79.86$

For an Italian restaurant Type_Italian = 1 and the estimated score is $\hat{y} = 67.4 + .573(20) + 3.04(1) = 82.90$

Thus, the satisfaction score increases by 3.04 points.

38. a. The Minitab output is shown below:

```
The regression equation is
Risk = - 91.8 + 1.08 Age + 0.252 Pressure + 8.74 Smoker

Predictor        Coef   SE Coef        T       P
Constant       -91.76     15.22    -6.03   0.000
Age            1.0767    0.1660     6.49   0.000
Pressure      0.25181   0.04523     5.57   0.000
Smoker          8.740     3.001     2.91   0.010

S = 5.757       R-Sq = 87.3%       R-Sq(adj) = 85.0%
```

```
Analysis of Variance

Source              DF        SS          MS          F         P
Regression           3      3660.7      1220.2      36.82     0.000
Residual Error      16       530.2        33.1
Total               19      4190.9
```

b. Since the p-value corresponding to $t = 2.91$ is $.010 < \alpha = .05$, smoking is a significant factor.

c. Using Minitab, the point estimate is 34.27; the 95% prediction interval is 21.35 to 47.18. Thus, the probability of a stroke (.2135 to .4718 at the 95% confidence level) appears to be quite high. The physician would probably recommend that Art quit smoking and begin some type of treatment designed to reduce his blood pressure.

39. a. The expected increase in final college grade point average corresponding to a one point increase in high school grade point average is .0235 when SAT mathematics score does not change. Similarly, the expected increase in final college grade point average corresponding to a one point increase in the SAT mathematics score is .00486 when the high school grade point average does not change.

b. $\hat{y} = -1.41 + .0235(84) + .00486(540) = 3.19$

40. a. Job satisfaction can be expected to decrease by 8.69 units with a one unit increase in length of service if the wage rate does not change. A dollar increase in the wage rate is associated with a 13.5 point increase in the job satisfaction score when the length of service does not change.

b. $\hat{y} = 14.4 - 8.69(4) + 13.5(6.5) = 67.39$

41. a. The computer output with the missing values filled in is as follows:

```
The regression equation is

Y = 8.103 + 7.602 X1 + 3.111 X2

Predictor         Coef      SE Coef            T
Constant         8.103        2.667         3.04
X1               7.602        2.105         3.61
X2               3.111        0.613         5.08

S = 3.35       R-sq = 92.3%        R-sq (adj) = 91.0%

Analysis of Variance

SOURCE            DF          SS          MS          F
Regression         2        1612         806       71.82
Residual Error    12      134.67     11.2225
Total             14     1746.67
```

b. $F_{.05} = 3.89$

$F = 71.82 > F_{.05}$; significant relationship

Actual p-value = .000

Because p-value $\leq \alpha = .05$, the overall relationship is significant

c. Using t table (12 degrees of freedom), area in tail corresponding to $t = 3.61$ is less than .005; p-value is less than .01

Actual p-value $= .0000$

Because p-value $\leq \alpha$, reject $H_0 : \beta_1 = 0$

Using t table (12 degrees of freedom), area in tail corresponding to $t = 5.08$ is less than .005; p-value is less than .01

Actual p-value $= .0003$

Because p-value $\leq \alpha$, reject $H_0 : \beta_2 = 0$

d. See computer output.

e. $R_a^2 = 1 - (1 - .923)\dfrac{14}{12} = .91$

42. a. The regression equation is

```
Y = -1.41 + .0235 X1 + .00486 X2
```

Predictor	Coef	SE Coef	T
Constant	-1.4053	0.4848	-2.90
X1	0.023467	0.008666	2.71
X2	.00486	0.001077	4.51

```
S = 0.1298    R-sq = 93.7%      R-sq (adj) = 91.9%
```

Analysis of Variance

SOURCE	DF	SS	MS	F
Regression	2	1.76209	.881	52.44
Residual Error	7	.1179	.0168	
Total	9	1.88000		

b. Using F table (2 degrees of freedom numerator and 7 degrees of freedom denominator), p-value is less than .01

Actual p-value $= .0001$

Because p-value $\leq \alpha$, there is a significant relationship.

c. for β_1: p-value $= .0302$; reject H_0: $\beta_1 = 0$

for β_2: p-value $= .0028$; reject H_0: $\beta_2 = 0$

d. $R^2 = \dfrac{SSR}{SST} = .937$

$R_a^2 = 1 - (1 - .937)\dfrac{9}{7} = .919$

good fit

43. a. The regression equation is

```
Y = 14.4 - 8.69 X1 + 13.52 X2

Predictor            Coef          SE Coef               T
Constant           14.448           8.191            1.76
X1                  -8.69           1.555           -5.59
X2                 13.517           2.085            6.48

S = 3.773      R-sq = 90.1%       R-sq (adj) = 86.1%

Analysis of Variance

SOURCE             DF            SS            MS          F
Regression          2        648.83       324.415      22.79
Residual Error      5         71.17        14.234
Total               7        720.00
```

b. $F_{.05} = 5.79$

$F = 22.79 > F_{.05}$; significant relationship.

Actual p-value = .0031

Because p-value $\leq \alpha = .05$, the overall relationship is significant.

c. $R^2 = \dfrac{SSR}{SST} = .901$

$R_a^2 = 1 - (1 - .901)\dfrac{7}{5} = .861$

good fit

d. for β_1: $t = p$-value = .0025; reject $H_0 : \beta_1 = 0$

for β_2: p-value = .0013; reject $H_0 : \beta_2 = 0$

44. a. A portion of the Minitab output follows:

```
The regression equation is
Buy Again = - 7.52 + 1.82 Steering

Predictor     Coef  SE Coef       T       P
Constant    -7.522    1.467   -5.13   0.000
Steering    1.8151   0.1958    9.27   0.000


S = 0.841071   R-Sq = 84.3%   R-Sq(adj) = 83.3%


Analysis of Variance

Source            DF      SS      MS       F       P
Regression         1  60.787  60.787   85.93   0.000
Residual Error    16  11.318   0.707
Total             17  72.105
```

Because the p-value = .000 < α = .05, there is a significant relationship.

b. The estimated regression equation provided a good fit; 84.3 % of the variability in the Buy Again rating was explained by the linear effect of the Steering rating.

c. A portion of the Minitab output follows:

```
The regression equation is
Buy Again = - 5.39 + 0.690 Steering + 0.911 Treadwear

Predictor     Coef  SE Coef       T       P
Constant    -5.388    1.110   -4.86   0.000
Steering    0.6899   0.2875    2.40   0.030
Treadwear   0.9113   0.2063    4.42   0.001


S = 0.572723   R-Sq = 93.2%   R-Sq(adj) = 92.3%


Analysis of Variance

Source            DF      SS      MS       F       P
Regression         2  67.185  33.592  102.41   0.000
Residual Error    15   4.920   0.328
Total             17  72.105
```

d. For the Treadwear independent variable, the p-value = .001 < α = .05; thus, the addition of Treadwear is significant.

45. a. A portion of the Regression tool output follows.

Regression Statistics	
Multiple R	0.8013
R Square	0.6421
Adjusted R Square	0.6409
Standard Error	3.4123
Observations	309

ANOVA

	df	SS	MS	F	Significance F
Regression	1	6413.2883	6413.2883	550.8029	1.79552E-70
Residual	307	3574.5628	11.6435		
Total	308	9987.8511			

	Coefficients	Standard Error	t Stat	P-value	Lower 95%	Upper 95%
Intercept	41.0534	0.5166	79.4748	8.1E-207	40.0370	42.0699
Displacement	-3.7232	0.1586	-23.4692	1.8E-70	-4.0354	-3.4110

Because the p-value corresponding to $F = 550.8029$ is .0000 < α = .05, there is a significant relationship.

b. A portion of the Excel Regression tool output follows.

Regression Statistics	
Multiple R	0.8276
R Square	0.6849
Adjusted R Square	0.6829
Standard Error	3.2068
Observations	309

ANOVA

	df	SS	MS	F	Significance F
Regression	2	6841.0876	3420.5438	332.6232	1.79466E-77
Residual	306	3146.7635	10.2835		
Total	308	9987.8511			

	Coefficients	Standard Error	t Stat	P-value	Lower 95%	Upper 95%
Intercept	40.5946	0.4906	82.7379	1.8E-211	39.6291	41.5600
Displacement	-3.1944	0.1701	-18.7745	7.43E-53	-3.5292	-2.8596
FuelPremium	-2.7230	0.4222	-6.4498	4.37E-10	-3.5537	-1.8922

c. For FuelPremium, the p-value corresponding to $t = -6.4498$ is $.000 < \alpha = .05$; significant. The addition of the dummy variables is significant.

d. A portion of the Excel Regression tool output follows.

Regression Statistics	
Multiple R	0.8554
R Square	0.7317
Adjusted R Square	0.7282
Standard Error	2.9688
Observations	309

ANOVA

	df	SS	MS	F	Significance F
Regression	4	7308.5436	1827.1359	207.3108	1.54798E-85
Residual	304	2679.3075	8.8135		
Total	308	9987.8511			

	Coefficients	Standard Error	t Stat	P-value	Lower 95%	Upper 95%
Intercept	37.9626	0.7892	48.1055	3.5E-144	36.4097	39.5155
Displacement	-3.2418	0.1941	-16.7007	6.97E-45	-3.6238	-2.8599
FuelPremium	-2.1352	0.4519	-4.7253	3.52E-06	-3.0243	-1.2460
FrontWheel	3.0747	0.5394	5.7005	2.83E-08	2.0133	4.1360
RearWheel	3.3114	0.5413	6.1174	2.92E-09	2.2462	4.3765

e. Since the p-value corresponding to $F = 207.3108$ is $.0000 < \alpha = .05$, there is a significant overall relationship. Because the p-values for each independent variable are also $< \alpha = .05$, each of the independent variables is significant.

46. a.   Type of Fund is a categorical variable with three levels. Let FundDE = 1 for a domestic equity fund
and FundIE = 1 for an international fund. The Excel output is shown below:

Regression Statistics	
Multiple R	0.7838
R Square	0.6144
Adjusted R Square	0.5960
Standard Error	5.5978
Observations	45

ANOVA

	df	SS	MS	F	Significance F
Regression	2	2096.8489	1048.4245	33.4584	2.03818E-09
Residual	42	1316.0771	31.3352		
Total	44	3412.9260			

	Coefficients	Standard Error	t Stat	P-value	Lower 95%	Upper 95%
Intercept	4.9090	1.7702	2.7732	0.0082	1.3366	8.4814
FundDE	10.4658	2.0722	5.0505	9.033E-06	6.2839	14.6477
FundIE	21.6823	2.6553	8.1658	3.288E-10	16.3237	27.0408

$\hat{y} = 4.9090 + 10.4658 \text{ FundDE} + 21.6823 \text{ FundIE}$

Since the p-value corresponding to $F = 33.4584$ is .0000 $< \alpha = .05$, there is a significant relationship.

b.   R Square = .6144. A reasonably good fit using only Type of Fund.

c.   The Excel output follows:

Regression Statistics	
Multiple R	0.8135
R Square	0.6617
Adjusted R Square	0.6279
Standard Error	5.3726
Observations	45

ANOVA

	df	SS	MS	F	Significance F
Regression	4	2258.3432	564.5858	19.5598	5.48647E-09
Residual	40	1154.5827	28.8646		
Total	44	3412.9260			

	Coefficients	Standard Error	t Stat	P-value	Lower 95%	Upper 95%
Intercept	1.1899	2.3781	0.5004	0.6196	-3.6164	5.9961
FundDE	6.8969	2.7651	2.4942	0.0169	1.3083	12.4854
FundIE	17.6800	3.3161	5.3315	4.096E-06	10.9778	24.3821
Net Asset Value ($)	0.0265	0.0670	0.3950	0.6950	-0.1089	0.1619
Expense Ratio (%)	6.4564	2.7593	2.3399	0.0244	0.8798	12.0331

Since the p-value corresponding to $F = 19.5558$ is .0000 $< \alpha = .05$, there is a significant relationship.

For Net Asset Value ($), the p-value corresponding to $t = .3950$ is .6950 $> \alpha = .05$, Net Asset Value ($) is not significant and can be deleted from the model.

d. Morningstar Rank is a categorical variable. The data set only contains funds with four ranks (2-Star through –5Star), so three dummy variables are needed. Let 3StarRank = 1 for a 3-StarRank, 4StarRank = 1 for a 4-StarRank, and 5StarRank = 1 for a 5-StarRank. The Excel output follows:

Regression Statistics	
Multiple R	0.8501
R Square	0.7227
Adjusted R Square	0.6789
Standard Error	4.9904
Observations	45

ANOVA

	df	SS	MS	F	Significance F
Regression	6	2466.5721	411.0954	16.5072	2.96759E-09
Residual	38	946.3539	24.9040		
Total	44	3412.9260			

	Coefficients	Standard Error	t Stat	P-value	Lower 95%	Upper 95%
Intercept	-4.6074	3.2909	-1.4000	0.1696	-11.2694	2.0547
FundDE	8.1713	2.2754	3.5912	0.0009	3.5650	12.7776
FundIE	19.5194	2.7795	7.0227	2.292E-08	13.8926	25.1461
Expense Ratio (%)	5.5197	2.5862	2.1343	0.0393	0.2843	10.7552
3StarRank	5.9237	2.8250	2.0969	0.0427	0.2048	11.6426
4StarRank	8.2367	2.8474	2.8927	0.0063	2.4725	14.0009
5StarRank	6.6241	3.1425	2.1079	0.0417	0.2624	12.9858

$\hat{y} = -4.6074 + 8.1713$ FundDE $+ 19.5194$ FundIE $+5.5197$ Expense Ratio (%) $+ 5.9237$ 3StarRank $+ 8.2367$ 4StarRank $+ 6.6241$ 5StarRank

At the .05 level of significance, all the independent variables are significant.

e. $\hat{y}$ = -4.6074 + 8.1713(1) + 19.5194(0) +5.5197(1.05) + 5.9237(1) + 8.2367(0) +6.62415(0) = 15.28%

47. a. A portion of the Minitab output is shown below:

```
The regression equation is
Salaried ($1000s) = 40.3 + 1.19 Hourly ($1000s)

Predictor            Coef    SE Coef      T      P
Constant            40.35      15.66    2.58  0.016
Hourly ($1000s)    1.1947     0.3050    3.92  0.001

S = 30.2639    R-Sq = 35.4%    R-Sq(adj) = 33.1%

Analysis of Variance

Source            DF       SS      MS       F      P
Regression         1    14049   14049   15.34  0.001
Residual Error    28    25645     916
Total             29    39694
```

b. Because the p-value = .001 < α = .05, there is a significant relationship.

c. A portion of the Minitab output is shown below:

```
The regression equation is
Salaried ($1000s) = 27.0 + 1.22 Hourly ($1000s)- 3.2 Size-Midsize
                  + 34.4 Size-Small

Predictor            Coef   SE Coef      T      P
Constant            26.97     14.00    1.93  0.065
Hourly ($1000s)    1.2240    0.2581    4.74  0.000
Size-Midsize       -3.21     12.63   -0.25  0.802
Size-Small         34.40     10.44    3.30  0.003

S = 25.4752    R-Sq = 57.5%    R-Sq(adj) = 52.6%

Analysis of Variance

Source            DF         SS       MS       F      P
Regression         3    22820.3   7606.8   11.72  0.000
Residual Error    26    16873.6    649.0
Total             29    39693.9
```

e. Hourly ($1000s): Significant because the p-value = .000 < α = .05.

Size-Midsize: Not significant because the p-value = .802 > α = .05

Size-Small: Significant because the p-value = .003 < α = .05

f. A portion of the Minitab output using Hourly ($1000s) and Size-Small as the independent variables follows.

```
The regression equation is
Salaried ($1000s) = 26.3 + 1.22 Hourly ($1000s) + 35.4 Size-Small

Predictor          Coef   SE Coef      T      P
Constant          26.26     13.49   1.95  0.062
Hourly ($1000s)  1.2176    0.2524   4.82  0.000
Size-Small       35.409     9.486   3.73  0.001

S = 25.0299   R-Sq = 57.4%   R-Sq(adj) = 54.2%

Analysis of Variance

Source          DF      SS      MS      F      P
Regression       2   22778   11389  18.18  0.000
Residual Error  27   16915     626
Total           29   39694

Source           DF  Seq SS
Hourly ($1000s)   1   14049
Size-Small        1    8730
```

48. a. The Minitab output is shown below:

```
The regression equation is
Win% = - 295 + 7.70 FG%

Predictor     Coef   SE Coef      T      P
Constant   -294.77     60.33  -4.89  0.000
FG%          7.697     1.346   5.72  0.000

S = 10.7930   R-Sq = 53.9%   R-Sq(adj) = 52.2%

Analysis of Variance

Source          DF      SS      MS      F      P
Regression       1  3807.7  3807.7  32.69  0.000
Residual Error  28  3261.7   116.5
Total           29  7069.4
```

Since the p-value corresponding to $t = 5.72$ or $F = 32.69$ is .000 < α = .05, there is a significant relationship between the percentage of games won and the percentage of field goals made.

b. An increase of 1% in the percentage of field goals made will increase the percentage of games won by 7.7%.

c. The Minitab output is shown below:

```
The regression equation is
Win% = - 408 + 4.96 FG% + 2.37 3P% + 0.005 FT% + 3.46 RBOff
       + 3.69 RBDef

Predictor     Coef   SE Coef      T      P
Constant   -407.97     68.95  -5.92  0.000
FG%          4.961     1.368   3.63  0.001
3P%         2.3749    0.8074   2.94  0.007
FT%         0.0049    0.5182   0.01  0.992
RBOff        3.461     1.346   2.57  0.017
RBDef        3.685     1.297   2.84  0.009
```

```
S = 8.26628    R-Sq = 76.8%    R-Sq(adj) = 72.0%

Analysis of Variance

Source           DF      SS      MS      F       P
Regression        5   5429.5  1085.9   15.89   0.000
Residual Error   24   1640.0    68.3
Total            29   7069.4
```

d. For the estimated regression equation developed in part (c), the percentage of free throws made (FT%) is not significant because the *p*-value corresponding to $t = .01$ is $.992 > \alpha = .05$. After removing this independent variable, the Minitab output is shown below:

```
The regression equation is
Win% = - 408 + 4.96 FG% + 2.37 3P% + 3.46 RBOff + 3.69 RBDef

Predictor       Coef  SE Coef      T       P
Constant     -407.58    54.22   -7.52   0.000
FG%            4.962    1.337    3.71   0.001
3P%           2.3736   0.7808    3.04   0.005
RBOff          3.458    1.277    2.71   0.012
RBDef          3.686    1.269    2.90   0.008

S = 8.09928    R-Sq = 76.8%    R-Sq(adj) = 73.1%

Analysis of Variance

Source           DF      SS      MS      F       P
Regression        4   5429.4  1357.4   20.69   0.000
Residual Error   25   1640.0    65.6
Total            29   7069.4
```

e. $\hat{y} = -408 + 4.96(45) + 2.37(35) + 3.46(12) + 3.69(30) = 50.37\%$